perspectives on science

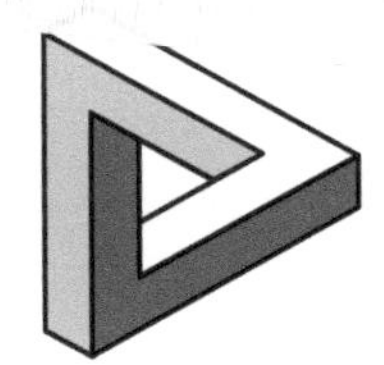

The History, Philosophy and Ethics of Science

Heinemann

Heinemann is an imprint of Pearson Education Limited, a company incorporated in England and Wales, having its registered office at Edinburgh Gate, Harlow, Essex, CM20 2JE.
Registered company number: 872828

Heinemann is a registered trademark of Pearson Education Limited

First published 2007

13

10 9 8 7 6 5 4 3

British Library Cataloguing in Publication Data is available from the British Library on request.

ISBN: 9780435569600

Project Editors: Elizabeth Swinbank and John Taylor

Heinemann editorial team: Sophy McHugh, Leslie Hopper

Edited by Ruth Holmes

Index compiled by John Holmes

Designed by Wooden Ark studio

Typeset by Tek-Art, Croydon, Surrey

Original illustrations © Harcourt Education Limited 2007

Illustrated by Tek-Art, Croydon, Surrey

Printed and bound in Great Britain by Ashford Colour Press Ltd

Cover photo: © Science Photo Library

Picture research by Catherine Bevan

Acknowledgements

The authors and publishers would like to thank the following individuals and organisations for permission to use copyright material: New Scientist p 3; The Guardian p 6T; Royal Society of Chemistry p 6B; The Times p 10T,10B, 11T, 11T, 12T, 12B, New Scientist p 18, 19T, 19M, 19B, 20, 21; Linnaean Society of London p 45, 46T, 46B, 47; Penguin p 71; Oxford University Press p 92; BMJ Publishing Group p 93, p 94; Bionews p 95; Blackwell p 98; BMJ Publishing Group p 99; Times Higher Education Supplement p 105, 106; The Royal Society p 108; Animal Aid p 110; BMJ Publishing Group p 112; Routledge p 115, 117; Journal of Commercial Biotechnology p 122; Times Higher Education Supplement p 123; Eric Hall p 125; BMJ Publishing Group p 129; Committee for Skeptical Inquiry p 140; spikedonline.co.uk p 149, 150T, 150B; The Times p 154; Oxford University Press p 159; Chicago Tribune p 162T; American Humanist Association p 162M; Institute for Creation Research p 162B; National Institute of Biology Teachers p 163; Berry et al p 164; Nature Publishing Group p 165; New Scientist p 170; New Scientist p 177; The Times p 182; University of York p 199.

The authors and publishers would like to thank the following individuals and organisations for permission to reproduce photographs: Corbis p 1; Zucchi Uwe/dpa/Corbis p 2; Eleanor Bentall/Corbis p 2; Science Photo Library p 5 T; Science Photo Library p 5 B; Science Photo Library p 9; Getty Images/PhotoDisc p 11; Ronald Grant p 14; Science Photo Library p 15; Getty Images/Photodisc p 24; Anthony Eva/Alamy p 25; Science Photo Library p 27; National Portrait Gallery p 33 L; Science Photo Library p 33 R; Science Photo Library p 35; Ted Spiegel/Corbis p 40; Dr Jeremy Burgess/Science Photo Library p 42; The Bridgeman Art Library p 43; Leonard de Selva/Corbis p 49 T; Science Photo Library p 49 M; Corbis p 49 B; Science Photo Library p 50; Mary Evans p 51; Science Photo Library p 52 T; Science Photo Library p 52 B; Science Photo Library p 53; Hulton-Deutsch Collection/Corbis p 54T; Science Photo Library p 54B; Science Photo Library p 56; Science Photo Library p 59; Macana/Alamy p 60; Science Photo Library p 61T; Science Photo Library p 61B; Bernard Bisson/Corbis Sygma p 64; Science Photo Library p 66 L; Science Photo Library p 66 M; Science Photo Library p 66 R; Science Photo Library p 68; Science Photo Library p 69; Science Photo Library p 73; Science Photo Library p 79; Science Photo Library p 80; Science Photo Library p 83; Getty Images/PhotoDisc p 85; Guenter Rossenbach/Zefa/Corbis p 89; Joseph Sohm; Visions of America/Corbis p 90 T; Catherine Bevan p 90 B; Science Photo Library p 97 L; Getty/Terry Vine p 97 R; Photofusion Picture Library/Alamy p 100; Science Photo Library p 101; Gary Braasch/Corbis p 104; David Pearson/Alamy p 106; Alamy p 108; Javajane p 110; Science Photo Library p 117; Corbis p 119; Corbis p 120; Adrian Arbib / Alamy p 122; Corbis p 123; Science Photo Library p 125; Science Photo Library p 127; Science Photo Library p 128; Peter Turnley/Corbis p 129; Murray Andrew/Corbis Sygma p 130; David Crausby/Alamy p 133; Getty Images/PhotoDisc p 137 T; Denis Scott/Corbis p 137 B; Science Photo Library p 139; Getty p 142 L; Photographers Direct p 142 R; Science Photo Library p 144; Getty p 145; Science Photo Library p 147; Tudor Photography p 148 T; Getty Images/PhotoDisc p 148 B; David Crausby/Alamy p 149; Rex Features p 150; Photolibrary.com p 152; Science Photo Library p 153; Corbis p 156; Illustrated London News Picture Library p 157; Getty Images/PhotoDisc p 158 T; Science Photo Library p 158 BL; Science Photo Library p 158 BR; Avid Sanger Photography/Alamy p 160; Getty p 162 T; Rex Features p 162 B; Science Photo Library p 163; Visual Arts Library (London)/Alamy p 164; Getty Images/PhotoDisc p 167; The Kobal Collection p 170; Tudor Photography p 172; Science Photo Library p 173; Science Photo Library p 175; Louie Psihoyos/Corbis p 178; Getty p 179 L; Science Photo Library p 179 R; Science Photo Library p 182; Wellcome Trust p 185; Science Photo Library p 187 TL; Science Photo Library p 187 TM; Catherine Bevan p 187 TR; David Pearson/Alamy p 187 C; Science Photo Library p 187 BM; Getty Images/PhotoDisc p 187 BR; Wellcome Trust p 188; Wellcome Trust p 194; Wellcome Trust p 204; Wellcome Trust p 206; Wellcome Trust p 208; Wellcome Trust p 209; Wellcome Trust p 211; Wellcome Trust p 215; University of York Science Education Group p 216 L; University of York Science Education Group p 216 R; Rune Hellestad/Corbis p 218 T; Wellcome Trust p 218 B; Wellcome Trust p 219; Wellcome Trust p 220; Wellcome Trust p 221.

Every effort has been made to contact copyright holders of material reproduced in this book. Any omissions will be rectified in subsequent printings if notice is given to the publishers.

Contents

The Perspectives on Science project

The *Perspectives on Science* project aims to support and promote the study of the History, Philosophy and Ethics of Science in schools and colleges.

Project development team

Jonathan Allday	Royal Hospital School, Ipswich
John Cartwright	University of Chester
Joanna Corden	Royal Society
Chris Edwards	Open University
Peter Ellis	Cranford House School, Oxfordshire
David Harrison	Cambridge University
Peter Fowler	British Society for the History of Science, Frances Bardsley School
Nancy Newton (administrator)	University of York
Becky Parker	Simon Langton Boys' School, Canterbury
Michael Reiss	Royal Society and Institute of Education, London
Elizabeth Swinbank	University of York
John Taylor (project director)	Rugby School
Mark Williams	St. George's School Edgbaston, Birmingham

Sponsors

The Wellcome Trust
The Royal Society
The Particle Physics and Astronomy Research Council

Authors

John Taylor
Elizabeth Swinbank
Michael Reiss
David Harrison
Peter Ellis
John Cartwright
Jonathan Allday

Advisors

Dr Graeme Gooday	University of Leeds
Professor Norman Greenwood FRS	University of Leeds
Professor Julia Higgins DBE FRS	Imperial College
Professor Peter Lipton	University of Cambridge
Dr William Newton-Smith	University of Oxford
Professor David Philips FRSC OBE	Imperial College
Professor Russell Stannard OBE	Open University
Professor Roger Trigg	University of Warwick

We also wish to thank the following for advice, assistance and support

Julian Baggini	Philosophers Magazine
Emma Barnes	University of Manchester
Sally Collins	Natural History Museum, London
Bob Crick	Simon Langton Boys' School
Peter Finegold (formerly of the Wellcome Trust)	Isinglass Consultancy
Kate Henderson	Natural History Museum, London
Prof Sir Alistair Macfarlane FRS	Former chair, Royal Society Education Committee
Prof Michael Hunter	Birkbeck College, London
Eleanor Lanyon	Wellcome Library
Sarah Leonard	Science Museum, London
Veronica McCabe	Wellcome Trust
Justine Millard	Natural History Museum, London
Ginny Page	Royal Society
Rachel Perkins	Natural History Museum, London
Rachel Thomas	Wellcome Trust
Jackie Titley	Wellcome Trust
Nick von Behr	Royal Society
Chris Wilmott	University of Leicester

The late Prof John Ziman FRS

About *Perspectives on Science*

Welcome to *Perspectives on Science*.

Have you ever become involved in an argument about science and its applications? (Should animal experiments be allowed? Is space research good use of government money?) Or wondered about deep questions underlying the study of science? (Was there a time before the Big Bang? Is the mind distinct from the brain?) If so, then this is the course for you!

Perspectives on Science is designed to help you address historical, ethical and philosophical questions relating to science. It won't provide easy answers, but it will help you to develop skills of research and argument, to analyse what other people say and write, to clarify your own thinking and to make a case for your own point of view.

You will spend approximately half the course developing key skills and vocabulary relating to historical research and to ethical and philosophical discussion and argument. Then you will carry out a project in which you research the 'story' behind a question with a scientific dimension, and explore ethical and philosophical aspects of that question. You will be asked to present the outcome of your research both orally and in writing.

About this book

The first three parts of this book use case studies and examples to focus on the history, ethics and philosophy of science. In the History part, the emphasis is on developing research skills – gathering and summarising information, and assessing information sources for reliability. The Ethics part introduces some helpful ways of thinking about ethical questions (so-called ethical frameworks), which you then apply to a range of scientific issues. The Philosophy part explores some philosophical questions relating to science, and shows how careful presentation and analysis of arguments can help you refine your ideas, deepen your understanding and communicate your views effectively.

The final part of this book contains information and advice to support your Research project. This includes guidance on planning and organising your work, and materials to help with written and oral presentation.

Each part of this book includes the following features:

Main text

This is the main reading material in the book, in which information is presented and ideas discussed. The text in each part is organised into sections which are subdivided into lessons – these may, or may not, coincide with the actual sessions arranged by your teacher/tutor/lecturer.

Within the main text, some words are printed in **bold**. These are key terms relating to the study of history, philosophy and ethics, and are defined in the *Glossary* printed at the back of this book (pages 223–8). You will probably need to use several of these terms in your Research project.

Activities

The text includes many *Activities*. Some are intended for individual work, while others are designed for groups. It is likely that you will be asked to carry out some of these activities in class or in private study time.

Activity 1

Questions

There are plenty of *Questions* in this book. Most of the questions are designed to help you think and get to grips with the ideas presented in the main text, and to summarise what you have learned. Some of the questions have definite, precise answers, but in many cases the process of thinking through the question is at least as important as your final answer.

Further work

Some activities and questions are designated as *Further work*. These are unlikely to be covered in formal class sessions, but you might tackle some of them during private study time.

Further work

Project hints

Within the first three parts of this book, you will find *Project hints*. These alert you to material that is of direct relevance to your Research project (though in fact all the material is of course relevant!), and include suggestions for topic areas that might be developed into research questions.

Project hint

The '5 W' questions provide a useful framework for analysing any source of information.

Course references

In the fourth part of this book, *Course references* direct you back to activities, lessons or sections that relate to aspects of your Research project.

Course reference

Lesson 2.3 in the Philosophy part of this course is about the careful use of language and techniques for defining terms.

Resource links

The notes headed *Resource links* guide you to additional resources relating to particular topics. You might use these in relation to activities during the first part of the course, or as pointers towards information sources for a Research project. Links to useful websites are provided on a dedicated 'hotlinks' page on the Heinemann website at www.heinemann.co.uk/hotlinks. When you access the site, the express code is 9600P.

Resource link

The Times archive can be accessed online.

Finally, while the material is presented as a textbook, the *Perspectives on Science* team hope you will treat it as a book to be read for interest and enjoyment. Above all, we hope it will make you think!

PART 1

RESEARCHING THE HISTORY OF SCIENCE

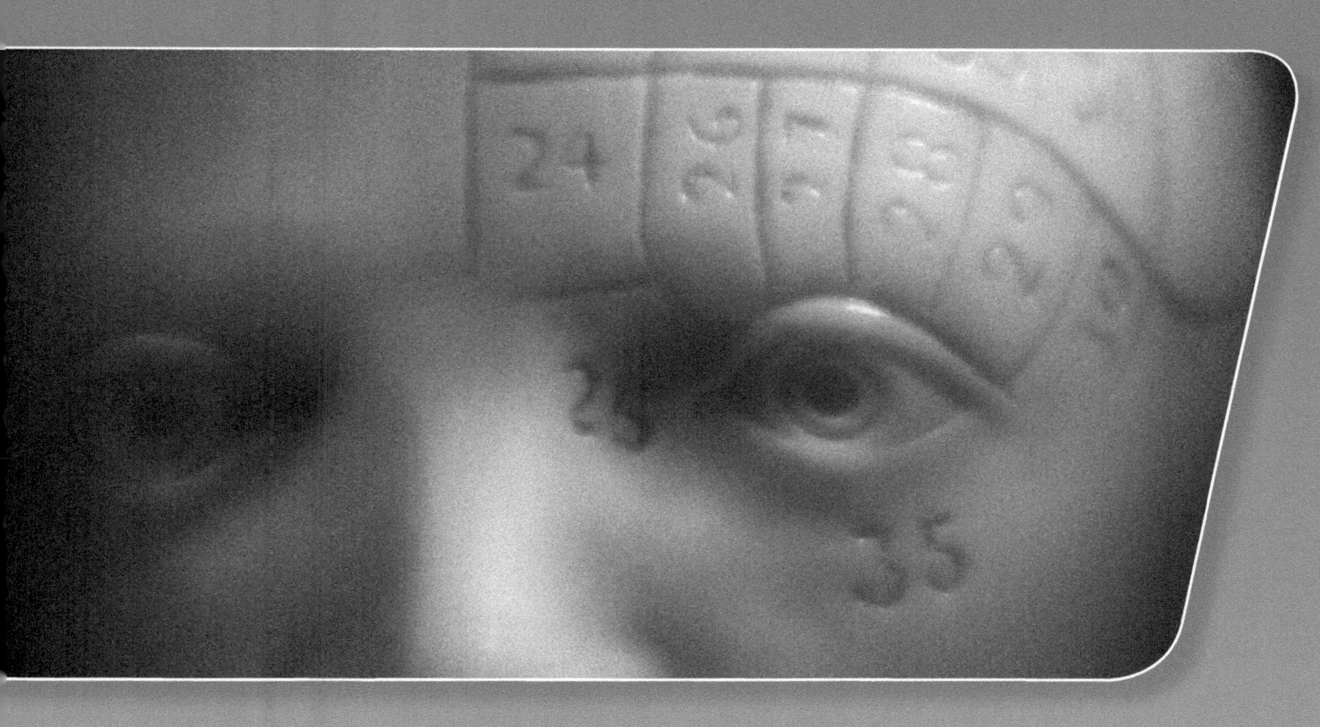

1 Introduction to researching the history of science

1.1 Questions, questions

Science and history

Not long ago it was quite unusual in the UK for a post-16-year-old student to study both history and science. The two subjects were seen as being very different. It was thought that students of each subject needed different strengths and qualities. Despite this, the history of science has attracted interest from scientists and historians for many years, and there have been many popular books on the subject. Some of the teachers of history of science courses and the writers of the books were originally scientists, some were historians and some are simply historians of science. Perhaps the differences between the two subjects are not that great (Figure 1).

▲ ***Figure 1*** *Stephen Hawking and Simon Schama: how different are they?*

Activity 1 *Science and history compared*

In small groups, discuss the following questions.

1 What do historians and scientists do that is similar?

2 In what ways are history and science different?

Asking questions

To be an historian of science, like both historians and scientists, you have to ask questions. Finding the right questions to ask may be the most difficult part of the work. When researching an historical event it is useful to start with the '5 W' questions:

- *What* happened?
- *Who* were the people involved?
- *When* did it happen?
- *Where* did it happen?
- *Why* did it happen?

The answers to these questions allow us to pose many more questions, such as what were the motives of the people involved, what were the influences on them, what were the consequences of the decisions and the actions that they made.

Note that some of the answers to these questions may be **objective facts** (dates, places, names) and others **subjective opinion** (motives, influences), and that the answers depend on the sources used. Some may also involve **speculation** (guessing!) about past or future events.

Project hint

The '5 W' questions provide a useful framework for analysing any source of information. Use them with the literature sources you consult for your Research project.

Activity 2 Finding answers

Practise answering the '5 W' questions listed on page 2 for a recent news item. The topic need not necessarily be scientific; it could be a sporting occasion or a celebrity event. Find out the answers to the '5 W' questions. What further questions would you like answered?

Historians and scientists need to be able to produce a report on their findings. Write a brief report (a few hundred words) on your chosen news item, ensuring that you answer all the questions that you have posed.

Further work

1. *This question may require you to look back on some work you would rather forget! Imagine that a scientific investigation that you have done previously (e.g. at GCSE) may be of historical significance. What questions should you pose and what answers would you give? Write a brief report on your historical research.*
2. *Read the following short extract from an article about killing pests. Analyse the article using the '5 W's and note any instances of speculation or opinion.*

“ ***Corpses of the dead kill the living***

A cheap eco-friendly alternative to pesticides will soon be tested in Tanzania.

The African army worm (*Spodoptera exempta*) can reach plague proportions, with over 1000 caterpillars per square metre, and wipe out over 90% of a maize crop. At the moment the only cost-effective way to control it is to bombard it with pesticides, but these have obvious disadvantages: a 1990 UN report estimated that 11 million farmers in Africa suffer from pesticide poisoning each year.

A more environmentally friendly solution is to use a kind of nucleopolyhedrovirus (NPV) that infects only the army worm. Applied in large quantities it can start a massive outbreak devastating the pest. But mass-producing viruses like NPV in the quantities required to tackle army worms costs more than pesticides.

So David Grzywacz at the University of Greenwich in London is instead copying a method used in Brazil to deal with outbreaks of the velvet bean caterpillar that feeds on soya. There, workers watch for outbreaks early in the season, infect the caterpillar with a virus, then collect tonnes of dead, virus laden caterpillars. The caterpillars can be mashed up and used as a spray to tackle later outbreaks.

This is significant because farmers are already used to spraying. 'The easier it is to use, the easier it will be to get them to adopt it,' says Grzywacz. He hopes mass production of NPV virus in Tanzania will enable the virus to be sold to farmers for just a tenth of the price of pesticides.

Randerson, J. (2003) New Scientist, ***2425***, *p.12* ”

1.2 Sources of evidence

Publishing scientific work

Answering questions requires **evidence**. To answer questions in the history of science there are a wide variety of sources of evidence. One important source of evidence is scientists' own accounts of their work. Scientists usually want to communicate their work to other scientists, and sometimes to the general public. They report on the work they have done by writing a paper for a scientific journal or by publishing a book or pamphlet.

Scientific journals began to appear in the late seventeenth century. For example, the Italian Galileo Galilei (1564–1642) described his discoveries in astronomy and mechanics early in the seventeenth century in books that he published (e.g. *The Starry Messenger* and *Discourses on Two New Sciences*). By the time that British scientist Isaac Newton (1642–1727) was discovering the law of gravitation, the Royal Society in London was producing its journal *Philosophical Transactions* – and it continues to do so in the present day. Today, there are thousands of scientific journals in many different languages. Some deal with particular topics in science while others cover a wider range of subjects. Many are published on the Internet as well as on paper.

For at least the last century, the accepted way of publishing scientific work has been by **peer review**. This means that the work is checked by other scientists before it is published.

Peer review and publication

The scientist (or, more commonly today, a group of scientists) writes a report on their work.

They choose which journal is appropriate for their work and send their report to the editor.

The journal editors (or their staff) look at the paper and decide who are the best qualified people to review it.

Copies of the paper are sent to the chosen reviewers. They read the paper, check it for errors and comment on whether the conclusions are justified.

The editor receives the comments from the reviewers and decides whether to publish the paper.

Peer review is usually anonymous, so the authors of the paper do not know who reviewed it.

Sometimes the editor may return the paper and ask for changes to be made before it is published; this sometimes involves passing on comments from the reviewers.

A paper refused by one journal may be accepted by another.

The process often takes months, but for exciting bits of research the editor may rush things through in a week or two.

Sometimes, if scientists want to establish their priority in a discovery, they can send a letter or a brief summary of their work to a journal which the editor may decide to publish without peer review.

Comment on a scientific discovery may be found in other papers written at about the same time by supporters and opponents of the main characters in the story. Contemporary magazines and newspapers may also provide commentary. Magazines such as *New Scientist* provide a week-by-week summary of scientific news and controversy.

Resource link

New Scientist can be accessed online.

A variety of sources

Project hint

You will need to consult a variety of resources for your Research project, such as those mentioned here.

Scientists usually keep notebooks to record their results and observations. Although scribbled notes often get thrown away, many scientists keep their laboratory notebooks safe so that they can refer to them at a later date. Marie Curie (Figure 2) discovered radium in 1898, and her notebook is well looked after – it's still radioactive a century after she did her work. Letters also provide an important source, especially as scientists often reported their discoveries to their contemporaries by this method.

▲ ***Figure 2*** Marie Curie (1867–1943), a Polish-French scientist who researched radioactivity.

As well as the written word there are other sources of information. For more recent history there may be audio-visual recordings of radio and TV news items or programmes, or recorded interviews with scientists.

There are also artefacts. Most scientists do experiments; while instruments, apparatus and materials are often reused, passed on or disposed of, many items are kept and sometimes locked away in cupboards and forgotten. One unusual artefact is the blackboard that Albert Einstein scribbled on during a visit to Oxford University. It is stored at the Museum of the History of Science in Oxford.

Finally, the place where the research took place may reveal answers to questions. Some of the places where famous scientists worked have been preserved (Figure 3), others have been neglected while many have totally changed.

All the sources of evidence mentioned so far have been **primary sources**. They are contemporary with the event or the lifetime of the characters. All the objects are produced or used by the people involved in the event, and the accounts are written or spoken by people who were either actively involved in the event or eye-witnesses to it.

Secondary sources include biographies, books, articles and programmes about scientific topics and general histories of science, usually written after the event and by people who were not directly involved. Such sources can be very useful to the historian, particularly to the student. This is because someone else has done the primary research for you.

▲ ***Figure 3*** Michael Faraday's laboratory at the Royal Institution in London is preserved as he left it in the 1860s.

A particular problem with relying on secondary sources for information about a historical event is that you are stuck with the writer's interpretation of the primary evidence. It may be a surprise to some people but historians and scientists can interpret the same evidence in a variety of ways. These viewpoints may be political so that, for example, you have the Marxist view of history or the feminist slant on discoveries. It is probably impossible to be totally objective in analysing a piece of evidence but you must be aware of the different viewpoints of writers and commentators.

Activity 3 *Comparing sources*

Either: Choose a recent discovery, invention or obituary of a scientist. Find reports about your chosen event in scientific journals, newspapers and any other medium that you have access to. Analyse each report by writing a few words in response to each of the '5 W's. Then write one or two sentences to answer the following questions:

- Does it answer the questions that you would pose?
- How is the event reported?
- Who is the intended audience?

Or: Compare the two extracts printed below. Analyse each report by writing a few words in response to each of the '5 W's. Then write one or two sentences to answer the following questions:

- Which readers are the articles aimed at?
- What differences are there in the way the information is presented? For instance, does one report present more details about the event/discovery? Is one account more supportive than the other?

" ***Global dimming***

Human activity is making the planet darker as well as warmer, scientists say. They believe levels of sunlight reaching the Earth's surface have declined by up to 20% in recent years because air pollution is reflecting it back into space and helping to make bigger, longer-lasting clouds.

The 'global-dimming' effect could have implications for everything from the effectiveness of solar power to the growth of plants and trees. 'Over the past couple of years it's become clear that the solar irradiance at the Earth's surface has decreased' said Jim Hansen, a climate scientist with NASA's Goddard Institute for Space Studies in New York.

Experts say that global dimming is probably down to tiny particles such as soot and chemical compounds such as sulphates accumulating in the atmosphere. 'Data from 100 stations around the world show that the amount of black carbon in the atmosphere is twice as big as we assumed' said Dr Hansen.

Guardian, *18 December 2003* "

" ***Organic catalyst breaks alcohol record***

A simple and effective catalyst for an important organic transformation has been disclosed by three chemists at the Universidad de Oviedo in Spain. Jose Gimeno, Victorio Cadierno and Sergio Garcia-Garrido looked at the ability of a readily available ruthenium complex to convert allylic alcohols into saturated aldehydes or ketones, and they struck gold.

An interest in green chemistry or, as the authors put it, in developing 'catalytic processes with atom efficiency in environmentally friendly media and with industrial application' provided all the motivation necessary. They chose to investigate this particular reaction, they say, because it is useful but generally requires two steps and is rarely successful in water.

The chemists show how their catalyst can quickly and completely synthesise ketones from allylic alcohols in one step and in water. The ruthenium complex they chose as a catalyst is stable in water and comes from a group of such complexes that are widely used in organic synthesis. Unusually, their ruthenium is in the +4 oxidation state; ruthenium(II) complexes are more commonly used.

'As far as we know this is the most efficient catalyst described to date for this important transformation', says Gimeno.

C. Evans, *Chem. World*, 2004, **1**(1), 15 and C. Evans, *Chem. Sci.*, 2004, **1**(1) C3 – *Reproduced by permission of the Royal Society of Chemistry* ”

Further work

1. *Look at the science section in a recent issue of a national newspaper. What topics are covered? Choose one topic. Summarise the content of the article. Does it answer the basic questions of historical evidence? What is the attitude of the author?*
2. *Most scientists are in favour of peer review but some oppose it. Discuss the advantages and disadvantages of peer review.*
3. *In what ways do you think the Internet might affect the communication of scientific work?*

1.3 Researching information

At this stage you might have the opportunity to visit an academic library, either in a university or as part of an organisation (such as the Wellcome Trust) specialising in the history of science, technology and medicine. During your visit, notice how publications are arranged and catalogued. Have a look at some scientific journals and see how papers are set out, with headings, references and acknowledgements. If possible, compare the styles of more recent journals with some from earlier centuries. Talk to the library staff and note the name of anyone who might be able to help you use the library on a future occasion.

Project hint

This sort of library can be a rich source of material for your Research project.

2 Cold fusion

This is the first of four case studies in the history of science. The history of science is a vast subject and it is impossible, in just a few weeks' work, to give a comprehensive treatment. Instead, we have presented four case studies to allow you to study some topics in depth. These case studies have been chosen from different areas of science and different periods of history. They are all controversial in some way and show that 'progress' in science can be far from smooth. All are designed to help you develop skills in historical research, and this should be the focus of your work rather than the learning of facts.

2.1 Out of the blue

Meet the press

On 23 March 1989, Stanley Pons and Martin Fleischmann, researchers at the University of Utah in the United States, issued a news release and called a press conference. They announced:

> “***A simple experiment results in sustained nuclear fusion***
>
> ... the discovery will be relatively easy to make into a usable technology for generating heat and power. ... this generation of heat continues over long periods and is so large that it can only be attributed to a nuclear process.”

At the press conference they described experiments in which a piece of palladium, about 2 cm long and 0.5 cm in diameter, had reached 100 °C within a few minutes. Power output from the palladium was about 26 W/cm^3, which was around four times the power they had supplied to it. At one stage, the apparatus had reached a temperature of several thousand degrees, vaporising the palladium and destroying a fume cupboard.

Their announcement of cold fusion attracted interest across the world and newspapers, TV and radio news reports were full of their discovery. You can read the full reports from *The Times* newspaper online.

Resource link

The *Times* archive can be accessed online.

The cold fusion men

Martin Fleischmann (Figure 4, left) is the senior scientist of the pair. He was born in Czechoslovakia in 1927 and his family fled to Britain at the outbreak of the Second World War. He was educated at Imperial College, London and

◀ ***Figure 4*** Martin Fleischmann (left) and Stanley Pons.

became a respected chemist and expert in electrolysis. In 1967 he became Professor of Electrochemistry at the University of Southampton in the UK. Fleischmann had the reputation of being thoughtful and methodical in his work and not prone to making wild statements.

Stanley Pons (Figure 4, right) is an American scientist born in 1943. He was a student of Fleischmann's and they worked together between 1985 and 1988. They had written over 20 scientific papers together on uncontroversial aspects of electrochemistry which were accepted by their scientific colleagues. Pons had been appointed to a job at the University of Utah. Pons was the enthusiast. He had apparently had the idea of cold fusion a few years before and persuaded Fleischmann to join him in the research. They invested $100,000 of their own money in their research. There was a third man in the team: Marvin Hawkins had made many of the measurements that Pons and Fleischmann reported, but he wasn't mentioned in the cold fusion paper.

Activity 4 *Cold fusion – hot news*

Refer to the *Times* extracts that follow on pages 10–13 and discuss the following questions. Spend a few minutes jotting down brief notes for each question then compare your ideas with other students.

1 What scientific observations led Fleischmann and Pons to claim they had produced cold fusion?

2 What was unusual about Pons and Fleischmann's announcement on 23 March 1989?

3 How do the reports treat the story over the week after the announcement?

4 From your reading of the events, what is your opinion of Pons and Fleischmann's discovery? Can you tell whether their discovery is correct? Why do you think they announced their discovery in this way?

5 Why did the world's media react in such an excited manner? (Not every scientific announcement gets such coverage.)

Cold fusion – hot news

“***Scientists claim energy breakthrough***

Two scientists from Britain and America last night claimed to have carried out controlled nuclear fusion in a test tube. If confirmed, their discovery could become the greatest breakthrough of the century. Professor Martin Fleischmann, of Southampton University, and Professor Stan Pons, of the University of Utah, released the results of research which could open the door to a limitless source of 'clean' energy. … their discovery came from a very modest experiment.

In studies costing a few thousand pounds, the two professors say they have succeeded where international research teams, spending hundreds of millions of pounds a year for the past 20 years, have failed. The scientists believe they have shown that the process of nuclear fusion, which includes the type of energetic reactions that power the sun and is the source of the destructive force of the H-bomb, can be reproduced in a test tube by electro-chemistry. …

Wright, P., Science Editor, The Times, *Edition 5*, Friday 24 March 1989*”

“***Fusion energy scientists defend claims***

The British and American scientists who claim to have solved the problem of harnessing fusion energy, opening the door to a limitless source of power, yesterday defended their results against the restrained scepticism of the scientific establishment. The two scientists … are under siege because they have released an outline of their experiments before publication of the full details. The announcement by the University of Utah contained too few technical details for an expert independent assessment. …

The scientists claim to have achieved what is known as cold fusion. Most attempts to achieve controlled hydrogen fusion have assumed that hydrogen must first be heated to a temperature near that of the Sun. The power generated in fusion is the huge amount of surplus nuclear energy that is released when two atoms of a light element, such as deuterium or tritium, are forced together to form a heavier one. Thousands of millions of pounds have been poured into attempts over the past 30 years to harness fusion energy. … But scientists have been unable to sustain a fusion reaction that mimics the Sun. Now the two professors have said this has been done at room temperature in a vessel that is comparable to a car battery. The acid is replaced by deuterium-containing heavy water and the plates, or electrodes, between which the electric current flows, are made in the fusion cell from precious metals, platinum and palladium. Powerful electric currents cause a reaction in which deuterium is absorbed by the palladium. … The scientists are convinced that fusion, rather than a conventional chemical reaction, is happening because of the very large amounts of heat released. …

Spokesmen for important fusion research centres … were reluctant to comment formally without more details. But they expressed private doubts.

Wright, P., Science Editor, The Times, *Edition 5*, Saturday 25 March 1989*”

“*Fizzing dream of nuclear fusion*

A liquid fizzing in a test tube at the Atomic Energy Authority's Harwell research establishment in Oxfordshire could realize or dash a scientific dream. … The dream, pursued for more than 30 years, is the achievement of nuclear fusion by chemical means. If surplus energy from fusion power can be harnessed, it promises a virtually unlimited source of energy because sea water can provide the basic fuel.

… Now a team of physicists, chemists, specialists in material science and energy experts, led by Dr David Williams, at Harwell, is trying to duplicate the Utah experiment. …

Wright, P. Science Editor, The Times, *Edition 1, Monday 27 March 1989* ”

“*Doubts growing on claims of nuclear fusion experiment*

Growing doubts are being cast on claims by a British scientist to have discovered a way of triggering nuclear reactions which could form a source of virtually limitless power. … Until now it has been widely believed that the only way to trigger fusion reactions was to use temperatures of tens of millions of degrees C to force the mutually repelling deuterium nuclei together. The team at Harwell may be the first to confirm that there is another, far simpler, electrical way of achieving the fusion and subsequent release of energy. However, there are growing indications that if fusion takes place in Professor Fleischmann's reaction vessel at all, it will be at such a low level that it may never be of practical use.

A rival fusion research team, at Brigham Young University also in Utah, has been running a similar experiment since last September. So far the team

◀ ***Figure 5*** Cold fusion could replace conventional power stations like this one.

has refused to divulge the results. However, *The Times* understands it has also found that fusion can be created electrochemically, but the amount of fusion taking place is so low it may be of academic interest only. Over the weekend researchers at Princeton University, site of one of the world's largest conventional fusion machines, have also tried to re-create the experiment, so far without success.

Professor Fleischmann said [that] in the best experiment so far, the vessel had produced 20 watts of [power], somewhat more than the amount put in. He said a better designed experiment should be able to produce 10 times more energy than it needed to start the reactions.

Matthews, R., Technology Correspondent, The Times, *Edition 5*, Tuesday 28 March 1989* ❞

❝ ***Scientist confident of fusion results***

The British scientist at the centre of claims to have discovered a new source of potentially limitless supplies of energy said yesterday that he was 'very confident' that backing for his claims would emerge in the next 12 weeks. …

However, fellow scientists have criticized his claims and how they were made public. Professor Fleischmann said: 'We went public because a lot of incorrect information was leaking out. My feeling is that we need to provide answers before the end of three months. At the moment I am very confident the experiment will be recreated. … I think people are entirely justified in being sceptical because this is something so extraordinary, but with my colleagues in the US we have got to the point where no other explanation will do, except that a form of fusion is produced.' However, nuclear fusion experts yesterday reiterated their view that whatever is responsible for the large amounts of heat being generated, it could not be nuclear fusion.

Matthews, R., Technology Correspondent, The Times, *Edition 3*, Wednesday 29 March 1989* ❞

❝ ***Wishing and fusing***

The bicycle was not a great breakthrough in scientific theory. All the necessary knowledge was already familiar to mathematicians. The same may yet be true of the new scientific sensation, test-tube nuclear fusion, which has been exciting both the lay and specialist public since the first results were announced with a flourish from the University of Utah. The theory is simple, no more complex than the theory of the bicycle, provided one can take the mysterious phenomenon of nuclear tunneling on trust. But apparently no one actually thought of doing what University of Utah scientists and Southampton colleagues too have now done. They have passed an electrical current through heavy water, using a cathode of palladium. They claim to have generated energy, in the form of heat, which cannot be explained by the normal theory of electrolysis; and they claim to have detected the emission of neutrons, suggesting that something very remarkable was taking place, low energy nuclear fusion at room temperature.

Other scientists are now attempting to reproduce their results. The focus of attention is on the nuclear laboratory at Harwell, where one of the originators of this technique, Professor Martin Fleischmann of Southampton University, is assisting. Fusion, particularly using heavy water, is the Holy Grail of nuclear science, the physicists' equivalent of a universal cure for cancer. It promises an energy supply which is almost unlimited, cheap, and virtually pollution free. If Professor Fleischmann and Professor Stan Pons of Utah really have unlocked its secrets, they will be entitled to Nobel prizes in profusion. But they will be well aware of how many reputations have been broken already on this wheel. The conventional wisdom so far has been that nuclear fusion can only be expected as a result of the expenditure of enormous quantities of energy in the most extraordinary circumstances, similar to the conditions in the interior of the sun.

The story resembles that of super-conductivity, which was long thought to occur only at temperatures close to absolute zero, but which now seems to be theoretically possible at room temperatures. This is undoubtedly part of the popular appeal of both projects. They transfer the domain of research from the exotic and even esoteric mysteries of the high energy or low temperature laboratory to the familiar world of the domestic kitchen, or at least the A-level physics class.

Scientists are naturally sceptical people. In this case they are particularly so, because the results have not been announced through the usual scientific channels, the learned article in a professional journal or paper at a professional symposium. It is an accepted custom in the scientific world that someone who claims to have made a discovery should issue publicly, through such channels, enough information for others to set up their own experiments to verify the results. For whatever reason, in which commercial considerations are no doubt present, the Utah-Southampton discovery has been made known with more than the usual amount of public relations hyperbole, less than the usual amount of technical detail. But there is all the difference in the world between scepticism and cynicism. The former simply asks for proof; the latter mocks. Until someone has disproved the phenomenon of test-tube nuclear fusion he who mocks is on no safer ground than he who boasts. We must all watch and wait; and the one thing that, above all else, is sure about scientific discovery is that wishes make no difference.

Leading Article, The Times, *Edition 1, Wednesday 29 March 1989* ”

Activity 5 *23/03/89 reviewed*

Using the *Times* articles above, write a summary account of the events answering the what, who, when, where, why questions. Look for examples of objective factual reporting, speculation and subjective opinion, and note these in your summary. Present your summary in the form of short notes, using headings and bullet points.

Project hint

When summarising information, aim to be brief and clear. Using headings and bullet points is often better than writing complete sentences. You will find this technique useful when gathering information for your Research project.

2.2 Fusion hot and cold

To understand the excitement over cold fusion we need to understand a little of the science behind the work and something of the history of fusion.

The power of the Sun

Nuclear fusion is the process that powers the stars, including the Sun, and makes them shine. Put simply, it is the joining together of light nuclei to form nuclei of heavier elements. Two of the nuclear reactions in the Sun are:

$^{2}_{1}H + ^{2}_{1}H \rightarrow ^{3}_{1}H + ^{1}_{1}H$

$^{2}_{1}H + ^{2}_{1}H \rightarrow ^{3}_{2}He + ^{1}_{0}n$

Nuclei are made up of protons, which have positive charge, and neutrons, which are uncharged.

$^{1}_{1}H$ is a nucleus of ordinary hydrogen. The lower '1' indicates that it contains one proton, and the upper '1' that it is made up of just one particle – so no neutrons. All hydrogen nuclei contain just one proton.

$^{2}_{1}H$ is a type of hydrogen called deuterium, which has a neutron in its nucleus as well as the proton (two particles in total, hence the upper '2'). It is sometimes represented by the symbol $^{2}_{1}D$ (or just D). An atom of deuterium has twice the mass of an ordinary hydrogen atom so it is sometimes known as 'heavy hydrogen'.

$^{3}_{1}H$ is another type of hydrogen, called tritium. It has three particles in its nucleus – one proton and two neutrons. Tritium also has the symbol $^{3}_{1}T$ or T.

$^{1}_{1}H$, $^{2}_{1}H$ and $^{3}_{1}H$ are all isotopes of hydrogen – the same element, but with different numbers of neutrons giving the nucleus different properties.

Nuclear reactions involve a redistribution of protons and neutrons. There is the same number of each before and after the reaction, but they are combined in different ways. In the second reaction given above, two deuterium nuclei produce a single nucleus of helium (symbol $^{3}_{2}He$, made of 2 protons and 1 neutron) and a 'spare' neutron, with symbol $^{1}_{0}n$.

The origin of the Sun's power was worked out in the 1930s and 40s. An important part of the story was Albert Einstein's theory of relativity, published in 1905, which included the famous equation $E = mc^2$. This equation shows that a small loss of mass, m, releases a very large amount of energy, E (c is the speed of light, 3×10^8 m/s). When light nuclei fuse together a small amount of mass is lost. The energy is released as electromagnetic radiation (gamma rays) and the reacting material gets hot.

There is one major problem in getting nuclei to fuse. They carry a positive charge, so when they get close together they repel one another. Usually this means that nuclei cannot get close enough together for fusion to occur. The Sun and other stars get around this because they are so massive. The force of gravity pulls the nuclei together and they become very hot. At the temperatures in the middle of the Sun, over ten million degrees Celsius, the nuclei are moving so fast that they slam into each other with enormous energy, and despite the repulsion they get close enough together for the fusion reactions to take place.

Weapons

The two nuclear bombs dropped on Japan at the end of the Second World War released the energy of nuclear fission. Fission occurs with some isotopes of heavy elements, such as uranium-235. The heavy nucleus splits up into fragments when bombarded by neutrons. The total mass of the fragments is less than the heavy nucleus, so energy is released.

Project hint

A question about the uses of nuclear fusion could form a good starting point for a Research project.

After the war, scientists in the USA, Britain and Russia (then the USSR) looked for ways of making nuclear weapons even more destructive. They realised that nuclear fusion was the answer. In the early 1950s each of the three countries developed what was called the hydrogen bomb (H-bomb) or thermonuclear bomb. In these weapons a small nuclear fission bomb made of uranium heats some tritium to a very high temperature so that it undergoes fusion reactions and releases even more energy.

Nuclear power

Alongside the nuclear weapons research, scientists were trying to find ways of using nuclear power for peaceful purposes – using the energy released from nuclear processes to drive machinery that generates electricity. Nuclear fission is relatively easy to control and the first nuclear-powered electricity-generating stations were built in the 1950s. But nuclear fusion has proved to be far more difficult (Figure 6). Since the 1950s scientists have been suggesting that the goal of producing a small sun in the laboratory was just around the

◀ ***Figure 6*** The JET prototype nuclear fusion reactor.

corner. Billions of dollars have been spent in the USA, Russia and Europe on experiments designed to achieve the conditions necessary for controlled fusion. Two main methods have been tried.

In the first, isotopes of hydrogen are heated to temperatures of 100 million degrees Celsius. Of course there is no material that can hold something this hot. Instead, magnetic fields are used to contain the fast-moving, positively charged nuclei. Keeping control of the nuclei, getting them to crash together and removing the energy produced has proved to be an immense engineering problem. Scientists have inched towards their goal but it is still said to be 50 years away.

The second method involves firing immensely powerful lasers at a tiny bead of solid tritium. The lasers squeeze the bead until the nuclei are forced together. The idea is sound but again the engineering problems have so far been too great for success to be achieved. Nuclear fusion has remained a source of energy that is tantalisingly out of our reach.

The principles of cold fusion

The experiment set up by Pons and Fleischmann is in two parts. First of all, so-called heavy water is electrolysed. Heavy water is water (H_2O) made from deuterium instead of ordinary hydrogen. When water is electrolysed, hydrogen is formed at the cathode (the negative electrode) and oxygen is formed at the anode (the positive electrode). The electrolysis of heavy water produces deuterium (heavy hydrogen) and oxygen. Pure ordinary water or heavy water does not conduct electricity very well so other substances have to be added. Pons and Fleischmann dissolved sodium chloride and other metal salts in their heavy water.

If electrodes made of carbon or copper are used, the hydrogen or deuterium is given off as a gas, but Pons and Fleischmann used palladium for the cathode (Figure 7). Palladium and a few other metals have the property of being able

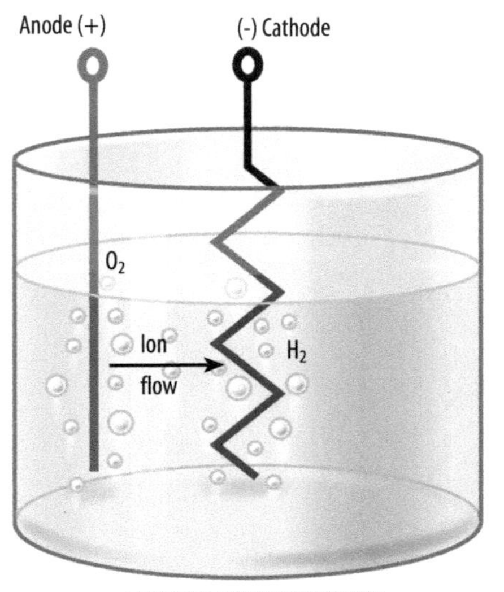

The cathode is palladium in a typical heavy water cell and nickel in a typical light water cell. The CETI cell contains layers of nickel palladium and copper.

The electrolyte is light or heavy water and a salt. The salt is usually lithium sulfate.

◀ ***Figure 7*** Schematic diagram of cold-fusion electrolysis apparatus.

to absorb hydrogen and deuterium. The small deuterium atoms are trapped in the gaps between the larger palladium atoms.

Pons and Fleischmann suggested that when they had been running their electrolysis for a while the deuterium atoms became so tightly packed into the palladium that they started to fuse together. They said that it was this fusion that produced the energy they had measured. They should also have been detecting the other products of fusion – helium atoms, tritium atoms, neutrons and high-energy electromagnetic radiation (gamma rays).

Alternative routes to cold fusion

Pons and Fleischmann were not the only scientists working on a route to nuclear fusion that did not require very high temperatures. Steve Jones at Brigham Young University, also in Utah, USA, had come up with another idea. Jones's plan involved swapping the electron around the deuterium atom with muons. Muons are rare particles that resemble electrons but with 200 times more mass. A deuterium atom with a muon instead of an electron would be very much smaller than a normal deuterium atom. Jones thought that it would be possible to pack these atoms together, perhaps in palladium, and achieve fusion.

Activity 6 *Understanding fusion*

Check your understanding of nuclear fusion by answering the questions below.

1 Explain, in one or two sentences, what is meant by nuclear fusion.

2 What is the difference between cold fusion suggested by Pons and Fleischmann and 'hot' fusion in stars and thermonuclear bombs?

3 Pons and Fleischmann said that their experiment gave out more energy than was put in. Why was an energy input needed?

4 What evidence would be required to show that fusion was taking place in Pons and Fleischmann's experiment?

5 From what you have learned about nuclear fusion, why were physicists surprised by Pons and Fleischmann's announcement?

2.3 The scientific world responds

Rush to replicate

The usual fate of a paper published in scientific journals is that many scientists will read it, some will mention it in their own work and a few may repeat the experiments. Only rarely will the announcement of a discovery spur scientists to put their own work aside in order to try out the new idea. Cold fusion was one such discovery.

The unusual way in which Pons and Fleischmann announced their results stirred scientists across the world to try out the experiment. Governments were interested too. The United States government was spending billions on 'hot' fusion research. Was all this investment wasted when fusion could be done on a bench top in a small electrolysis cell? Scientists in university and government labs were instructed to test Pons and Fleischmann's claims.

The University of Utah set up the National Cold Fusion Institute to patent Pons and Fleischmann's invention and continue the research. (Patenting a discovery is a legal process designed to ensure that the owner of the patent keeps the right to any profit made from the discovery.) The university invested $5 million and asked the USA government for another $25 million. Soon the journals and newspapers were reporting the findings.

Activity 7 Does cold fusion work?

Below are some extracts from articles in *New Scientist* magazine from April to July 1989. (If you have access to the *New Scientist* archive then you can read the whole articles). Read the extracts then discuss and write answers to the questions that follow.

1. Did the initial reports accept or reject Pons and Fleischmann's claims about cold fusion?
2. Pons and Fleischmann are chemists. What was the attitude of physicists to the discovery? Why might the attitude of physicists be different from that of chemists?
3. The reports reprinted here came just a few weeks after the original announcement of cold fusion. Do you think this is time for accurate attempts to replicate Pons and Fleischmann's experiment?
4. Why do you think the groups in Tokyo, Texas and at Brigham Young University in Utah reported their results so quickly?
5. At this point in the story, what is your opinion of Pons and Fleischmann's work?

Resource link

The *New Scientist* archive can be accessed online.

“***Japanese mimic cold fusion***

A group led by Noboru Koyama at the Tokyo University of Agriculture and Technology's Faculty of Engineering has duplicated the room-temperature nuclear fusion reaction achieved by researchers at Utah University, the Japanese newspaper *Nihon Keizai Shimbun* reported on Tuesday.

The group used the same method as the Utah groups, in which a palladium cathode applied an electric current through heavy water. The Tokyo team said that large amounts of heat were evolved, and gamma-rays and uranium detected, suggesting that nuclear fusion had occurred. However, neutron release has yet to be confirmed. The group plans to begin joint experiments with the Japan Atomic Energy Research Institute to confirm whether the reaction releases neutrons.

New Scientist, *8 April 1989*”

“ *Test-tube fusion experiment repeated*

An American nuclear physicist confirmed last week the recent claims of two chemists that by electrolysing heavy water in a simple cell at room temperature they achieved nuclear fusion. However, Steven Jones of Brigham Young University in Utah warned that his group's experiments produced only extremely small amounts of energy – in fact, 13 orders of magnitude lower than that claimed by the chemists.

Hall, N. and Beard, J. New Scientist, *8 April 1989* ”

“ *Texans repeat cold fusion*

Scientists in Texas said this week that they may have duplicated the experiment in Utah last month that reportedly created heat from 'cold' fusion in a test tube. The electrochemical reaction, carried out at Texas Agricultural and Mechanical University in College Station, produced between 50 and 80 per cent more energy than was put in.

New Scientist, *15 April 1989* ”

“ *Physics community strikes back in debate over cold fusion*

Physicists debunked claims of cold fusion in a test tube this week at the annual meeting of the American Physical Society. It was the first time physicists have gathered to compare notes on the claim, made in March by two chemists in Utah, that through fusion produced in a test tube, they generated at least four times as much heat as they put into the experiment. Since then, scores of laboratories around the world have tried, and generally failed, to replicate the experiment, by Martin Fleischmann of the University of Southampton and Stanley Pons of the University of Utah.

As strongly as chemists tried to support the claims at the meeting last month of the American Chemical Society, physicists here all but ridiculed it. The bluntest assessment came from Steven Koonin, a theoretical physicist from the University of California at Santa Barbara. 'We are suffering from the incompetence and perhaps delusion of doctors Pons and Fleischmann,' he said.

The longest applause, however, went to a chemist, Nathan Lewis of the California Institute of Technology. After exhaustive attempts to duplicate the Pons-Fleischmann experiment, Lewis's team found no signs of unusually high heat. Nor did the investigators detect neutrons, tritium, gamma-rays or helium, all of which would accompany a fusion reaction.

Joyce, C. (Baltimore) New Scientist, *6 May 1989* ”

“ *Science: Physicists deal cold fusion a theoretical blow*

Cold nuclear fusion cannot occur on a significant scale in an electrochemical cell. This is the conclusion of Anthony Leggett and Gordon Baym of the University of Illinois at Urbana-Champaign after taking a close theoretical look at fusion. The argument that the two theorists have developed will be very difficult to refute because it is based on general considerations.

Ojha, P. New Scientist, *29 July 1989* ”

Further work

Write a summary report of the work done in support of, and opposition to, cold fusion in April–July 1989. Use the '5 W's to help you decide what to include. Present your summary in the form of headings and brief, clear notes.

2.4 The tide turns

As summer turned to autumn in 1989, more and more laboratories reported the results of their experiments on cold fusion. Many people were now involved and millions of dollars were being spent to check Pons and Fleischmann's claims.

Activity 8 *Opposition to cold fusion*

Read the extracts from *New Scientist* magazine and the articles on the websites listed in the resource link. Then discuss and answer the questions that follow.

(Note: A calorimeter is an instrument for measuring the heat given out in a reaction.)

1. Did Lewis and Williams detect heat given out by the cold fusion cells as Pons and Fleischmann claimed?
2. If the heat was not produced by cold fusion, what did Lewis think caused it?
3. What did Williams think was the reason for Pons and Fleischmann's conclusion?
4. Since they found no evidence of cold fusion, was Lewis and Williams' work a waste of time?
5. Why was Williams' work at Harwell important in determining scientists' attitudes to cold fusion?
6. What do you think was the outcome of the Department of Energy report?

Resource link

The USA Department of Energy inquiry into cold fusion report is available online.

“ ***Cold water on cold fusion***

A jury of scientists judging claims on 'cold' fusion is expected to register a distinct lack of enthusiasm when it presents its verdict in Washington DC this week. 'We are not persuaded,' John Huizenga, chairman of a panel that has studied such claims since May, said on Monday. The panel's report to the Department of Energy advises against spending the $25 million that adherents of cold fusion in Utah want. Instead, it recommends only 'modest' support through normal, peer-reviewed procedures.

New Scientist, *11 November 1989* ”

“ *Science: Test-tube fusion fails the final test*

Cold fusion has staggered back into the headlines with the announcement last week that two teams in Japan had repeated the process (*This Week*, 9 December). However, their announcements come just after the appearance of two scientific papers which raise doubts about the measurements of energy production and the interpretation of these measurements made by the first team to create 'test-tube fusion' …

Nathan Lewis and a team of researchers at the California Institute of Technology (Caltech) in Pasadena have analysed the data produced by Fleischmann and Pons. They say: 'The raw data that reflect the actual magnitude and conditions of the observed excess power production were not presented in the original description of the work' (*Science*, vol. 246, p. 793). In other words, when Fleischmann and Pons presented the results of their work in a 'preliminary paper' – a follow-up has yet to see the light of day – they did not publish their data (*Journal of Electroanalytical Chemistry*, vol. 261, p. 301).

Lewis and his colleagues present the raw data and their analysis of the measurements. They find some strange increases after a time in the temperature of the electrochemical cells – Fleischmann and Pons have always said that it takes time for the process to begin. However, they go on to say: 'These changes were clearly caused by changes in the heat transfer from the cells, rather than by some additional heating mechanism …'

After they had recalibrated the cells, the scientists found that the heat produced was no more than they would have expected, given the electrical input. 'Without recalibration of the cell,' they say, 'such temperature increases could have been interpreted in terms of increased power production.'

A second team of scientists has also tried to repeat the experiments. David Williams and a team from the Harwell laboratory of the United Kingdom Atomic Energy Authority, and Imperial College, London, had Fleischmann as a consultant. They point to problems with the calorimeters used to measure the heat output from the cells (*Nature*, vol. 342, p. 375).

Williams and his team used three different types of calorimeter, including copies of the design used by Fleischmann and Pons. Of the latter, the Harwell researchers say: 'We found these to be inaccurate instruments with some very subtle sources of error …'

The Harwell scientists also counted the neutrons produced by their cells. Their equipment was between 100,000 and a million times as sensitive as the neutron detectors employed by Fleischmann and Pons. They conclude: 'It seems unlikely that any greatly enhanced fusion process associated with the absorption of deuterium into palladium, giving rise to neutron emission, is occurring.'

New Scientist, *16 December 1989* ”

Ups and downs

Despite the reports dismissing cold fusion, the story refused to fade away. In December 1989, Japanese researchers announced that they had proof that hydrogen absorbed by palladium underwent fusion. In March 1990, 200 people attended a conference at the University of Utah to report work done at the National Cold Fusion Institute. Pons was still very confident and the Director of the Institute, Fritz Will, said that they had made 'solid progress'. The Institute continued to receive the support of the President of the University of Utah, Chase Peterson.

While the conference was celebrating, another Utah researcher, Michael Salaman, was publishing a damning paper on cold fusion. Salaman had attempted to measure the gamma rays supposedly given off by Pons's own apparatus but had failed to find any. He concluded that cold fusion was not happening. The row that followed between Pons and Salaman created as much heat as the cold fusion experiment.

Support for cold fusion drained away. In June 1990 Peterson was forced to retire from his position at the university. Pons and Fleischmann still refused to divulge all their data saying that it could harm their patent applications. The patents were published in November 1990 and proved to be just as vague as Pons and Fleischmann's press announcements.

In November 1990, Pons was due to appear before a panel that was judging whether the University of Utah's money had been well spent. Pons failed to appear. Even his lawyer did not know where he was. In an unusual move, Pons faxed the university asking for a year away from his post starting immediately. Meanwhile, Fleischmann was back in the UK and not fully aware of what was happening in Utah.

Further work

1. *Why do you think Pons and Fleischmann were reluctant to publish all their work or let other people close to their apparatus?*
2. *What could be the reasons for Pons' disappearance and failure to attend the panel reviewing his work?*
3. *Outline the role of the University of Utah in the story.*

2.5 The return of cold fusion

Cold fusion then and now

In January 1991, Frank Close, a distinguished British physicist, published a book on the cold fusion saga (*Too hot to handle*, published by W H Allen). Close accused Pons of altering some data to fit his conclusions and of giving contradictory answers to questions. He also pointed out that up to March 1989, Pons and Fleischmann had not done control experiments with ordinary water replacing the heavy water in their electrolysis cell.

Close's dismissal of cold fusion did not put everyone off. John Bockris at Texas Agricultural and Mechanical University continued to defend cold fusion. He admitted the difficulty in getting the experiments to replicate Pons and Fleischmann's results but he was convinced that something remarkable was happening.

Nevertheless, support for Pons and Fleischmann at Utah had ebbed away and they were sacked from the National Cold Fusion Institute. They had not given up, however, and got new backers from Japan to support their work at a private research laboratory in France. In the years that followed they made further announcements of their success.

Work continued elsewhere as well. In January 1992 an explosion occurred in a laboratory in California, killing one scientist. The cause of the explosion was deuterium reacting with oxygen given off in a cold fusion cell. Then, in 1994, the Japanese company, Canon, applied for patents for a different type of cold fusion.

Long after stories of cold fusion had disappeared from the journals, it was reported that the United States navy was still interested. A report in 2002 from navy scientists did not use the term cold fusion but it was clear from the description of the work they had done that they were repeating Pons and Fleischmann's experiment. The results were still unclear but the story is not over yet (see Davis, B. (2003) Reasonable doubt, *New Scientist,* **2388**, p. 36).

Activity 9 *Cold fusion in the 1990s*

Discuss the questions below. First jot down your own ideas then compare them with those of other students.

1 Why was it possible nearly two years after Pons and Fleischmann's first announcement for scientists still to disagree about whether cold fusion really happens?

2 Why do you suppose the US Navy was interested in cold fusion?

3 Until the US Navy was revealed to have carried out cold fusion research, most of the research that continued after 1991 was done in Japan and India. Why do you suppose these countries continued the research but not the USA or UK?

Activity 10 *Cold fusion news*

Search the Internet for recent reports of work on cold fusion (aim to find two to five reports in total). Make a short summary of what you find, noting which reports seem to describe genuine research and which are 'wacky' speculation.

Activity 11 *Summing up cold fusion*

Review all the information you have collected about cold fusion, Pons and Fleischmann and the other people involved in the story. Make a note of aspects of the story that involve the following:

- peer review of scientific work
- different types of source material (primary, secondary) and their reliability
- speculation and opinion being confused with factual reporting.

2.6 Making history

Cold fusion now

Since Pons and Fleischmann made their dramatic announcement of cold fusion, the initial flurry of activity has died down. Cold fusion has not had the scientific impact of work such as the Human Genome Project or the Hubble Space Telescope (Figure 8), nor has it, apparently, set off a new area of research. But the topic hasn't disappeared completely.

Perhaps the story of cold fusion is more like the development of high-temperature superconductors, which hit the headlines in 1987 and have since not achieved the results hoped for. Or perhaps Pons and Fleischmann and all their supporters have just been mistaken or misled into thinking that cold fusion was real.

Now it is the turn of historians of science to have their say – and you to have yours.

▲ ***Figure 8*** Pictures from the Hubble Space Telescope were revolutionary.

Activity 12 *What do you think of cold fusion?*

For each of the statements listed below, make a table with two columns headed 'agree' and 'disagree'. Use your table to summarise reasons and evidence for agreeing and disagreeing with each statement. If you agree with a statement, try to think of reasons why other people might disagree – and vice versa. Discuss each statement with the rest of your class and use evidence to try to persuade other people of your point of view. Finally, vote on whether you agree or disagree with each statement.

1. Pons and Fleischmann really did achieve nuclear fusion in their experiment reported in March 1989.
2. Pons and Fleischmann should have published their work through the normal process of peer review.
3. The time and money spent by the scientific community in checking the claims for cold fusion was a waste of resources.
4. The scientific establishment's opposition to cold fusion was based on sound scientific methods.

Project hint

A key part of your Research project will involve stating your point of view on a scientific question and presenting arguments for and against your point of view.

Further work

Write a report of the discussion in Activity 12.

3.1 March 1953

A lunchtime announcement

It is not often that someone at a pub bar tells you that they have solved the meaning of life, but that is what happened to lunchtime drinkers in the Eagle public house in Cambridge one day in March 1953. Francis Crick was the person making the bold statement, and although his side-kick, James Watson, wasn't certain at the time, his claim was almost true.

That morning they had pieced together the final clues to the structure of deoxyribonucleic acid (DNA) and had an insight into how living cells replicate their genes. On 25 April a brief announcement of Watson and Crick's discovery appeared in the journal *Nature*. From that time on, the science of genetics was never the same and millions of people came to know of the fascination of the double helix.

In this lesson and those that follow, you will learn about events that led up to Crick's lunchtime announcement and about what happened afterwards. It is quite a complex story, involving a large number of people working in several different countries, and it brings in scientific ideas from biology, chemistry and physics.

▲ **Figure 9** The Eagle pub in Cambridge.

Activity 13 *The race for DNA*

Read the following account. As you read it, make a summary of events in chronological order. Your summary should be a list of dates, with a few brief notes under each date using the '5 W' questions.

Project hint

Making a chronological list can be a useful way to summarise information when you are working on your Research project.

Fame, priority and scientific etiquette

Crick and Watson, and to a lesser extent Maurice Wilkins and Rosalind Franklin, became famous because of their work on the structure of DNA. The story of the discovery has been told many times and various myths have grown up around it. Unlike most scientific work, the events of early 1953 seem to have moved fast.

As described later by James Watson in his book *The Double Helix*, there was great excitement as he and Crick strove to be the first to arrive at the correct structure. But there is more to the story than the announcement in the pub suggests – there are questions about how science is done, who deserves the credit and the ownership of scientific data. Many people contributed to Crick and Watson's big idea and many people had an interest in the outcome. We need to explore exactly what happened in early 1953.

Crick and Watson's brief letter in the 25 April edition of *Nature* was not the only article on DNA. It was followed by two slightly longer papers by Maurice Wilkins and his colleagues Alec Stokes and Herbert Wilson, and by Rosalind Franklin and her assistant Ray Gosling, all from King's College London. These two papers reported experimental work that gave support to Crick and Watson's suggested structure. There was also an article by Linus Pauling and Robert Corey of Caltech describing Pauling's own suggestion for the structure of DNA. As we shall see, all three groups were intimately involved in the story.

Cambridge, London and California

In Cambridge, Francis Crick was the established scientist while James Watson was the young visitor from the USA. However, Crick was only a junior member of the physics department led by Sir Lawrence Bragg with senior colleagues Max Perutz and John Kendrew.

Bragg was one of the founding fathers of the science of X-ray crystallography and Perutz and Kendrew were leaders in the field, working out the structure of proteins. Crick, too, was supposed to be working on proteins, the large molecules that control the processes that give us life. Watson arrived in 1951 from the USA via Copenhagen. He was principally a biologist with little knowledge of chemistry but a passion for DNA.

Watson teamed up with Crick and soon had him interested in DNA too. Work on DNA was not then being done at Cambridge but it was a topic of research at King's College London, where New Zealand–British biophysicist Maurice Wilkins had been joined by chemist and crystallographer Rosalind Franklin. They were trying to get better X-ray pictures of DNA and, although they did not work together happily, they were making progress.

Crick knew Wilkins quite well and so he and Watson were able to get a look at Wilkins' data. Unknown to Franklin, they were also able to have a look at one of her fine pictures of DNA. This was enough to give them the information about the helical structure of DNA.

Meanwhile in California, American chemist Linus Pauling was becoming interested in DNA too. Pauling was already famous for his work on chemical bonding and the X-ray crystallography of proteins (for which he would receive a Nobel Prize in 1954). Crick and Watson feared that once Pauling looked at the problem of the structure of DNA he would solve it. One of Pauling's favourite methods of tackling similar problems was to build models of molecules; this is what Crick and Watson decided to do.

Modelling DNA

Crick and Watson already knew that DNA was made up of three types of chemical compound: sugars and phosphate joined into a chain, with bases

A, C, G and T attached. (You will find out more about these later.) They had metal models of these units made and started trying to fit them together. They came up with three strands of the sugar-phosphate chain wound together in a helix, with the bases sticking out.

They proudly announced their structure to their Cambridge colleagues and to Wilkins and Franklin. It didn't take long for Franklin to point out their errors. The chemistry was wrong; the structure couldn't exist naturally. Crick and Watson were told by Bragg to forget DNA and get back to their protein work. But they wouldn't give up on DNA.

Coincidentally, Pauling's son Peter arrived at Cambridge and Jerry Donohue, another American, shared an office with Jim Watson. More information on the bases in DNA arrived from Austrian–American biochemist Erwin Chargaff. Peter Pauling announced that his father had a structure for DNA and Crick and Watson were able to get a preview of it before Pauling's paper appeared in the April 25 edition of *Nature*. They soon saw that Pauling had made a similar mistake in proposing a three-strand structure. Crick and Watson were fired with enthusiasm once again but worried that Pauling would soon find his mistake. They had now realised that a double helix was more likely with the bases on the inside but still could not work out what held them together.

Chargaff had found that in all samples of DNA the amount of base A was always equal to T and the amount of C was always equal to G. At first this was no help to Watson as he couldn't get the structures to fit. Jerry Donohue pointed out that the shapes published in all the text books were wrong. When he gave Watson the correct molecular structures for the four bases, Watson made cardboard cut-outs of each base. By moving them around he discovered that the two pairs of bases, A with T and C with G, could link together by hydrogen bonds. The paired bases had identical shapes and would hold the two strands of DNA together.

All the parts of the structure fell into place on that morning in March 1953.

◀ ***Figure 10*** *Crick (right) and Watson with their double helix model.*

Informing the world

Returning from their pub lunch, Crick and Watson realised they had work to do. A proper scale model of their DNA structure had to be built and checked to make sure it worked chemically (see Figure 10). The King's College group would have to be informed again and then a paper written to establish their priority for discovery. This time Wilkins and Franklin liked the model and, while they would not confirm that it was correct until they had done their calculations, they agreed that it fitted all the data so far. So it was that on 25 April 1953, *Nature* contained the three short papers from Cambridge and London and, coincidentally, Pauling's paper with the incorrect structure.

Crick and Watson had been struck immediately by one feature of their structure. It was obvious that DNA could replicate itself and carry a code for the genes. A three-line paragraph in their 25 April paper referred to this. On 30 May they returned to this subject with a slightly longer paper in *Nature* with the title 'The Genetic Implications of the Structure of DNA'.

Activity 14 *The announcement of the double helix*

Read Crick and Watson's brief paper in *Nature* (25 April 1953, **4356**, p. 737) and, if they are available, look at Wilkins and Franklin's papers that follow. Do not worry about the chemical and crystallographic details. Answer the questions below.

1 Why do Crick and Watson start by referring to Pauling and Corey's structure of DNA?

2 What is the 'novel' feature of Crick and Watson's structure (see second column, paragraphs 3 and 5)?

3 Why is the mention of Donohue, Wilkins and Franklin important (last paragraph)?

4 Why was it important that Wilkins and Franklin's papers should be published with Crick and Watson's?

Resource link

Free copies of the original paper on DNA from 1953 can be found on *Nature's* website.

Further work

1 *If you had been one of the people in the Eagle pub on that day in March 1953, what would have been your opinion of Crick?*

2 *What do you think are the advantages and disadvantages of model building as a method for working out the structures of molecules?*

3 *Why was it useful that Peter Pauling should arrive at Cambridge while Crick and Watson were working on DNA?*

4 *Compare the styles of Crick and Watson's paper with those of Wilkins and Franklin that follow. What differences are there?*

3.2 The science of DNA

Explaining the double helix

Crick and Watson had quite a lot of chemical information to start their work on DNA. Chemists had analysed samples and knew that it was a large molecule made up of carbon, hydrogen, oxygen, nitrogen and phosphorus atoms. Not all DNA is the same, however, and the composition varies slightly from one species to another. Further work showed that DNA was made of three particular parts:

- a ribose sugar – this contains carbon, hydrogen and oxygen atoms arranged in a ring
- phosphate links – a group of a phosphorus atom and four oxygen atoms that link the sugar groups together in a chain
- the bases – these are compounds of carbon, hydrogen, oxygen and nitrogen that have alkaline properties. There were known to be just four types of base in DNA called adenine (A), thymine (T), guanine (G) and cytosine (C). Each has a flat (planar) structure made up of one or two rings of carbon and nitrogen atoms.

DNA is a polymer (a long chain molecule) in which these units are repeated over and over again. One sugar unit, a phosphate link and one of the four bases forms the repeat unit, called a nucleotide. Rosalind Franklin's X-ray pictures that Jim Watson sneaked a look at told Francis Crick how wide the helix was, how tightly it was twisted, and how the two strands of DNA were wound around each other.

What holds the strands together? The answer is hydrogen bonds. These are relatively weak chemical bonds that bind some hydrogen atoms of one molecule to the oxygen or nitrogen atoms of other molecules. Hydrogen bonds between water molecules are what give snowflakes their shape and are responsible for the relatively high melting and boiling points of water. In a large molecule such as DNA, a lot of hydrogen bonds keep the strands locked together.

It is the particular shape of the bases that allows them to pair up, A with T and C with G. The bases stick out at right angles from the sugars and hold each other firmly like the north and south poles of a magnet. The paired bases form the steps in the DNA spiral staircase, with the sugar–phosphate chain forming the banisters.

The genetic code

Crick and Watson realised that the pairing of the bases meant that DNA could replicate itself. The order of the bases on one strand complements the order on the other, e.g. if the order of the bases on one strand is AGCATC then on the other it must be TCGTAG. In their paper of 30 May 1953, they explained that if a DNA double helix unravelled, two identical DNA molecules could be constructed by pairing new bases with the existing strand and building up the sugar–phosphate backbone. This would be a vital stage in the formation of new cells.

Activity 15 Pairing bases

Copy and cut out the diagrams of the four bases in Figure 11. Select pairs and fit them together so that the dotted lines representing hydrogen bonds match. When you have two pairs that match, note the shape of the combination. Check that your pairs are the same as Watson's.

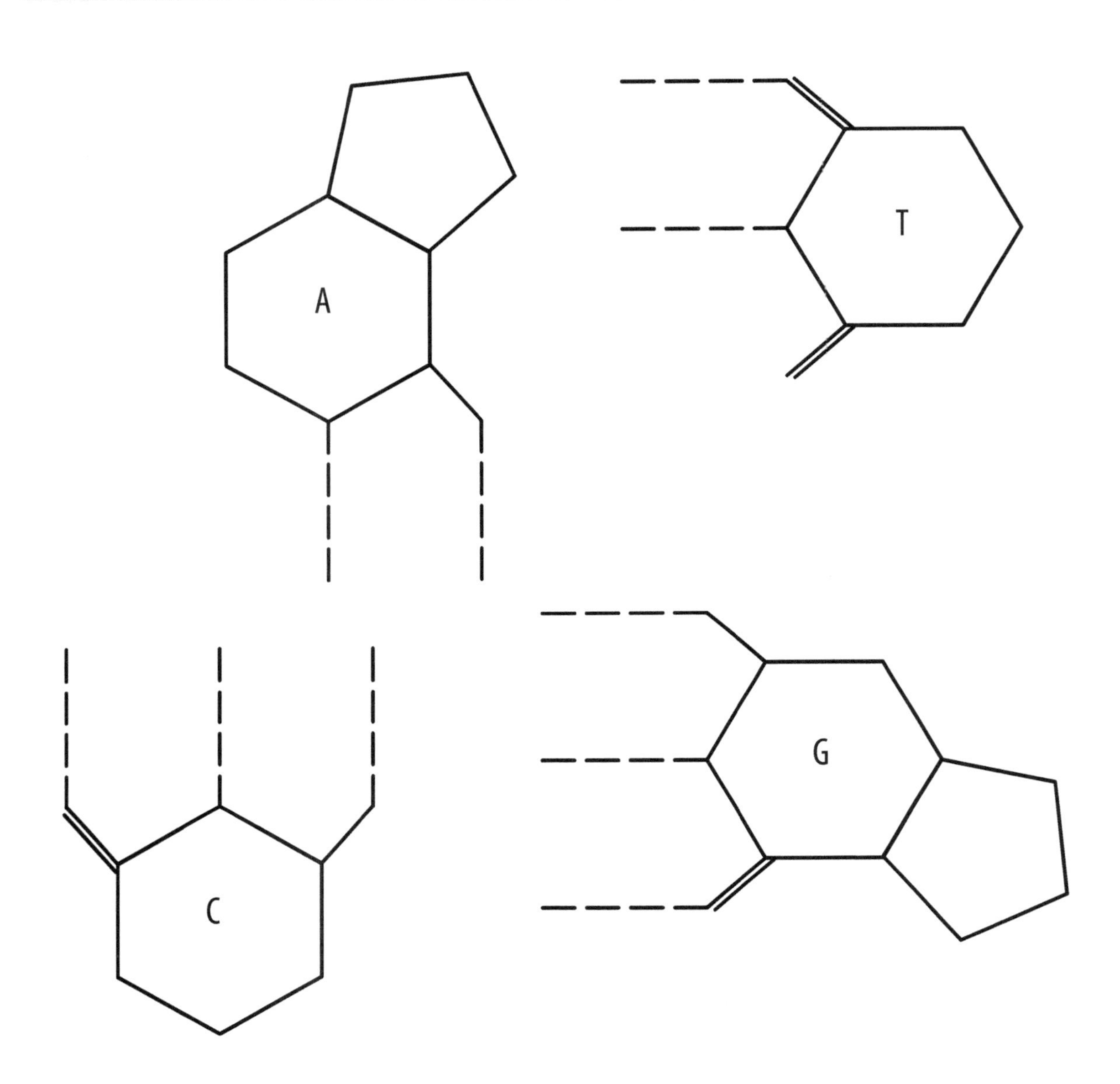

▲ ***Figure 11*** *Schematic diagrams of the four bases A, T, C and G.*

Crick and Watson also realised that the order of the bases could act as a code for the genes in an organism. Every process that takes place in cells involves proteins; in the 1950s it was realised that the gene was responsible for the production of a particular protein. Before Crick and Watson suggested their structure of DNA, it wasn't known what genes actually were.

X-ray diffraction

While chemists could determine the composition of DNA and modellers like Crick and Watson could fit the bits together to build a possible structure, it was X-ray crystallography that provided the evidence that hinted what the structure should be and showed whether it was correct.

X-rays were discovered in 1895 by German physicist Wilhelm Röntgen (1845–1923) and it was soon realised that X-rays are a form of electromagnetic wave, similar to light but with a much shorter wavelength. In fact their wavelength is less than the diameter of an atom. Another German physicist, Max von Laue (1879–1960), realised that the wavelength of X-rays was small enough for them to be diffracted by the gaps between atoms in crystals.

Diffraction is a property of waves that means they spread out after passing through a gap comparable in size to their wavelength. Sound waves are diffracted by doorways and corridors, which is why we can hear noises in other rooms. If there are lots of gaps close together, the diffracted waves overlap. Sometimes they add together crest on crest, and sometimes they cancel out, crest on trough. This means that just a few strong beams emerge in certain directions. In the case of light or X-rays, these beams can be detected as bright spots on a photographic film. The first recorded example of X-ray diffraction by a crystal was produced in 1912 using copper sulfate.

Activity 16 *Demonstrating diffraction*

Figure 12 shows waves being diffracted by two gaps. The curved lines represent the crests of the waves. Draw a line between A and B to represent a photographic film. Mark on the line where bright spots will appear.

If you have access to suitable apparatus, observe diffraction of light through a narrow gap.

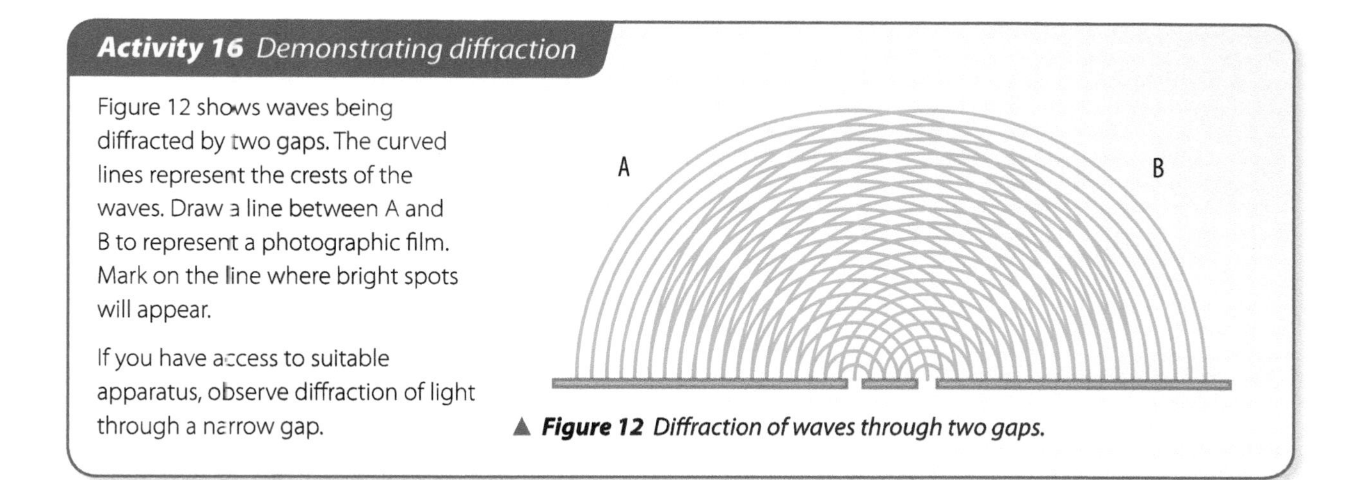

▲ ***Figure 12*** *Diffraction of waves through two gaps.*

X-ray crystallography

British scientists Lawrence Bragg (1890–1971) and his father William Bragg (1862–1942) were pioneers in the use of X-ray diffraction to determine crystal structure. They made the first steps in developing the mathematical interpretation of the X-ray photographs. The X-ray diffraction pattern of a crystal is a series of spots of varying brightness in a geometric pattern. The shape of the pattern, the distance between the spots and the pattern of brightness of the spots all give information about the arrangement of atoms in the crystal.

In the 1920s and 30s Linus Pauling led the development of X-ray crystallography to find the structures of more and more complicated molecules. In the 1940s some of the simpler proteins were worked out (Dorothy Hodgkin worked out the structure of penicillin) but the calculations were long and difficult.

When Maurice Wilkins and Rosalind Franklin worked on DNA in 1953, they had to do the calculations using only simple mechanical calculators. This work took months or years. Today the work is done by computers in seconds. Their first problem, however, was to get good X-ray pictures of DNA. DNA is an awkward material for crystallography. When it is drawn into fibres the molecules take up a regular pattern like in a crystal. But the fibres absorb water readily and change shape depending on how much water is present. Franklin had the patience and skill necessary to get X-ray photographs of just one form of DNA that were clear and useful.

There are two approaches to using X-ray crystallography. Franklin was working through her calculations to reveal the number of strands in the DNA helix, how tightly wound the helices were and the diameter of the helix. Eventually she would work out where each atom was situated in the molecule. Crick and Watson's model-building approach relied on X-ray crystallography to suggest the right structure and to check whether their model was correct.

Further work

1 *A sample of DNA contains 20% adenine and 30% guanine. What are the percentages of cytosine and thymine?*

2 *Why was the order of the bases on the DNA chain significant?*

3 *Why did the use of X-ray crystallography to determine the structure of proteins follow a long time after its use on metals and ionic crystals such as sodium chloride?*

4 *Franklin's X-ray photo of DNA clearly shows the X shape typical of a helix structure. Why was this not sufficient on its own to prove Crick and Watson's structure?*

3.3 DNA people

Who were the key players?

As we have seen, there were at least three groups of scientists working on the structure of DNA. They were Crick and Watson at Cambridge, Franklin and Wilkins (Figures 13 and 14) at King's College London and Linus Pauling at Caltech in California. In addition, there were other people who played an important role in the DNA story. For instance, at Cambridge there was Sir Lawrence Bragg who led the department in which Crick and Watson worked. In the same department, Max Perutz and John Kendrew were working on the structure of biological molecules. At Kings College London, the department head who had appointed Rosalind Franklin without Wilkins' knowledge was Sir John Randall. Wilkins worked with Stokes and Wilson, while Franklin

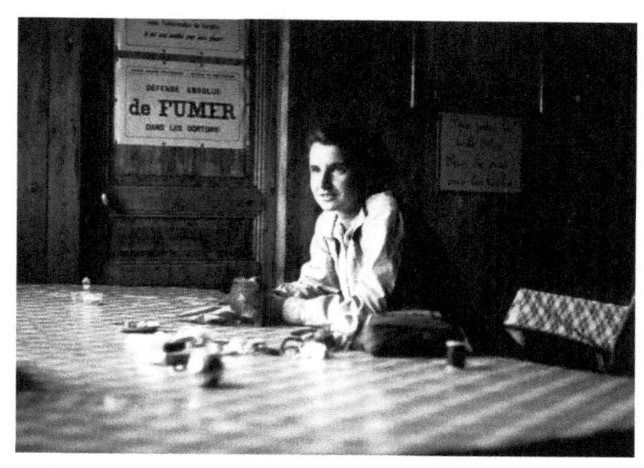

▲ ***Figure 13*** *Rosalind Franklin.*

▲ ***Figure 14*** *Maurice Wilkins.*

had Gosling as her research student and assistant. Pauling was very much an individual but he had his own team of assistants including Robert Corey. Pauling's son Peter, also a scientist, played a significant role as well.

How can we find out more about the people involved in the DNA story? The starting point for a search for biographical data is the entry on the person in biographical dictionaries. For scientists, there are a number of these. The most accessible are the *Oxford Dictionary of Scientists* and the *Cambridge Dictionary of Scientists*. If you can get to a large library you will find other biographical sources such as the *Oxford Dictionary of National Biography* and *Notable Twentieth-Century Scientists*.

Project hint

These sources of information will also be useful for your Research project.

These dictionaries are all secondary sources which rely on information about people provided from a variety of sources. They should be fairly accurate about the facts but will give little hint about the personality of the subjects.

The next stage is to look up biographies and autobiographies. These obviously tell you more about the characters but they are often biased and subjective in their opinions. An example is James Watson's account of the DNA story, *The Double Helix*, which is an exciting story but highly coloured by Watson's own opinions of people. Books telling the DNA story or the history of genetics or more general histories of science will also be useful. These may be more objective but still offer just one interpretation of the primary sources.

Typing the person's name into an Internet search engine (e.g. Google) can provide information. But be careful: you might find details of a totally different person with the same name, and information from websites is not necessarily reliable as it has often not been carefully checked.

Finally, there is primary research where you go back to the papers, books, letters and other personal material relating to the character and contemporary accounts of his or her work. You may already have looked at Crick and Watson's paper in *Nature* and the papers by Wilkins and Franklin that accompanied it. These tell you what the scientists were doing and give some indication of how they worked.

Activity 17 DNA people

Find out what you can about the life and work of someone involved in the race for DNA then write a short biography of this character (a few hundred words). For this activity, the first stage of biographical research (looking through dictionaries coupled with some reading of other accounts of the story) will be all that time allows.

Make a list of all the sources that you use. References to books should be recorded as:

- title, author (where available), publisher, date of publication.

Articles in journals should be recorded as:

- authors, journal title, date and/or volume and issue number, page number. (The title of the article is not necessary as it may be rather long.)

Project hint

When you are gathering information for your Research project, it is important to record the details of all the sources you use. This information will be needed for the bibliography of your report and in case you need to consult the source again.

Activity 18 Connecting people

Working with other students who have researched different people in Activity 17, draw a spider diagram to show how the main characters are linked to the story of DNA and to one another.

Project hint

A spider diagram can be a good way to summarise and present information. You might find such diagrams useful when doing your Research project.

Further work

1 *Many of the characters in the DNA story were caught up in the events of the Second World War. Make a list of the war activities of the character you researched in Activity 17. What influence do you think the events of the war had on his/her later work?*

2 *Rosalind Franklin is the only woman to figure in the DNA story. Why are so few women visible in the history of science up until at least the 1960s?*

3.4 Before and after the double helix

Leaning on shoulders

It is clear from James Watson's telling of the DNA story in *The Double Helix* that he and Crick stood no chance of discovering the structure of DNA on their own. Wilkins and Franklin were the unsuspecting suppliers of the X-ray crystallography data. Peter Pauling kept them up to date on his father's work and Jerry Donohue put Watson right on the chemistry of the bits that make up DNA. There were others who provided the links in the chain of discovery that led to the double helix. We have to go back a further 80 years for the origins of the story.

◀ ***Figure 15*** *The former site of Mendel's garden.*

Inherited characteristics

One of Charles Darwin's unanswered questions in his work on evolution was 'how do characteristics get passed from one generation to another?' Darwin himself had no answer to this question although he favoured some blending of characteristics between the parents of offspring. While he was publishing his books *The Origin of Species* and *The Descent of Man*, Darwin had no idea that a monk in what is now the Czech Republic was collecting data that gave an answer.

Gregor Mendel spent over 10 years patiently growing pea plants, crossing different varieties and determining his laws of inheritance. In a paper of 1866 he suggested that an organism carries two 'factors' for every characteristic such as tallness, colour of flowers, texture of peas, etc. Each parent passes on one copy of each factor to their offspring. The factors can either be dominant or recessive. The journal that published Mendel's paper in 1865 was not distributed widely and neither Darwin nor other scientists interested in inheritance came across it. Mendel had other tasks as abbot of the monastery and gave up his scientific work.

It was not until 1900 that other scientists came across Mendel's work and realised its importance. Mendel's factors were renamed 'genes' and the science of genetics was born.

Studies of cell reproduction showed that the cell nucleus contained a number of chromosomes which separated and split during cell division. It was realised that genes were somehow carried by the chromosomes. During the first half of the twentieth century, geneticists began to determine which chromosome carried genes for various characteristics. An American biologist, Thomas Hunt Morgan, was one of the pioneers of this field. He chose the fruit fly *Drosophila melanogaster* as his subject, as it has just four chromosomes, a short life cycle and mutates readily. By 1911, Morgan had begun to map genes on to the chromosomes.

In the years that followed, geneticists modified Mendel's laws of inheritance, developed statistical methods for handling their data and mapped lots of genes. But they did not know what was in the chromosomes that actually carried the genes.

DNA discovered

In 1869, Swiss scientist Friedrich Miescher discovered a new substance in the nuclei of dead white blood cells (otherwise known as pus). The new substance was acidic. He found it was a complicated molecule and obtained a simple formula – $C_{29}H_{49}O_{22}N_9P_3$ (which is not completely correct). Unlike other compounds in cells, it was not a protein, a carbohydrate or a fat. By 1900 chemists had found that the substance could be broken down into a sugar, phosphate and four bases. No one knew how the three bits were linked together.

Russian chemist Phoebus Levene, who emigrated to the USA in 1891, discovered in 1929 that the sugar was deoxyribose and the compound acquired its name deoxyribonucleic acid (DNA). Levene also showed that the sugars were linked together by the phosphates in a chain and the bases were attached to the sugars as branches. He called each unit of phosphate, sugar and base a nucleotide. Levene thought that there might be just 12 such units in a molecule of DNA. He also thought that there were the same amounts of each of the four bases and that they repeated in the same order along the whole DNA chain.

Proteins or DNA?

Levene's work suggested that DNA was a fairly simple regular molecule which had no way of carrying the complex information of the genes. There were other substances in the nuclei of cells, however: proteins. Proteins come in many different varieties made up of chains of about 20 different amino acids. Proteins are very complicated and only in the 1940s was any progress made in determining their shape. Surely the order of amino acids in the proteins in the nucleus could act as the letters in the genetic code? Thus DNA was relegated to a supporting role as the framework of chromosomes holding the proteins.

Until the 1920s it was thought that molecules were relatively small collections of atoms, a few hundred at the most. Then it was discovered that substances such as polythene had many thousands of atoms linked together; they were called polymers. Proteins were polymers too, yet more confirmation that they were complicated enough to carry the code of life. DNA was shown to be a polymer in the 1930s but with Levene's regular pattern of bases it was considered too straightforward to carry any information.

DNA steps forward

In 1944, Oswald Avery, a Canadian-born scientist working in New York, announced that it was DNA, not proteins, that carried the genetic material. He had started work in 1932 on transferring material from the nuclei of one strain of bacteria into others. This had the effect of giving the characteristics of the first type of bacteria to the other – he was performing genetic engineering. Avery and his team used enzymes in their work. Enzymes that destroyed the proteins in the nuclear materials had no effect on the ability to transfer the genetic code. Only enzymes that broke up DNA stopped the transfer working. Levene and others did not support Avery's conclusion but the importance of DNA gradually became accepted.

The detailed chemical structure of DNA was still a mystery. In 1944 Alexander Todd became Professor of Organic Chemistry at Cambridge University. A few years later he succeeded in making the four bases in DNA and worked out their structure His team also showed that, despite having the different bases attached to them, the connections between all the nucleotides in DNA were the same, making the backbone of the chain very regular. Todd and his team worked closely with Crick and Watson's department in Cambridge.

Also late in the 1940s, Linus Pauling had shown that large molecules, particularly proteins, could coil up into a helical shape. Could DNA be a helix too? Did it have two, three or four strands wound around each other?

Base ratios provide the key

Erwin Chargaff was born in Ukraine, studied in Vienna and settled in the USA in 1935. He used the new technique of paper chromatography to investigate fragments of DNA broken up by enzymes. He discovered that Phoebus Levene was wrong: the amount of each of the four bases was not equal. Indeed, the amounts of each base varied from one species to another. He concluded that each species had its own variation of DNA. Incidentally, he also found that in all the samples he had studied the amount of adenine (A) was equal to thymine (T) and the amount of cytosine (C) equalled that of guanine (G). Although he mentioned this fact in his paper of 1950 he didn't make much of it. Nevertheless, these simple base ratios provided the key for Crick and Watson's work.

Activity 19 *Before the double helix*

Draw up a time line of events in the DNA story from the publication of Darwin's *The Origin of Species* in 1859 to Crick and Watson's announcement in 1953.

Project hint

A time line can be a good way to summarise and present information. You might find such diagrams useful when doing your Research project.

Cracking the code

Francis Crick's announcement to the occupants of the Eagle pub was bold, but the discovery of the structure of DNA did indeed go a long way to explain the mechanism of life. So what happened after Crick and Watson's brief paper in *Nature*?

Crick and Watson's 30 May article in *Nature* gave more detail of the structure of DNA and also suggested the possible way in which it could be replicated in the cell. They imagined the double helix unravelling and parting and then new sugar–phosphate–base groups joining on to both chains. The pattern of base A with T and C with G ensured that the two new double chains were exact duplicates of the original. However, they couldn't explain how the unravelling occurred or what brought the new bits to the chain at the correct moment.

Watson had been inspired by a book by Erwin Schrödinger (1887–1961), a physicist and pioneer of quantum mechanics. In *What is Life?*, Schrödinger said that genes could consist of a chemical code which specified how proteins should be put together. The order of the bases on the DNA was just the code Schrödinger had imagined. The genetic information DNA carries is used to make proteins that perform all the functions of a cell.

It was known that the many thousands of different proteins in a cell were built up from just 20 smaller molecules called amino acids. Another physicist, George Gamow, whose main interest was the Big Bang, suggested that groups of bases could act as a code for each amino acid. With just four letters to choose from (A, C, G and T), coding for 20 amino acids, he reasoned that the code for each amino acid must have at least three letters. This gives 64 possible combinations.

Francis Crick and a South African, Sydney Brenner, tackled the problem. By 1961 they had confirmed that the code was indeed a triplet of bases, or 'codon' as they called it. In the same year, Marshall Nirenberg and Johann Matthaei in Washington worked out the code of the first amino acid. They found that phenylalanine had the code AAA. Soon the codes for all 20 amino acids were obtained – they are the same for all life on the planet. Most amino acids have at least two possible codes. There are three codons that do not code for an amino acid but act as punctuation marks showing where a gene on the DNA chain stops.

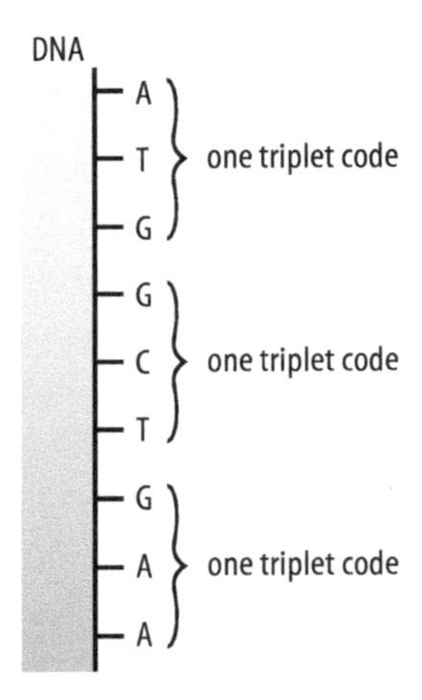

▲ ***Figure 16*** DNA triplets.

Now molecular biologists knew that a gene consisted of hundreds or thousands of bases listing the order in which amino acids were to be linked together to form proteins. But how was the information used?

The protein-building machine

During the 1950s and early 1960s, Crick and Brenner in Cambridge and Watson at Caltech and then Harvard, along with others, worked out how DNA actually builds proteins. The process involves another molecule, RNA, that had been found in cells some time before. RNA, or ribonucleic acid, is very similar to DNA, being a single chain of sugar–phosphate with bases attached. RNA is slightly different to DNA in the sugar part and has the base uracil (U) instead of thymine (T). U and T have very similar shapes so U can link with A like T does. There are actually three types of RNA which together convert the DNA code into proteins.

By the early 1960s molecular biologists understood how DNA worked. This knowledge opened up the possibility of DNA sequencing, DNA fingerprinting, genetic testing and genetic engineering. The consequences of Crick and Watson's discovery for science and society are still being felt.

Activity 20 *After the double helix*

Investigate one of the areas of research that followed from the discovery of the structure of DNA, for example:

- Alec Jeffreys and DNA fingerprinting
- Frederick Sanger and DNA sequencing
- Paul Berg and genetic engineering
- James Watson, John Sulston, Craig Venter and the Human Genome Project.

Use the Internet, books and journals to find out about the people and what they did. Comment on the effects of their work on society.

Make brief notes on your findings. Decide how best to structure your notes for easy future reference. (Use the '5 W' questions as headings? Draw a time line?)

Further work

1. *Sometimes it is said that every discovery creates more questions than it answers. Discuss the extent to which this statement applies to the DNA story.*
2. *Explain the importance of international cooperation in science in the DNA story and in other areas of science that you know of.*
3. *It might be said that discovery of the structure of DNA was the most important event in the history of biology. Discuss the extent to which you think this statement is true and give your reasons.*
4. *Find out more about the people mentioned in this section, e.g. Phoebus Levene, Oswald Avery, Alexander Todd, Erwin Chargaff, Sidney Brenner.*

3.5 The Prize

In 1953 everyone working on DNA knew that discovering its structure would be an achievement worthy of a Nobel Prize. Who would win it? Crick and Watson had the inspiration and built the model. Wilkins and Franklin, perhaps unknowingly, provided the data that set Crick and Watson on the correct path and had the evidence to support their model. Chargaff's work on the ratio of the bases in DNA was vital. Linus Pauling's discovery of the helical shape in proteins also influenced Crick and Watson.

Nobel Prizes

The Nobel Prizes were set up in 1901 with the legacy of the will of Alfred Nobel (Figure 17), a Swedish industrialist who had made a fortune manufacturing explosives. Three science prizes are awarded each year, for chemistry, for physics and for physiology or medicine. Who should receive the prize is decided by the Swedish Academy of Sciences. People are nominated secretly and the committee makes its decision behind closed doors. The prize is a very large sum of money and, from the start, was seen as the most prestigious award in the sciences.

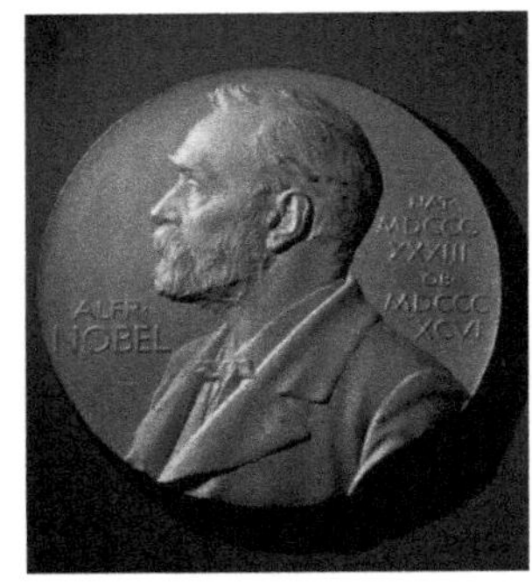

▲ ***Figure 17*** *Alfred Nobel, as he appears on the front of each Nobel medal.*

A Nobel Prize is generally awarded only when the work that is being celebrated has been proven to have an important place in science. Some winners had to wait many years before their discoveries were recognised. For instance, Linus Pauling's chemistry prize in 1954 was for work he did on chemical bonding in the late 1920s and 30s. Other prizes are awarded more rapidly: Alex Müller and Georg Bednorz received the Physics Prize in 1987, just a year after announcing their discovery of high-temperature superconductors.

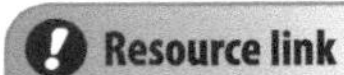

Resource link

The Nobel Foundation website gives details of all Nobel Prizewinners.

From the beginning it was decided that the prize would only be awarded to living scientists and it became accepted that each prize could be divided between no more than three people.

Throughout its history the announcement of the winners of the prizes has been eagerly awaited. The ceremony, held in Stockholm where the King of Sweden presents the prizes, is an annual occasion to rival the Oscars – except that the recipients of a Nobel Prize have to make a proper speech.

Activity 21 *Choosing a winner*

Take part in a balloon debate to decide who should receive a Nobel Prize for the discovery of the DNA structure. Choose one of the characters mentioned in the story who is a possible recipient of the Nobel Prize. Give a short presentation to make the case for your character to win the prize. When all the nominations have been made, choose no more than three of the characters to be the winners.

Aim to present your case in just 2 minutes – this is not long! To help prepare for this debate, look back at your notes from Activities 13, 14, 17 and 18. For your chosen character, make some brief notes setting out what was his/her single most important contribution to the discovery of the double helix structure. If there is time for discussion, decide how you will argue that your character's work is the most important. What evidence will you use to support your case? Try to anticipate what other people will say about their character. Practise speaking for 2 minutes to make your case. You need to get straight to the point and say what the person did and why it mattered – don't spend time talking about details of his/her life.

The Nobel Prize for Physiology or Medicine was finally awarded for the discovery of the DNA structure in 1962. The winners were Francis Crick, James Watson and Maurice Wilkins. Coincidentally, the Chemistry Prize that year was awarded to Max Perutz and John Kendrew for their work on determining the structure of proteins. People sometimes say that Rosalind Franklin was left out of the Nobel Prize. The fact is that she had died of cancer in 1958 and so was ineligible for the prize in 1962. However, there are still some questions that we can ask about the award.

Project hint

Activity 21 is good preparation for the oral presentation that will form part of your report on your Research project.

- Why was the award not made until 1962 when the proof was available and the importance of the discovery was clear years earlier?
- Did the awarding body wait until there were just three deserving recipients left to receive a prize?
- Should the award have gone to Crick, Watson and Franklin?
- Did Crick and Watson deserve the prize for just a bit of model building when all the data that supported the double helix structure were provided by other scientists?

Activity 22 *Prize questions*

What are your responses to the questions listed above? Discuss your ideas with other students.

Further work

1 *Write a summary of the DNA story. Discuss the part played by each of the characters and the importance of their contribution.*

2 *If Crick and Watson hadn't got there first, someone else would have discovered the structure of DNA, probably before the end of 1953. Who do you think would have been the first to the double helix? Give reasons for your suggestions.*

3 *Is winning a Nobel Prize important? Discuss your response.*

4 Evolution

4.1 Joint declaration

The Linnean Society of London, 1 July 1858

On 1 July 1858, about 25 fellows of the Linnean Society of London (a scientific society) assembled to hear the eminent geologist, Charles Lyell (1797–1875), recite an obituary to their former president, Robert Brown (1773–1858). Brown was a highly respected Scottish botanist known today for his discovery of Brownian motion. The fellows, largely amateur botanists and zoologists, got more than they expected.

Following the obituary there were papers from other fellows. Finally the secretary of the Society read some papers handed to him by Lyell. The papers had two authors. One was the well known naturalist Charles Darwin (1809–82), and the other the lesser known traveller and collector, Alfred Russel Wallace.

▲ **Figure 18** Charles Darwin.

Neither Darwin nor Wallace was at the meeting. Darwin was at home in Kent grieving over the death of his baby son, Charles, the tenth child of his marriage to Emma Wedgwood. Wallace was halfway around the Earth, exploring the jungles of Malaysia. Neither of the authors intended their work for a public reading but both presented a new theory to the world – the theory of evolution by natural selection.

Scientific societies

In the seventeenth century, the growth of interest in science and technology led to the emergence of the first scientific societies. Originally they were groups of people with a common interest in science who met regularly to exchange ideas. Members would write a paper giving an account of their work, which they would present for discussion at a meeting, and papers were sometimes circulated to members by post. As the societies grew, the circulation of written papers became more formal and papers were collected together to form a journal. These were the forerunners of today's journals that publish peer-reviewed accounts of scientific work.

In England, the most important scientific society was the Royal Society (founded in 1660) which draws together all areas of science. Other scientific societies focus on more specialist interests. In the UK, these include the Linnean Society (botany), the Physical Society (now incorporated into the Institute of Physics) and the Royal Astronomical Society. Other examples of scientific societies include the American Chemical Society, the European Physical Society and the French Academie des Sciences.

Nowadays, most professional scientists belong to at least one scientific society. Some societies are open to all with an interest in the field, but some restrict their membership or fellowship to those who have a proven track record of work. In the UK, the most exclusive and prestigious is the Royal Society, where only the most eminent scientists are eligible to become FRS (Fellow of the Royal Society).

▲ ***Figure 19*** *The red bird of paradise studied by Wallace in Malaysia.*

Darwin receives a letter

Two weeks earlier, in June, a letter had arrived at Charles Darwin's house in Kent. He wrote a lot of letters and in return received a sack of mail nearly every day. This letter had travelled from the other side of the world, an uncommon but not unique event. Darwin recognised the handwriting. It was from a young explorer, Alfred Wallace, whom he had corresponded with before. Darwin hoped that the letter would inform him that Wallace was sending skins of birds that he had found in his travels around Indonesia and Malaysia (Figure 19). In fact the letter gave Darwin the biggest shock of his life.

Wallace, writing in February 1858, asked for Darwin's opinion on an idea he had had as a result of his explorations and asked Darwin to pass on the letter to Charles Lyell to advise whether it was worth publishing. There followed 20 pages in which Wallace explained his idea of evolution of species of plants and animals by natural selection. Darwin was astounded because the idea was his own. For 20 years he had been working on it, collecting evidence from his own research and that of others who wrote to him, developing his arguments and slowly writing a massive manuscript. He knew that the theory was controversial and would cause pain and anguish to fervent Christians, including his wife, so he had delayed publicising his ideas. Only his closest friends, especially Charles Lyell and Joseph Hooker (1817–1911), knew anything of his theory of evolution. Now it looked as if Wallace had come up with the same conclusions; he even used the same phrases as Darwin. What was Darwin to do?

Activity 23 *Darwin's dilemma*

For any scientists who value their work, priority is vital. The first person to announce a discovery or propose a theory draws the fame associated with it. Darwin held in his hand the paper that could take away his priority of development of the theory of natural selection, his life's work. He thought of three options.

1 He could destroy the letter, ignore it completely, and announce the theory himself. If Wallace ever enquired about it he could say that he had never received the letter.

2 He could put the letter to one side while he announced his theory. In a few months' time he could reveal the letter as if it had just arrived.

3 He could do as Wallace requested and forward the letter for publication and thereby lose priority.

What should Darwin do? Justify each course of action and comment on the outcome.

You could work with two other students. Each person has to justify one of the actions before you all vote on what to do.

(Bear in mind that the postal service from the jungles of southeast Asia in 1858 was slow and unreliable.)

Lyell and Hooker hatch a plot

Darwin was fundamentally an honest man. He agonised over Wallace's letter but within a day or two passed it on to Charles Lyell. Darwin's baby son had fallen ill with a fever and was suffering dreadfully. Darwin was distraught.

Lyell immediately recognised the significance of Wallace's paper but also knew that Darwin had been working on his theory of evolution for many years. He had told Darwin he should publish his ideas less than two years earlier. He did not want to let his friend lose the priority to a young, almost unknown collector. Lyell and Darwin's other close friend, Joseph Hooker, a botanist, came up with a plan. They (and Darwin) were on the committee of the Linnean Society. The Society was shortly to have a special meeting to commemorate the death of Robert Brown. This would be an opportunity to present both men's ideas.

Unfortunately Darwin was in no state for writing a brief paper, his son was fighting for his life, and anyway to establish his priority he must show that he had had the idea first. Luckily Darwin kept notes and jottings for years. He had an outline of his theory from 1844 which he had shown to Hooker, and a copy of a more recent letter to Asa Gray, Professor of Zoology at Harvard University in the USA. Lyell and Hooker took extracts from Darwin's two writings and cobbled together a paper. It was this and Wallace's letter that were read to the unsuspecting members of the Linnean Society on 1 July.

The audience listened to the papers in long-suffering silence. They were not particularly interested and asked no questions. Afterwards, over tea, Hooker did hear some quiet words spoken about the content of the papers, but the theory of evolution had had its first public airing without shattering the peace.

Activity 24 *'On the tendency of species to form varieties'*

Read the extracts on pages 45–7 from Darwin's and Wallace's papers from the *Journal of the Proceedings of the Linnean Society* and answer the questions below.

1 Darwin's paper was read first. What effect did this have?

2 Why was it a good idea for the two scientists' papers to be read at the same time?

3 Lyell and Hooker wrote an introduction to the paper explaining that Darwin and Wallace had apparently come up with the same idea, but they emphasised that Darwin had been urged by them for years to publish his work. Why was this introduction by Lyell and Hooker important?

4 In Darwin's first contribution he says: 'Lighten any check in the least degree, and the geometrical powers of increase in every organism will almost instantly increase the average number of the favoured species'. What does he mean by the terms:

a 'lighten any check'
b 'geometrical powers of increase'
c 'favoured species'?

5 In Darwin's second passage he says: 'during millions of generations individuals of a species will be occasionally born with some slight variation, profitable to some part of their economy'.
  a What does he mean by 'profitable to some part of their economy'?
  b How would Darwin's idea fit in with the idea that the Earth was just 6000 years old?

6 In Wallace's paper he says: 'The possibility of procuring food during the least favourable seasons, and of escaping attacks of their most dangerous enemies, are the primary conditions which determine the existence both of individuals and of entire species'. Why does Wallace call this 'the struggle for existence'?

7 Wallace goes on to say: 'Most or perhaps all the variations from the typical form of a species must have some definite effect, however slight, on the habits or capacities of the individuals'. What does Wallace mean by:
  a 'variations from the typical form'
  b 'habits or capacities'?

8 If you have been able to read the whole paper delivered by Lyell and Hooker, compare the contributions of Darwin and Wallace. How similar are their ideas? Whose ideas seem to be the better prepared?

"Darwin's first contribution, second paragraph

Many practical illustrations of this rapid tendency to increase are on record, among which, during peculiar seasons, are the extraordinary numbers of certain animals; for instance, during the years 1826 to 1828, in La Plata, when from drought some millions of cattle perished, the whole country actually swarmed with mice. Now I think it cannot be doubted that during the breeding-season all the mice (with the exception of a few males or females in excess) ordinarily pair, and therefore that this astounding increase during three years must be attributed to a greater number than usual surviving the first year, and then breeding, and so on till the third year, when their numbers were brought down to their usual limits on the return of wet weather. Where man has introduced plants and animals into a new and favourable country, there are many accounts in how surprisingly few years the whole country has become stocked with them. This increase would necessarily stop as soon as the country was fully stocked; and yet we have every reason to believe, from what is known of wild animals, that all would pair in the spring. In the majority of cases it is most difficult to imagine where the checks fall—though generally, no doubt, on the seeds, eggs, and young; but when we remember how impossible, even in mankind (so much better known than any other animal), it is to infer from repeated casual observations what the average duration of life is, or to discover the different percentages of deaths to births in different countries, we ought to feel no surprise at our being unable to discover where the check falls in any animal or plant. It should always be remembered, that in most cases the checks are recurrent yearly in a small, regular degree, and in an extreme degree during unusually cold, hot, dry, or wet years, according to the constitution of the being in question. Lighten any check in the least degree, and the geometrical powers of increase in every organism will almost instantly increase the average number of the favoured species. Nature may be compared to a surface on which rest ten thousand sharp wedges touching each other and driven inwards by incessant blows. Fully to realize those views much reflection is requisite. Malthus on man should be studied; and all such cases as those of the mice in La Plata, of the cattle and horses when first turned out in South America, of the birds by our calculation, &c., should be well considered. Reflect on the enormous multiplying power inherent and annually in action in all animals; reflect on the countless seeds scattered by a hundred ingenious contrivances, year after year, over the whole face of the land; and yet we have every reason to suppose that the average percentage of each of the inhabitants of a country usually remains constant. Finally, let it be borne in mind that this average number of individuals (the external conditions remaining the same) in each country is kept up by recurrent struggles against other species or against external nature (as on the borders of the Arctic regions, where the cold checks life), and that ordinarily each individual of every species holds its place, either by its own struggle and capacity of acquiring nourishment in some period of its life, from the egg upwards; or by the struggle of its parents (in short-lived organisms, when the main check occurs at longer intervals) with other individuals of the same or different species. ”

“ *Darwin's second contribution, fourth paragraph*

Now take the case of a country undergoing some change. This will tend to cause some of its inhabitants to vary slightly—not but that I believe most beings vary at all times enough for selection to act on them. Some of its inhabitants will be exterminated; and the remainder will be exposed to the mutual action of a different set of inhabitants, which I believe to be far more important to the life of each being than mere climate. Considering the infinitely various methods which living beings follow to obtain food by struggling with other organisms, to escape danger at various times of life, to have their eggs or seeds disseminated, &c. &c., I cannot doubt that during millions of generations individuals of a species will be occasionally born with some slight variation, profitable to some part of their economy. Such individuals will have a better chance of surviving, and of propagating their new and slightly different structures; and the modification may be slowly increased by the accumulative action of natural selection to any profitable extent. The variety thus formed will either coexist with, or, more commonly, will exterminate its parent form. An organic being, like the woodpecker or mistletoe, may thus come to be adapted to a score of contingencies—natural selection accumulating those slight variations in all parts of its structure, which are in any way useful to it during any part of its life. ”

“ *Wallace's paper, fourth paragraph*

The life of wild animals is a struggle for existence. The full exertion of all their faculties and all their energies is required to preserve their own existence and provide for that of their infant offspring. The possibility of procuring food during the least favourable seasons, and of escaping the attacks of their most dangerous enemies, are the primary conditions which determine the existence both of individuals and of entire species. These conditions will also determine the population of a species; and by a careful consideration of all the circumstances we may be enabled to comprehend, and in some degree to explain, what at first sight appears so inexplicable—the excessive abundance of some species, while others closely allied to them are very rare. ”

“ *Wallace's paper, seventh paragraph*

Most or perhaps all the variations from the typical form of a species must have some definable effect, however slight, on the habits or capacities of the individuals. Even a change of colour might, by rendering them more or less distinguishable, affect their safety; a greater or less development of hair might modify their habits. More important changes, such as an increase in the power or dimensions of the limbs or any of the external organs, would more or less affect their mode of procuring food or the range of country which they inhabit. It is also evident that most changes would affect, either favourably or adversely, the powers of prolonging existence. An antelope with shorter or weaker legs must necessarily suffer more from the attacks of the feline carnivora; the passenger pigeon with less powerful wings would sooner or later be affected in its powers of procuring a regular supply of food; and in both cases the result must necessarily be a diminution of the population of the modified species. If, on the other hand, any species should produce a variety having slightly increased powers of preserving existence, that variety must inevitably in time acquire a superiority in numbers. These results must follow as surely as old age, intemperance, or scarcity of food produces an increased mortality. In both cases there may be many individual exceptions; but on the average the rule will invariably be found to hold good. All varieties will therefore fall into two classes—those which under the same conditions would never reach the population of the parent species, and those which would in time obtain and keep a numerical superiority. Now let some alteration of physical conditions occur in the district—a long period of drought, a destruction of vegetation by locusts, the irruption of some new carnivorous animal seeking "pastures new"—any change in fact tending to render existence more difficult to the species in question, and taking its utmost powers to avoid complete extermination; it is evident that, of all the individuals composing the species, those forming the least numerous and most feebly organized variety would suffer first, and, were the pressure severe, must soon become extinct. The same causes continuing in action, the parent species would next suffer, would gradually diminish in numbers, and with a recurrence of similar unfavourable conditions might also become extinct. The superior variety would then alone remain, and on a return to favourable circumstances would rapidly increase in numbers and occupy the place of the extinct species and variety. ”

4.2 Genesis and all that

Where did the species come from?

Darwin and Wallace weren't the first to provide an answer to the question 'where did the species we see today come from?' For most people in Christian countries the answer was simple – God's Creation – but from the middle of the eighteenth century some bold and revolutionary figures began to think about alternatives. At the time when Darwin and Wallace proposed their theory, there were essentially three types of theory under discussion in western Europe.

Activity 25 *Alternative theories*

For each of the three theories outlined below, summarise their main features and note the names of the main proposers and supporters. Compare and contrast their views on the following:

- Stability of species – do species change over time?
- Fossils – how can they be accounted for?
- The age of the Earth.
- Evidence – what use is made of evidence to support the theory and to attack rival theories?

You could use a table to record your notes for this activity. On an A4 sheet of paper, make a table with three columns (one for each theory) and four rows (one for each of the points listed above). Write brief notes in each space.

Project hint

When working on your Research project, you might find it useful to make a table when comparing different points of view or possible courses of action.

Alternative theories

Divine Creation

For many Christians in the eighteenth and nineteenth centuries, the Bible provided the answers to all questions. Most believed that the Bible had been written by a succession of prophets, leaders and apostles who were inspired to write down God's words. They weren't commentaries or interpretations but literally God's own thoughts delivered through the medium of his servants. It was thought that the first five books of the Bible were written by Moses who led the Israelites out of Egypt to the Promised Land and on the way gave them God's Ten Commandments.

The first book of the Bible is *Genesis*, and here Christians find the evidence for the origin of the universe, world, and all the living species in it including humans. God's words described the creation of the universe in seven days and it was accepted that this is what happened. The species God created was understood to have remained unchanged since then, so any idea of evolution was heretical.

In 1650, James Ussher, Archbishop of Armagh in Ireland, had added up the lifetimes of the descendants of Adam and Eve and decided that the Creation had been completed on Sunday 21 October 4004 BC. While the exact date may not have troubled people, a universe that was 6000 years old was fine for most believers. It covered the whole span of human history and was short enough for people to feel that God was still taking an interest in his creation (Figure 20).

▲ ***Figure 20*** The Ancient of Days, *painted by William Blake in 1794.*

A problem arose in the late eighteenth century when it was recognised that the strangely shaped stones that were found on beaches, in quarries and in cliff faces were the fossilised bones of animals. Many of these animals did not resemble anything living today. Where had these examples of God's Creation gone? One answer was that they had failed to get a ride on Noah's Ark and had been drowned in the flood that covered every bit of dry land on Earth, their remains sinking into the mud at the bottom of the world ocean.

In 1802 William Paley put forward a version of the 'Argument from Design'. This suggested that the mechanism of organs such as the eye was so complex and perfect for its task that it must be evidence of the work of a Perfect Designer. He used the analogy of finding a pocket watch in the desert as evidence that a designer must have been present.

Catastrophe

Early in the nineteenth century, anatomists and geologists were amassing data that posed awkward questions for believers of the literal truth of the Bible stories. The anatomists included the great Georges Cuvier of France (1769–1832, Figure 21). Cuvier spent his career at the Museum of Natural History in Paris, examining the bodies of creatures and noting the minute details of their anatomy. He also examined the fossils that he discovered around Paris and that were sent to him from further afield. He was able to suggest the type of creature and its size from tiny fossilised remains. The geologists included Reverend William Buckland of Oxford University, who struggled to see order in the strata of rocks and the fossils that were dug out from them.

▲ ***Figure 21*** *Georges Cuvier.*

Cuvier observed that the fossils in one layer of rock were different from those in another layer. There were sharp divisions between the layers. A layer of rock containing fossil sea creatures lay above a layer containing freshwater animals and plants, and then there was another marine layer and so on. Layers of mudstone occurred in many places. Cuvier came to the conclusion that there had been more than one occasion when animals and plants had become suddenly extinct. He reasoned that a great worldwide catastrophe was necessary for the mass extinctions that he thought had occurred. These catastrophes, earthquakes and eruptions (Figure 22) had either covered the Earth with ocean or left the land exposed. He realised that this process of dramatic change required more than 6000 years and reckoned the Earth to be hundreds of thousands of years old.

▲ ***Figure 22*** *A volcano: just a taste of a catastrophe.*

Buckland accepted the catastrophe idea but struggled to marry it with the Bible stories. Perhaps Noah's flood represented the last great catastrophe. Others thought that after each catastrophe new species had been created to fill the environmental niches left by the extinct creatures, but still species were thought to be unchangeable.

Everlasting change

Despite the weight of Church dogma that said that species remained as God created them, some brave, or perhaps foolhardy, souls dared to suggest theories of evolution. In the 1790s, Erasmus Darwin, Charles's grandfather, published *Zoonomia*. In this he suggested that species underwent change caused by the environment in which they lived. His ideas were largely ignored. However, 15 years later Jean Baptiste Lamarck (1744–1829, Figure 23) arrived at a similar theory. Lamarck was a colleague of Cuvier's at the Natural History Museum in Paris. He had changed his mind during his lifetime and decided that species did evolve.

▲ **Figure 23** *Statue of Lamarck in the Jardin des Plantes, Paris.*

Lamarck suggested, in *Zoological Philosophy* (1809), that during its lifetime a creature may be forced by its environment to develop certain organs and limbs. For instance, a short-necked ancestor of the giraffe may have had to stretch to the top of tall bushes to find the most nutritious leaves and its neck had become elongated. Lamarck's big step was to suggest that these acquired characteristics could be passed on to offspring. Successive generations of giraffes would be born with longer and longer necks. Cuvier totally rejected Lamarck's theory and made life difficult for him at the Museum. Lamarck died in poverty.

In 1844 a remarkable book called *Vestiges of the Natural History of Creation* appeared. The author, not surprisingly, remained anonymous since the book suggested that evolution of species could occur without God's designing hand. The author turned out to be a publisher called Robert Chambers. He suggested that animals and plants had slowly developed from primitive forms found in the fossil record to more complex species. Chambers could not explain how such change took place but imagined that there was a law of species development that acted as generally on living matter as the law of gravitation that pulled on all objects. Chambers' theory suggested that a creature would give birth to a more complex organism. *Vestiges* caused a storm of outrage and did not gain many followers. Charles Darwin, however, was pleased that it had been published as it prepared the ground for his more scholarly attack on the problem of evolution.

Further work

1. *Why were Christians opposed to any suggestion of the evolution of species?*
2. *What apparent evidence gave Cuvier the idea that catastrophes drove species to extinction?*
3. *What are the main differences between the catastrophe theory and the Creation story of the Bible?*
4. *Lamarck's theory seemed to fit the fossil record it and was testable. Suggest an experiment to test his prediction that a variation acquired during an animal's lifetime may be inherited by offspring.*
5. *Why were Christians opposed to Chambers'* Vestiges of Creation?

4.3 Darwin, Wallace and friends

The dispute that never was

You might think that Alfred Wallace would have been a little put out by Darwin's treatment of his letter. Wallace had asked for it to be forwarded to Lyell for comment and perhaps eventual publication. Instead it was used in its unedited form to back up Darwin's theory. Did Wallace complain? Did he fight for his name to be given priority? Did he despise Darwin for the treatment he received? The answer was no to all these questions. The dispute over priority that Darwin feared never happened. Wallace respected Darwin as a great naturalist and role model. Far away in Malaysia he was in no position to exercise his claims on the theory of evolution and it seems he was quite happy to stay there while the debate raged. He may have been disappointed that his name was not on everyone's lips as was Darwin's, but he continued to give his support. (At least, he did until Darwin published *The Descent of Man*. Wallace could not support the evolution of humans from apes because he thought that man's 'spiritual essence' could not have developed through natural selection.)

Activity 26 *Lives of the evolutionists*

Prepare a presentation on the life of either Charles Darwin or Alfred Wallace. Major landmarks are summarised below. Use whatever sources are available to you for additional information. The presentation could be a written paper or an oral presentation using PowerPoint.

Aim to consult at least two other sources to supplement the information given below. For each source, record its details (as if for a bibliography) and make brief clear notes to sum up the information given. Note whether each source is primary or secondary and say how reliable you think it might be. Decide how best to organise the information for written or oral presentation.

Lives of the evolutionists

Charles Robert Darwin

Born 1809, Shrewsbury; father a GP; educated at Shrewsbury School.

1825	Studies medicine at Edinburgh University.
1827	At Cambridge University to train for the Church.
1831–6	Sails on HMS *Beagle* (Figure 25) to map and explore the South American continent.
1839	Publishes his account of *A Naturalist's Voyage on the Beagle.*
1839	Marries his cousin, Emma Wedgwood. They settle at Down House in Kent and have ten children.
1840s & 1850s	Working at Down on his theory of natural selection and on the natural history of barnacles; breeding pigeons.
1858	Theory of natural selection announced.

▲ **Figure 24** *Charles Darwin and his sister, Catherine.*

▲ ***Figure 25*** HMS *Beagle.*

1859	*The Origin of Species* published.
1871	*The Descent of Man* published.
1881	Publishes book on the role of earthworms in the soil.
1882	Dies; buried in Westminster Abbey.

Alfred Russel Wallace

Born 1823, Usk, Wales. Family moved house frequently. Attended elementary school only.

1837	Joins older brother to train as a surveyor.
1844	Becomes a school teacher in Leicester.
1848	Sets off for South America with friend, Henry Bates, a naturalist. Explores the Amazon basin, collecting specimens of animals and plants.
1853	Many of his specimens are lost in a fire on-board ship. Publishes an account of his travels up the River Amazon.
1854	Travels to Malaysia.
1858	Sends letter with an outline of his theory of evolution by natural selection to Darwin.
1862	Returns to the UK.
1866	Marries Annie Mitten, the 20-year-old daughter of a friend. Writes and lectures about his travels and the geographical distribution of species; campaigns against vaccination and for the nationalisation of land, women's rights, socialism and spiritualism. Opposes the application of evolutionary theory to humans.
1880	Awarded a government pension of £200 per year.
1905	Publishes *My Life.*
1913	Dies.

Resource link

You can find out more about Wallace and his work by visiting the Natural History Museum online Wallace Collection.

▲ ***Figure 26*** *Alfred Russel Wallace.*

Activity 27 Darwin's friends

Read the following information about three key people in Darwin's working life and answer these questions.

1 In what ways was Darwin's trip on HMS *Beagle* important to his career?

2 Summarise the results of Darwin's friendships with Lyell, Hooker and Huxley.

3 Imagine you are Alfred Wallace sitting in your tent in the Malaysian jungle. You receive an account of the announcement of evolution by natural selection in London. What would your feelings be?

4 Compare and contrast the lives and careers of Darwin and Wallace. Explain why you think they arrived at similar if not identical theories.

Darwin's theory and book would never have entered the limelight if it hadn't been for his friends. Darwin was often weak and sick, was not keen on public speaking and was afraid of the public reaction to his ideas and its effect on his family. His wife, Emma, was a devout Christian and he knew his views troubled her. It was Lyell and Hooker who drove Darwin to publish and Huxley who became 'Darwin's bulldog', slugging it out on the public stage.

Darwin's friends

Charles Lyell (1797–1875)

Lyell (Figure 27) was born to a wealthy Scottish family and went to Oxford University to study law. He attended William Buckland's lectures on geology and became fascinated by the subject. He travelled around Europe observing geological formations and met Cuvier and the explorer von Humboldt. He developed his own ideas on geology and in 1830 published the first volume of *Principles of Geology*. This book had a huge influence on Darwin. When Darwin returned to England they became friends. Lyell spent a short time as Professor of Geology at Kings College London but preferred the freedom of his private income to travel and revise his books. By the 1850s Lyell was an important figure in the scientific establishment with the authority to promote an unpopular theory.

Lyell had developed the theory of uniformitarianism first suggested by James Hutton. The theory suggested that geological processes summarised in the rock cycle take place slowly and produce constant change in the environment. The Earth had existed for millions of years, if not eternity, in this constant state of change. Lyell thought that species periodically appeared or became extinct but he did not see signs of progression in the fossil record. Despite pressing Darwin to publish *Origin*, at first he did not accept Darwin's theory. It was 10 years before he included a mention of evolution by natural selection in his *Principles of Geology*.

▲ **Figure 27** Charles Lyell.

Joseph Hooker (1817–1911)

Hooker (Figure 28) was born in Suffolk and attended Glasgow University where his father was Professor of Botany. He studied medicine and was also a keen naturalist. In 1839 he joined HMS *Erebus* for a four-year voyage around the Antarctic and Australasia. He was officially assistant surgeon on the ship but had enough time to acquire specimens for a six-volume account of the natural history of the places they visited. Darwin praised this publication and he and Hooker became close friends. In 1844 Darwin told Hooker of his theory of evolution by natural selection.

In the late 1840s Hooker travelled in India and returned with the rhododendron, which became a popular plant in gardens. In 1855 he was appointed to assist his father who was Director of Kew Gardens and 10 years later became Director himself. In his 20 years in charge he turned the Gardens into a leading centre for botanical research. He wrote a great deal on plants. He retired in 1885 through ill health but continued his work until he died.

▲ **Figure 28** *Joseph Hooker.*

Thomas Huxley (1825–95)

Huxley (Figure 29) was born in London, the seventh child of a school teacher. He had only two years of schooling but taught himself sufficiently well to be admitted to Charing Cross Hospital to study medicine. After graduation in 1845 he joined HMS *Rattlesnake* as surgeon for an expedition to Australia and Papua. On the voyage he studied the marine life and wrote an important paper on jellyfish that brought him membership of the Royal Society. He became a lecturer on Natural History at what was to become Imperial College in London. This gave him sufficient income to marry his Australian fiancée in 1854. He made a detailed study of primates.

His knowledge of natural history drew him to Darwin's theory of evolution and he became its most public and vociferous supporter. Huxley was very active in the scientific societies of England and shaped the way that science was taught in the late nineteenth century, particularly in the new colleges that became the universities of Manchester, Birmingham and Johns Hopkins University, Baltimore, USA. His most formidable opponent was Sir Richard Owen, an anatomist and palaeontologist, whom he pushed out of positions of authority. His grandchildren include the writer Aldous Huxley (author of *Brave New World*), Nobel Prize-winning physiologist Andrew Huxley and biologist Sir Julian Huxley, who was the first Director-general of Unesco.

▲ **Figure 29** *Thomas Huxley.*

4.4 *The Origin of Species*

A revolutionary book

Following the announcement of his and Wallace's theory on 1 July 1858, Charles Darwin set to work to turn his manuscript into a publishable book. It appeared in November 1859 and its print run of a little over 1000 copies quickly sold out. Over the next 12 years the book went through five revisions and reprintings. The title was *The Origin of Species by Means of Natural Selection*. Very quickly people took sides, some admiring the book for its vision and others detesting its thesis. What was so special about *Origin*?

Struggle for existence and natural selection

Darwin's book rarely mentions the word evolution. What Darwin is concerned with are the individuals that make up varieties of species. There are two ideas central to his discussion: the struggle for existence and natural selection.

The first wasn't really Darwin's own idea. In 1838, shortly after his return to England, Darwin read *An Essay on the Principle of Population* written by an economist, Thomas Malthus, in 1798. This pointed out that human populations grow much faster than food production and that in the future (quite soon, Malthus thought) humans would be competing for declining food stocks. Darwin realised that this struggle applied to all living things; that competition exists between species and between individuals of a species for food, water, light, living space, shelter from predators, mates and other needs.

Both Darwin and Wallace separately arrived at the second idea, that the environment provided the conditions and the competitive surroundings that gave certain individuals the advantage over others. The individuals that survived had offspring. Why did certain individuals survive and not others? This was Darwin's vital observation – that the members of a species or even the members of a variety of a species varied in one or more characteristics. It was these variations that may or may not confer an advantage. Those individuals that were most suited to their habitats were those that multiplied, or 'survival of the fittest' as Wallace put it.

Evidence

Look around you at the people close to you. You recognise them and you can tell them apart. Although we all belong to the human species we are all different. Small variations set us apart. The same is true for every individual of every species. This observation was a revelation for Darwin which set him apart from the biologists of his time. They looked for similarities between individuals so that they could be classified in to varieties, species, phyla and kingdoms. The aim was to generalise in the same way that physics and chemistry have general laws which apply to specific conditions. Generalisation had the effect of making species seem fixed and unchanging. Darwin showed that this was wrong and he backed it up with evidence, lots of it.

The first chapter of *Origin* considers variation in domesticated species of plants and animals. A Chihuahua and a Great Dane are both dogs brought into existence by successive selective interbreeding by humans. Agricultural breeding methods can give rise to discrete varieties in a relatively short period of time. For instance, the first tomato was brought to Europe in the sixteenth century but by the end of the nineteenth century there were dozens of distinct cultivated varieties. Darwin himself bred pigeons. Many people, Lyell included, thought that there was something special about the domesticated

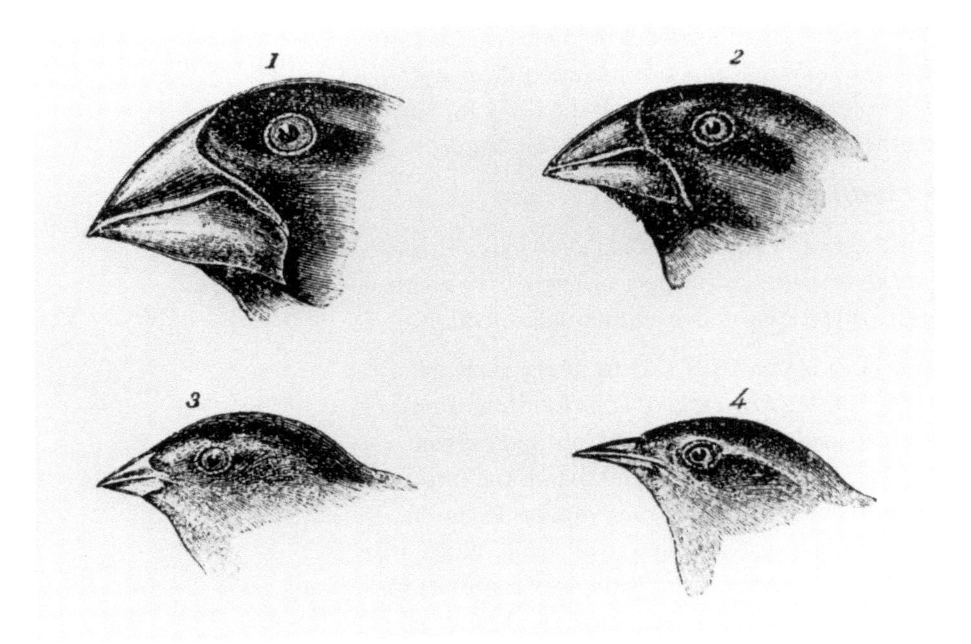

▲ ***Figure 30*** *Darwin's drawings of finches in the Galapagos Islands.*

species that somehow made variation easy to bring about. Darwin showed that such variation occurred naturally and that farm breeders only accelerated and exaggerated the changes.

In the following chapters of *Origin*, Darwin explores many examples of variation found in natural environments. Some of the most famous are the finches he encountered on the Galapagos Islands (Figure 30). After his return he discovered that 13 different types of bird originated as one species. The different varieties, with their different-shaped bills, had sprung up on different islands where the birds had to depend on different sources of food. Darwin showed that survival meant dependence on particular habitats.

Variability and inheritance

Darwin reasoned that variations arose in individuals. He did not know how they arose but suspected that it occurred before or during conception. However, later in life he did accept to some extent the Lamarckian view that variation might occur during an individual's lifetime. A variation that conferred an advantage on an individual would be passed on to offspring. After several generations the population which carried the variation would constitute a new species and was very likely to have replaced the earlier species.

The Descent of Man

The Origin of Species says little about the evolution of humans but it is obvious that Darwin thinks that mankind has been, and maybe is still, going through the process of natural selection. Man is a primate like chimpanzees and gorillas so it was obvious to assume that they had a common ancestor. Darwin took up the challenge of human evolution in his book *The Descent of Man,* published in 1871.

Darwin's problems

While convinced that he was right, Darwin knew that he did not yet have the answers to all the questions that would be asked. There were two particular problems:

- Inheritance – Darwin did not know how characteristics of one individual were passed on to offspring. He thought that some kind of blending occurred but this would result in new variations being lost. He did not know that at the same time as *Origin* was published, a monk in eastern Europe was performing genetic experiments that would reveal the answer. But then, no one took any notice of Mendel's work until 1900.
- Gaps in the fossil record – Darwin's theory predicted a gradual change in species as variation after variation modified plants and animals. Sometimes this was apparent from the sequence of fossils extracted from rocks of different ages, but all too often new species appeared in the fossil record with no sign of earlier types. Darwin was confident that further exploration would reveal fossils that filled the gaps, but today some gaps still remain.

Activity 28 *Reading* The Origin of Species

Read the following extracts (pages 57–8) from *The Origin of Species* and answer these questions.

1 What is the 'mystery of mysteries'? (Extract 1)

2 When does Darwin say he sketched his conclusions? (Extract 1)

3 How does Darwin differentiate between varieties and species? (Extract 2)

4 What does Darwin mean by the term 'natural selection'? (Extract 2)

5 How does Darwin explain that wolves are thin and fast? (Extract 3)

6 Why does Darwin refer to greyhounds? (Extract 3)

“*From Author's Introduction to* The Origin of Species

When on board HMS *Beagle*, as naturalist, I was much struck with certain facts in the distribution of the inhabitants of South America, and in the geological relations of the present to the past inhabitants of that continent. These facts seemed to me to throw some light on the origin of species – that mystery of mysteries, as it has been called by one of our greatest philosophers. On my return home, it occurred to me, in 1837, that something might perhaps be made out on this question by patiently accumulating and reflecting on all sorts of facts which could possibly have any bearing on it. After five years' work I allowed myself to speculate on the subject, and drew up some short notes; these I enlarged in 1844 into a sketch of the conclusions, which then seemed to me probable: from that period to the present day I have steadily pursued the same object. I hope that I may be excused for entering on these personal details, as I give them to show that I have not been hasty in coming to a decision. ”

“ *From Chapter 3*

Again, it may be asked, how is it that varieties, which I have called incipient species, become ultimately converted into good and distinct species, which in most cases obviously differ from each other far more than do the varieties of the same species? How do those groups of species, which constitute what are called distinct *genera*, and which differ from each other more than do the species of the same *genus*, arise? All these results, as we shall more fully see in the next chapter, follow inevitably from the struggle for life. Owing to this struggle for life, any variation, however slight and from whatever cause proceeding, if it be in any degree profitable to an individual of any species, in its infinitely complex relations to other organic beings and to external nature, will tend to the preservation of that individual, and will generally be inherited by its offspring. The offspring, also, will thus have a better chance of surviving, for, of the many individuals of any species which are periodically born, but a small number can survive. I have called this principle, by which each slight variation, if useful, is preserved, by the term of Natural Selection, in order to mark its relation to man's power of selection. We have seen that man by selection can certainly produce great results, and can adapt organic beings to his own uses, through the accumulation of slight but useful variations, given to him by the hand of Nature. But Natural Selection, as we shall hereafter see, is a power incessantly ready for action, and is as immeasurably superior to man's feeble efforts, as the works of Nature are to those of Art. ”

“ *From Chapter 4*

In order to make it clear how, as I believe, natural selection acts, I must beg permission to give one or two imaginary illustrations. Let us take the case of a wolf, which preys on various animals, securing some by craft, some by strength, and some by fleetness; and let us suppose that the fleetest prey, a deer for instance, had from any change in the country increased in numbers, or that other prey had decreased in numbers, during that season of the year when the wolf is hardest pressed for food. I can under such circumstances see no reason to doubt that the swiftest and slimmest wolves would have the best chance of surviving, and so be preserved or selected – provided always that they retained the strength to master their prey at this or at some other period of the year, when they might be compelled to prey on other animals. I can see no more reason to doubt this, than that man can improve the fleetness of his greyhounds by careful and methodical selection, or by that unconscious selection which results from each man trying to keep the best dogs without any thought of modifying the breed. ”

Further work

1 What did Malthus have to say that influenced Darwin?

2 What does 'survival of the fittest' mean?

3 What does *Origin* reveal about Darwin's skill as an observer?

4 Why does *Origin* begin with an examination of domesticated species?

5 *The Origin of Species* has the subtitle *Preservation of Favoured Races in the Struggle for Life.* What is meant by this subtitle?

4.5 An ongoing debate

Opposition to Darwin

The forgotten hero of the first half of nineteenth-century palaeontology, Richard Owen (Figure 31), wielded a huge amount of power at the time of the publication of *The Origin of Species*.

▲ **Figure 31** *Richard Owen.*

Owen was born in Lancaster where he began his training as a surgeon. He became interested in the study of anatomy. He moved to London where he was given a junior position at the Hunterian Museum, a collection of anatomical specimens attached to the Royal College of Surgeons. Owen was a master at manipulating people and events to his own advantage and was not afraid to use other people's data and ideas in his own papers. Before long he had married the daughter of the Curator of the Museum and begun a swift rise up the ladder of success. He was skilled at identifying fossils and he became acquainted with the aging Georges Cuvier. Soon he was the leading fossil anatomist in the country. In 1841, at a meeting of the British Association for the Advancement of Science, he delivered a paper on fossil reptiles that made his reputation, and shortly afterwards he introduced the term 'dinosaur' to the world. He chaired the committees of important scientific societies and became friendly with Prince Albert, Queen Victoria's husband. The Prince supported Owen's plans for a huge 'city of science' in South Kensington. As Owen's power waned the plans were cut back but the Natural History Museum was his lasting achievement. He died a forgotten and embittered old man.

Owen supported Cuvier's catastrophe theory and maintained the general truth of the Bible. He kept quiet about inconsistencies that he saw in the evidence of fossils and living creatures. He was quick to see flaws in Darwin's theory, the gaps where Darwin lacked evidence or explanation. He opposed evolution, perhaps because he thought the establishment, of which he was a leader, could win the argument quickly. Instead, he was the one who was defeated and displaced.

As Darwin expected, the publication of *The Origin of Species* brought condemnation from Church people, but a small group of scientists saw the value of his theory. Huxley was soon seen as the leading spokesperson for Darwin's supporters. It would not be long before the theory was debated in public.

Activity 29 *The Oxford debate*

Read the following account of a famous debate and discuss these points. For each, jot down some brief notes then compare your views with those of other students.

1 The debate is often portrayed as a victory for Darwin's theory of evolution. Do you agree?

2 What do you think was the attitude of the popular press to Darwin's theory?

3 Why do you think Wilberforce spoke at the Oxford meeting and not Owen?

4 Why do you think Huxley was reluctant to attend the meeting?

The Oxford debate

The British Association for the Advancement of Science was formed in the 1830s. Each year the BA meets in a university town for lectures and debates on many matters of scientific interest. In the summer of 1860 the conference was in Oxford. The conference met in the Oxford Museum (Figure 32), the university's new centre for scientific research. This year evolution and Darwin's book was a major topic of conversation. The Botany and Zoology section was busier than ever before. Thomas Huxley and Richard Owen had an argument about the comparison between gorilla and human brains. Owen thought that the differences between apes and humans were so great they could not be related while Huxley thought the opposite. One session was listed as a talk on 'Darwinism' by Professor John Draper of New York, but everyone knew it was an opportunity for the opponents of evolution to make their case.

▲ **Figure 32** *The Oxford Museum.*

Five hundred or more people turned up for the meeting so it had to be moved to a larger room in the Museum. The centre of the hall was packed with clergymen (at that time all Oxford and Cambridge university fellows had to be ordained members of the Church). Near the front sat the Bishop of Oxford, Samuel Wilberforce (Figure 33). A few of Darwin's supporters stood at the sides of the room. Thomas Huxley hadn't intended going to the meeting as he expected the anti-evolution feeling to be overwhelming. Nevertheless, he had been persuaded to attend. He took his place on the stage as a BA committee man.

▲ ***Figure 33*** *Samuel Wilberforce.*

When Draper sat down after an hour-long, boring speech, the audience were impatient for the fun to begin. Huxley was invited to comment but declined. Then Wilberforce rose to his feet and looked around the room noticing Huxley's presence. 'Soapy Sam' Wilberforce had been coached in evolutionary theory by Richard Owen. He was an excellent speaker and delivered Owen's arguments with skill and humour. But then it seems he decided to improvise. He turned to Huxley and 'begged to know whether it was through his grandmother or grandfather that he claimed descent from a monkey'. The laughter gave Huxley his opportunity to reply. He put forward the sound evidence that Darwin had for his theory, finishing with a withering retort to Wilberforce, 'I would not be ashamed to have a monkey for an ancestor but would be ashamed to be connected with a man who used great gifts to obscure truth'. The meeting erupted into laughter and argument and one of the ladies present fainted. The meeting was reported in the newspapers and magazines such as *Punch*. For the first time a scientific theory was of popular interest and the name of Darwin was talked about up and down the country (Figure 34).

▲ ***Figure 34*** *Cartoon of 1878 ridiculing Darwin and his theory.*

The debate between Wilberforce and Huxley didn't end the arguments; they were only just beginning. The supporters of evolution became confident enough, however, to continue to present the evidence for evolution and gradually the idea took hold. Changes were taking place in the universities, and new colleges were springing up in the industrial towns. The younger, evolution-supporting scientists, such as Huxley, were gaining authority and power and the old guard, including Richard Owen, were being sidelined. Some Christians found that they could assimilate evolution into their religious beliefs. There was even a paper in Hebrew that found support for evolutionary theory in the Old Testament. But the debate never ended.

The debate continues

Most scientists accept the general principles of evolution by natural selection as modified by recent developments in genetics and molecular biology. Nevertheless, the battle still rages, with fundamentalist religious groups who deny evolution and stick with the literal interpretation of the Bible and other religious texts. For example, some followers of Islam accept Darwinian evolution as applying to all species with the exception of human beings, who they believe were divinely created. Where fundamental Christians have wielded power, such as in the southern states of the USA, there have been legal arguments about what should be taught in schools. At one time teaching about evolution was banned in these states. Now the argument is for 'creationism' or 'creation Science' to be given equal standing in science lessons with the study of evolution. The argument is not restricted to the USA. The title of the anti-evolution theory changes from time to time; '**intelligent design theory**' is one such current title.

Activity 30 *Exploring creationism*

Carry out an Internet search for creationist ideas. Use the key words creationism, creation science, intelligent design.

What evidence do the sites use to support views of Creation derived from the Bible or other religious texts? What arguments do the sites use to discredit evolutionary theory?

For each site you visit, make a note of its URL and any information you can find about the person or organisation responsible for the site. Make brief notes to summarise the content of the site and the arguments presented, and try to distinguish between fact, opinion and speculation. It might be helpful to structure your notes in a table, as in Activity 25.

Further work

Why do you think Darwin's theory became so widely known amongst the general public?

4.6 After Darwin

Evidence for Darwinian evolution

In the twentieth century the sciences of genetics and molecular biology revealed the mechanism for inheritance and mutation of which Darwin was ignorant. Darwin's examples of evolution concern the varieties of plants and animals and the transformations undergone by extinct creatures as shown by fossil evidence. Evolution takes a long time to act on creatures with long lifetimes, but the study of bacteria has provided further evidence to support Darwin's idea of evolution by natural selection.

Three years after the publication of *Origin,* Louis Pasteur discovered that microbes in the air and water are responsible for fermentation and decay. It was several more years before the 'germ theory of disease' was accepted. The rapid growth and reproduction of microbes allows microbiologists to witness evolution in action. The emergence of strains of bacteria resistant to penicillin and other antibiotics is a perfect example of natural selection taking place (Figure 35).

In any population of bacteria there is variation. A chance change in the DNA may bring about a resistance to an antibiotic. Normally this confers no advantage on the bacteria, but when the antibiotic is administered all the non-resistant bacteria are killed. The resistant ones survive (they are the 'fittest' for the new environment) and no longer have competition for nutrients. The resistant bacteria multiply and in time replace the non-resistant strain as a new variety of bacteria.

Since Darwin's time, his theory has been modified in the light of new discoveries that were unknown to him. And there are still plenty of arguments about the details of evolution. Richard Dawkins and Stephen Jay Gould are

 **Project hint**

Some of these topics could provide interesting questions for investigation in your Research project.

SUPER BUG CASES 'ON THE RISE' IN UK

A report out today highlights a rise in deaths caused by so called 'super bugs' in UK hospitals.

The published data, compiled by an independent research body, claims that deaths involving MRSA, *Staphylococcus aureus* and *Clostridium difficile* have risen by nearly twenty percent in the last twelve months.

The report goes on to suggest a raft of new measures that may help combat the rise. It highlights the success of campaigns nationwide to increase hand washing, but states clearly that more funding for key cleaning services and new technologies such as nanotechnology antibacterial paint is needed.

The shadow health secretary claimed that these findings were merely the tip of the iceberg, and that super bugs are 'out of control' in NHS hospitals.

'Government spending has ignored areas like hygiene while focussing too much on issues like waiting lists and management pay rises' she announced in a press conference yesterday afternoon.

▲ ***Figure 35*** *Hospital 'superbugs' often make the news.*

two leading supporters of the theory of evolution and yet they were able to engage in a career-long debate about the finer points of the theory.

Using Darwinism

During the latter decades of the nineteenth century, Darwin's theory, or at least some of its most notable phrases, entered popular consciousness. In particular the slogan 'survival of the fittest' was frequently heard, albeit with little understanding of Darwin's detailed arguments. After the publication of *The Descent of Man* in 1871, politicians and social reformers used Darwin's theory to justify their policies.

The domination of the white colonialists over the native populations of Africa and the black former slaves of the Americas was taken as evidence of the more evolved state of white humans. This idea was used to legitimise apartheid policies in South Africa and the USA (Figure 36).

▲ ***Figure 36** Racial apartheid in South Africa.*

Another movement that emerged was eugenics. This was founded by anthropologist and explorer Francis Galton (1822–1911), a cousin of Charles Darwin. After travelling and making a name for himself in Africa, Galton settled in England and studied human inheritance. He became convinced that intelligence was inherited and not affected by the environment in which people lived. He suggested that human evolution should be given a helping hand by encouraging the intelligent to breed while preventing the dim, by which he meant the poor and disadvantaged, from having offspring. Many educated people adopted Galton's policies, and in the early years of the twentieth century the eugenics movement gained considerable power. As a consequence of this view, mentally handicapped people were sterilised without their consent.

The Nazis in Germany used the arguments of eugenics to proclaim the superiority of their 'master race' and to dispose of Jews, Romanies (Gypsies), mentally handicapped people and homosexuals. When the horrors of the Nazi concentration camps became known at the end of the Second World War, the eugenics movement was discredited.

Project hint

In your Research project, you will need to present evidence and arguments to support your point of view on your Research question, and you will need to identify and address counter-arguments.

Activity 31 *Darwinism today*

Hold a debate on one or more of the following propositions. Prepare for the debate by setting out arguments and evidence for and against the propositions.

- Evolutionary theory has contributed to racial hatred in the world today.
- The human race has ceased to evolve.
- Darwin's theory of evolution by natural selection is as good a theory as Newton's law of gravitation.

For each proposition being debated, make two lists to summarise points for and against it, and decide whether you agree or disagree with the proposition. Plan how best to argue your case. Make notes on the evidence and arguments that you can use to support your views. Try to anticipate what other people will say who disagree with you, and think how you will try to convince them of your own point of view.

Further work

1 Write a summary of Darwin's and Wallace's development of the theory of evolution and the events surrounding it.

2 Why do you think that eugenics appealed to so many people in the early twentieth century?

5 Oxygen

5.1 The Retro-Nobel Prize

Oxygen: the play

In 2001, two very distinguished scientists, Roald Hoffmann (a Polish-American chemist and Nobel Prizewinner) and Carl Djerassi (Austrian-American, one of the chemists who synthesised the first oral contraceptive), wrote a play called *Oxygen*. Since it was written, the play has been publicly performed a number of times in the UK, Germany and the USA.

The basic idea of the play is to imagine that the Royal Swedish Academy of Sciences has decided to award a 'Retro-Nobel' Prize for work done before 1901, and the Nobel Committee for Chemistry has to decide upon a suitable chemist to receive it. They eventually decide to give it to the discoverer of oxygen. But there were three competing candidates: Karl Scheele, Joseph Priestley and Antoine Lavoisier (Figure 37). Who did discover oxygen? This section is a variation on the plot of the play.

Over the next few pages you will study the story of the discovery of oxygen. The conclusion of this section will be a debate in which you argue the case for one of the candidates. But first let us learn what we can about the discovery of oxygen.

▲ **Figure 37** *(From left to right:) Lavoisier, Priestley and Scheele.*

The naming of oxygen

Today, most people are familiar with the name oxygen. They know it is a gas needed for respiration and they may recognise its role in combustion. But for chemists the word stands for a whole theory which underpins much of modern chemistry: the oxygen theory of combustion. The naming of oxygen was the culmination of a controversy that involved Joseph Priestley, Antoine Lavoisier, Karl Scheele and many other scientists in the eighteenth century. We have yet to decide who discovered oxygen but it was Lavoisier who gave it its name.

Lavoisier used the term oxygen for the first time in 1779. In his book *The Elements of Chemistry* (1789) he explained his reasoning.

> "We have already seen, that the atmospheric air is composed of two gases, or aeriform fluids, one of which is capable, by respiration, of contributing to animals' life, and in which metals are calcinable, and combustible bodies may burn; the other, on the contrary, is endowed with directly opposite qualities; it cannot be breathed by animals, neither will it admit of the combustion of inflammable bodies, nor of the calcinations of metals. We have given to the base of the former, or respirable portion of the air the name of oxygen, from oxus, acidum, and geinomai, gignor (i.e genesis or to generate); because in reality, one of the most general properties of this base is to form acids, by combining many different substances."

Lavoisier's language, or rather this translation of his French, may be a little difficult to understand but the essence is that oxygen is a made-up word meaning 'acid maker'. In German this is translated directly as 'sauerstoff'. Lavoisier had observed that substances such as carbon, sulfur and phosphorus burned readily in oxygen and formed substances that were acids. Lavoisier went on to suggest that all acids contained oxygen.

If it wasn't until 1779 that oxygen got its name, what was it called before? How can a gas that is in the air all around us be 'discovered'? What do Priestley and Scheele have to do with it, and who was Lavoisier? These are questions we will answer in the next lessons.

Activity 32 Oxygen men

Who were Priestley, Scheele and Lavoisier? Choose one of these three characters and find out about him and his life. Where and when did he live? What notable events occurred during his life?

Working in a group, begin to prepare a short presentation on the life of your character. In later lessons you will learn more about the work of your character and this will contribute to your presentation. In the final lesson your group will make a presentation and argue in support of your character. The entire presentation should be no more than 8 minutes.

Use dictionaries of scientists, scientific histories and the Internet to aid your research.

For each source you consult, keep a careful note of the title, author and date of publication. For websites, record the URL. Note whether each is a primary or a secondary source, and whether it is likely to be reliable.

Decide how best to organise your notes. Use lists, tables, time lines and diagrams to summarise the information you find.

Further work

1 Read the passage from Lavoisier's book again.
 a What is the gas in the air, other than oxygen, that Lavoisier refers to?
 b What do you think 'calcinable' means?
 c Name an acidic substance formed when sulfur is burned in air.

2 *a* Can you name any acidic substances that do not contain oxygen?
 b Can you give any examples of elements that react with oxygen to give substances that are not acids?
 c What significance do your answers to ***a*** and ***b*** have for Lavoisier's choice of name?

5.2 Before oxygen: the phlogiston theory

The beginnings of the phlogiston theory

In 1669 the German chemist Johann Joachim Becher (1635–82) proposed a theory to account for combustion. Until then, alchemists (those who studied the properties of substances and the changes they underwent) had adhered to a theory developed by the Greek philosophers Empedocles (c. 490–430 BC) and Aristotle (384–322 BC). In this theory there were just four 'elements' that made up all matter and accounted for its behaviour: fire, earth, air and water.

Becher suggested that there were three kinds of 'earth'. These were:

- mercurious earth, which gave substances properties of metallicity, fluidity and volatility
- fatty earth, which gave rise to oily, sulfurous and combustible properties
- vitreous earth, which enabled substances to fuse into glasses and glazes.

The important earth for our story is the fatty earth because Becher suggested that when objects burn they release this fatty earth, and that objects that burn well are rich in this substance.

The next step towards a comprehensive theory of combustion was taken by another German chemist, Georg Ernst Stahl (1660–1734, Figure 38). Stahl was a Professor of Medicine at the University of Halle and physician to the King of Prussia. His first book, *Zymotechnia Fundamentalis* (1697) concerned the fermentation of wine and beer. In 1713 he renamed Becher's oily earth as phlogiston (meaning 'flame principle', from the Greek *phlox*, meaning flame). He suggested that matter now consisted of four elements: mercurious earth, vitreous earth, water and phlogiston. But Stahl's greatest contribution was to realise that the combustion and the calcination of metals (that is, turning a metal back to its powdery ore) were similar processes.

▲ ***Figure 38*** *Georg Stahl.*

Combustion and calcinations

According to Stahl and his followers, all substances that were combustible were said to contain phlogiston, something that was lost to the air on burning. Non-combustible substances were devoid of phlogiston or had been dephlogisticated (i.e. phlogiston had been removed from them). The early phlogistonists almost certainly regarded phlogiston as a 'principle' rather than a solid substance. The English chemist Richard Watson was one of these. In his *Chemical Essays* (1781) he wrote:

> “You do not surely expect that chemistry should be able to present you with a handful of phlogiston separated from an inflammable body; you may just as reasonably demand a handful of magnetism, gravity or electricity to be extracted from a magnetic, weighty or electric body.”
>
> *(Quoted in Toulmin and Goodfield, 1962, p. 240)*

As the century unfolded, however, many chemists began to assume that phlogiston was actually a material substance. Those substances which left the least residue on combustion were thought to be especially rich in phlogiston. Many materials left no residue and were thought to be phlogiston itself. Charcoal, hydrogen and sulfur, at one time or another, were proposed as candidates for nearly pure phlogiston. The appearance of flames as objects burned was explained as the whirling motion caused by the escape of phlogiston.

Both rusting and calcination (what we would now call the oxidation of a metal to its oxide or calx) were regarded by Stahl as the removal of phlogiston. Metallurgists had known for centuries that to extract a metal from its ore it must be heated with charcoal (Figure 39). This process was interpreted as the addition of phlogiston from a phlogiston-rich substance:

calx or ore + charcoal (rich in phlogiston) → metal (phlogisticated ore)

▲ ***Figure 39*** *Copper smelting in the sixteenth century.*

Activity 33 Demonstrating the phlogiston theory

If you have access to a laboratory and suitable apparatus, observe some chemical reactions and try to use the phlogiston theory to explain what is happening.

Gases, airs and weight changes

Ideas about the gaseous state in the eighteenth century were rather vague and inconsistent. Generally, chemists thought all gases to be different forms of air. Gases that we now call hydrogen, methane and carbon monoxide were all termed 'inflammable air' since they could burn in common air. Gases that could not support combustion were called 'phlogisticated airs'; these included gases we now call carbon dioxide, sulfur dioxide and nitrogen. They were phlogisticated in the sense that, since objects did not burn in them, something must be preventing the phlogiston leaving the object.

A substance such as charcoal, for example, was thought to be rich in phlogiston since in ordinary air it burns with little residue and is able to turn a metal ore or calx to the metal. However, carbon will not burn in nitrogen. It follows that nitrogen must be already full with phlogiston – it is saturated, so to speak.

It was eventually discovered that air played a vital role in combustion. It is hardly surprising then that refinements to the theory of phlogiston and finally its overthrow came from the study of gases – pneumatics as it was then called. Many gases, known as 'firedamp', 'inflammable airs', 'mofette', 'afterdamp' and 'marsh gas', were familiar to eighteenth-century miners and brewers, but it was not clear whether these were different substances or simply variations of common air.

Today it seems obvious that to understand chemical reactions we must weigh the reactants and products very carefully. In the eighteenth century, however, it was not at all clear that this would be a useful thing to do. For a start, there was the sheer difficulty of weighing gases. Secondly, why should weight be important? The chemists had yet to accept the principle of the conservation of mass. More importantly, there was the problem of 'imponderables' and 'incorporeals'. These were entities or phenomena that seemed to have no weight such as electricity, magnetism and light.

Objections and explanations

It was Thomas Huxley (see Lesson 4.3), in the nineteenth century, who said that 'many a beautiful theory has been slain by an ugly fact' and in the long run this is true of much of science. We can also see in science many examples where an 'ugly fact' can be beautified and made to fit a theory. Such was the case with the change in weight of the reactants following combustion. It was indeed difficult for these early chemists to investigate weight changes. Very often they were led astray because the heating (usually by the sun's rays focused through a lens) caused such an increase in temperature that the substance vaporised and some of it was lost, and therefore appeared lighter after the reaction. But eventually it was realised that the calx formed following combustion was actually heavier than the original metal. The problem of course was that since calcination is supposed to be the loss of something (phlogiston) it should become lighter – weight gain is the ugly fact. Chemists wedded to phlogiston (it was one of the few theories they had, after all) could accommodate this apparent anomaly. Some of the explanations offered were as follows:

- The departure of phlogiston increased the density of a substance – an idea proposed by a number of chemists including Pott, Stahl, Scheffer and Wallerius.
- The presence of phlogiston weakened the gravitational attraction of bodies – argued by J. Ellicot (1780).
- Secondary accretion (another substance) from the air took the place of the phlogiston. This became the common response and we can conceptualise it as shown in Figure 40.

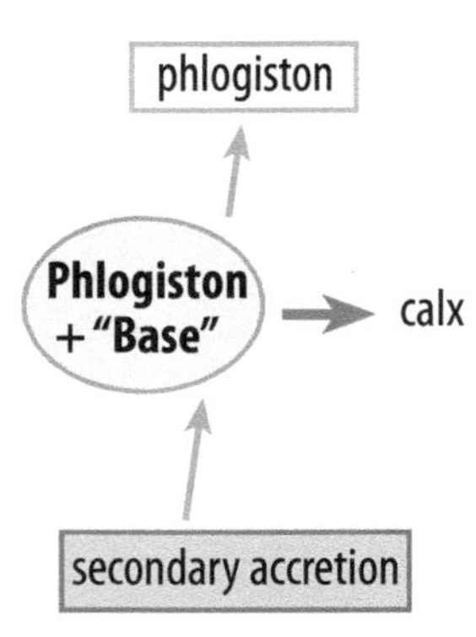

▲ ***Figure 40*** *Explaining weight gain in combustion.*

Activity 34 *Morveau's explanation for weight change*

One ingenious explanation for the gain in weight when a substance lost phlogiston came from the Frenchman Louis Bernard Guyton de Morveau (1737–1816). He explains his reasoning by means of an analogy (quoted below).

Discuss Morveau's analogy. What things are playing the part of phlogiston, a metal, a metal calx and the air? Rewrite Morveau's explanation in your own words.

> "Place one upon the other in each pan of a balance two lead cubes each weighing 573 grains. They are in equilibrium in air and in water. Between one pair put a strip of cork, the so-called absolute weight of which is 6 grains. The pan containing the cork descends in air with a force exactly as the 6 grains. Immerse both pans in water; the pan with the cork rises with a force as the excess of the specific gravity of water over that of the cork, and 28 grains must be added to restore equilibrium. And thus an addition of matter here produces a decrease of weight in water.
>
> *(Dissertation sur le phlogistique, in Crosland, M. (Ed) (1971)* The Science of Matter, *Penguin, Harmondsworth)*"

(Note: A grain is a unit of mass.)

Activity 35 *The difficulty of refuting the phlogiston theory*

Soon after it was proposed by Stahl, the theory of phlogiston faced criticism but remarkably it was able to explain away any supposed objections. Table 1 shows some critical points that were made against the theory. Select the most appropriate response from the phlogistonists and insert it alongside the objection in a copy of the table.

Discuss whether you think that the critics of the phlogiston theory were convinced by these arguments.

Table 1 Defending the phlogiston theory.

Objection to phlogiston theory	*Response*
A If rusting and combustion of iron are the same process (they both produce iron calx) how come the latter gives off heat and flames whilst the former does not?	
B For both rusting and combustion, air is necessary, so surely something in the air is the vital principle.	
C When combustion of a metal takes place the calx is heavier than the original metal, yet phlogiston is supposed to be lost.	

The phlogistonists' responses

1 When phlogiston leaves an object quickly, it generates heat and light.

2 When an object burns it takes in a secondary accretion from the air.

3 Air is the medium which carries phlogiston from one place to another.

Further work

1 Another analogy for the phlogiston theory is the following:

Consider a lump of plasticine with a hydrogen balloon attached. The plasticine and balloon are weighed together in air. The string of the balloon is now cut and the balloon floats upwards.

a What happens to the weight on the scales when the string is cut?

b In this analogy, what represents:

i phlogiston *ii* a metal ore or calx *iii* a metal?

c What property of the hydrogen balloon explains the readings on the scales?

2 Why do you think scientists were reluctant to reject the phlogiston theory even when they recognised that it had weaknesses?

5.3 Priestley, Lavoisier and dephlogisticated air

Priestley at Bowood

In 1773 Priestley became librarian and household tutor to William Petty, the second Earl of Shelburne, at his large castle in Bowood, Wiltshire. Petty opposed the attitude of George III to the American colonists and favoured the breaking away of America from British rule. Priestley shared these views.

Priestley's most famous discovery at Bowood was dephlogisticated air (oxygen). Priestley described his experiments in his book *Experiments and Observations on Different Kinds of Air* (1775).

Activity 36 *Priestley on different kinds of air*

Read the extract from Priestley's book (below and overleaf) and discuss the questions that follow.

1 What role does Priestley think chance played in his discovery? Try to think of any other case where chance has played a role in scientific discovery.

2 In what ways does Priestley's account of his work differ from a more recent scientific paper?

3 What experiments revealed that Priestley's gas was not common air?

4 As a follower of the phlogiston theory, Priestley used the theory to explain the formation of his gas. Explain the reasoning behind his naming of the gas 'dephlogisticated air'. ('Mercurius calcinatus' or mercury calx is mercury without phlogiston).

5 What evidence does Priestley offer to suggest that breathing dephlogisticated air may be beneficial?

6 In the final paragraph, how does Priestley suggest that others might be interested in his discovery?

“The contents of this section will furnish a very striking illustration of the truth of a remark, which I have more than once made in my philosophical writings, and which can hardly be too often repeated, as it tends greatly to encourage philosophical investigations viz that more is owing to what we call chance, that is philosophically speaking, to the observation of events arising from unknown causes, than to any proper design, or pre-conceived theory in this business.

From my own part, I will frankly acknowledge, that, at the commencement of the experiments recited in this section, I was so far from having formed any hypothesis that led to the discoveries I made in pursuing them, and they would have appeared very improbable to me had I been told of them; and when the decisive facts did at length obtrude themselves upon my notice, it was very slowly, and with great hesitation, that I yielded to the evidence of my own senses.

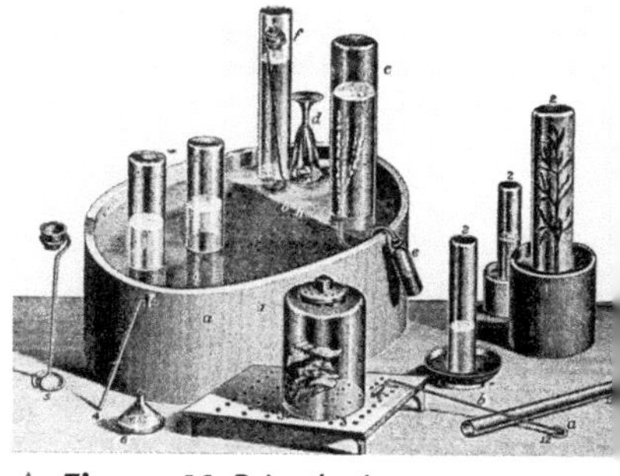

▲ ***Figure 41*** *Priestley's preparation of dephlogisticated air.*

With this apparatus [Figure 41], after a variety of other experiments, an account of which will be found in its proper place, on the 1st of August, 1774, I endeavoured to extract air from mercurius calcinatus per se; and I presently found that by means of the lens air was expelled from it very readily. Having got about three or four times as much as the bulk of my materials, I admitted water to it, and found that it was not imbibed by it. But what surprised me more than I can well express was, that a candle burned in this air with a remarkably vigorous flame.

On the 8th of this month [March, 1775] I procured a mouse, and put it into a glass vessel, containing two one-ounce measures of the air from mercurius calcinatus. Had it been common air, a full-grown mouse, as this was, would have lived in about a quarter of an hour. In this air, however, my mouse lived a full half hour, and though it was taken out seemingly dead, it appeared to have been only exceedingly chilled; for, upon being held to the fire, it presently revived, and appeared not to have received any harm from the experiment.

My reader will not wonder, that, after having ascertained the superior goodness of dephlogisticated air by mice living in it, and the other tests above mentioned, I should have the curiosity to taste it myself. I have gratified that curiosity, by breathing it, drawing it through a glass-syphon, and, by this means, I reduced a large jar full of it to the standard of common air. The feeling of it to my lungs was not sensibly different from that of common air; but I fancied that my breast felt peculiarly light and easy for some time afterwards. Who can tell but that, in time, this pure air may become a fashionable article in luxury.

Being at Paris in the October following [1775], and knowing that there were several very eminent chemists in that place, I frequently mentioned my surprise at the kind of air which I had got from this preparation to Mr Lavoisier, Mr le Roy, and several other philosophers, who honoured me with their notice in that city; and who, I daresay, cannot fail to recollect the circumstance. ”

Lavoisier's combustible air

Lavoisier was thinking about phlogiston and air before Priestley visited Paris in 1775. The train of reasoning that led Lavoisier to devise his new system of chemistry probably began in spring 1772 when he read the article on phlogiston by Guyton de Morveau (see page 71). Lavoisier thought this explanation to be absurd and suggested that something from the air must be fixed when metals were heated. It is probably significant that Lavoisier did not come to chemistry by the traditional routes of pharmacy, medicine or metallurgy, as did many of his peers. The formative influences on Lavoisier were the physical sciences and mathematics. With this training he approached chemistry with a critical eye for detail and, more importantly, was convinced of the need for a quantitative approach.

In October of 1772, Lavoisier noted that a large fraction of air became 'fixed' (i.e. would not support combustion) after sulfur and phosphorus were burnt. He began to think that perhaps something was taken from the air on combustion, that this perhaps was typical of all combustion and that the increase in weight of metal calxes was due to the same cause. Over the next two years Lavoisier began a search for the gas that was taken up from air but he made little progress. The breakthrough came when Lavoisier learned from Priestley of the special characteristics of mercury and what today we would call its oxides. We now realise that mercuric oxide decomposes to metal and oxygen when heated below red-heat without the presence of charcoal. When mercury metal is heated in air at atmospheric pressure it forms the oxide or calx.

The crucial period when Lavoisier began to think in very different terms from Priestley was sometime between 1775 and 1777. In 1775 he thought the gas released from heating calx of mercury (mercuric oxide) to be common air, but by May 1777 he realises it is 'eminently respirable air' (oxygen). We know this because Lavoisier first announced his findings before the French Academy of Science on 27 April 1775. But when he came to publish this paper in 1778 he had revised it considerably.

Lavoisier's paper of 1778 describes the reactions that he carried out. He reacted mercury calx (mercury oxide) with charcoal. As predicted by the phlogiston theory, mercury was formed. However, Lavoisier collected the gas given off and tested it. He found that it was fixed air (carbon dioxide). (The fraction of air that will not support combustion – 'fixed air' – is in fact mainly nitrogen. But it is only carbon dioxide that is produced and takes part in the reactions studied by Lavoisier and his contemporaries.)

Activity 37 *Lavoisier's new idea*

In the following passage, Lavoisier describes his next experiment. Read the passage and answer the questions below.

(A pouce is a unit of length, so a cubic pouce is a volume; ounce, gros and grain are units of mass.)

1 What evidence does Lavoisier give for the gas being similar to common air?

2 What evidence does Lavoisier give for the new gas not being fixed air (carbon dioxide)?

3 Why does Lavoisier say that 'respirable air' is a purer form of common air?

4 In the final paragraph, Lavoisier outlines his new theory of combustion. Describe Lavoisier's theory in your own words.

" It then only remained to examine this calx alone, to reduce it without adding anything, to see if some elastic fluid were evolved from it, and, supposing there were, to determine its nature. To this end I placed in a retort of 2 cubic pouces capacity, 1 ounce of precipitated mercury per se alone, arranged the apparatus in the same manner as in the preceding experiment, and operated so that all the circumstances would be exactly the same. The reduction took place this time with a little more difficulty than when charcoal was added; more heat was required, and there was no sensible change until the retort began to become slightly red. Then the air was evolved little by little, passed into the bell, and, holding the same degree of fire during two and one-half hours, all the mercury was reduced.

The operation completed, there was found, on the one hand, partly in the neck of the retort, and partly in a glass vessel which I placed beneath the water under the exit of the retort, 7 gros and 18 grains of fluid mercury, and on the other hand, the quantity of the air which had passed into the bell was found to be 78 cubic pouces; whence it follows that by supposing that the whole loss of weight should be attributed to the air, each cubic pouce should weigh a little less than two-thirds of a grain – a value not far removed from that of common air.

After having thus fixed the first results, I had only to submit the 78 cubic pouces of air which I had obtained to all the tests necessary to determine its nature, and I found with much surprise:

1. That it would not combine with water on shaking
2. That it did not precipitate limewater but only gave it a nearly imperceptible turbidity
3. That it failed to unite at all with fixed or volatile alkalis
4. That it failed entirely to diminish the causticity of these
5. That it could be used again to calcine metals
6. Finally, that it had none of the properties of fixed air.

In contrast to the latter, animals did not perish in it and it seemed more suitable to their respiration. Candles and inflamed materials were not only not extinguished, but the flame widened in a very remarkable manner and shed much more light and brilliancy than in common air. Charcoal burned therein with a brilliance nearly like that of phosphorus, and all combustible materials in general were consumed with astonishing rapidity. All these circumstances have fully convinced me that this air, far from being fixed air, is in a more respirable, more combustible state and in consequence is more pure even than the air which sustains us.

It appears to be proved from the above that the principle which combines with and increases the weight of metals when they are calcined is nothing other than the purest portion of the air itself which surrounds us and which we breathe – this it is which in calcination passes from the expansible state to the solid one. If, then, this principle is obtained in the form of fixed air in all metallic reductions in which carbon is used, it follows that this is due to the combination of this latter with the pure portion of the air, and it is very probable that all metallic calces would, like mercury, give only eminently respirable air if we could reduce them all as we do precipitated mercury per se.

(Memoir on the Nature of the Principle which Combines with Metals during their Calcination and which Increases their Weight, from (1778) Memoires de l'Academie Royale des Sciences for 1775*, pp. 520–6, translation of the 1778 text taken from Leicester, H. M. and Klickstein, H. S. (1952)* A Source Book in Chemistry, 1400–1900, *McGraw Hill, New York)* ”

5.4 Meanwhile, in Sweden …

Scheele in Uppsala

In 1770 Karl Wilhelm Scheele moved to Uppsala to become a laboratory assistant. At the time Sweden's best known chemist was Torbern Bergman who worked in Uppsala. Scheele got to know Bergman and received his help. Between 1771 and 1772 Scheele heated a variety of different substances and obtained an unknown gas. One of his first methods involved heating a mixture of manganese oxide and sulfuric acid (then known as oil of vitriol). As a result Scheele began calling the gas 'vitriol air'.

Scheele was in touch with other scientists such as Priestley and Lavoisier. Lavoisier may have heard of Scheele's experiments, perhaps from Bergman. In 1774 Lavoisier sent two copies of a book he had published to Wargentin, the Secretary of the Academy of Sciences in Stockholm, one to be passed on to Scheele.

Scheele wrote to thank Lavoisier. Lavoisier didn't reply to Scheele's letter and never acknowledged that he had received it. However, the letter was found many years later amongst the papers of Lavoisier's wife, Marie Anne.

Scheele didn't write up his work until 1775. Bergman was supposed to be supporting the publication but there were delays until 1777. By this time

Scheele had heard of Priestley's discovery of dephlogisticated air and of Lavoisier's experiments with the gas.

In his book Scheele now referred to the gas as 'fire air'. He described the methods he used to generate it and showed how it supported aquatic life as well as air-breathing creatures. He said that common air was a mixture of his fire air and what he called 'foul air'. Nevertheless, Scheele still tried to explain his observations using the phlogiston theory.

Activity 38 *Scheele's letter to Lavoisier*

The letter Scheele wrote to Lavoisier in 1774 is reproduced below. Read it and discuss the following points.

1 What is the tone of the letter? Where does Scheele place himself in relation to Lavoisier?

2 Assuming that Lavoisier did read the letter, do you think the experiment that Scheele suggests would have influenced Lavoisier in any way?

(Note: Scheele's experiment would first form silver nitrate. The addition of the alkali of tartar precipitates silver tartrate which on heating breaks down first to silver oxide, carbon dioxide and water, and then the silver oxide breaks down to silver and oxygen. Carbon dioxide (fixed air) is the toxic gas which combines with alkalis such as quicklime in water. He may also have obtained solid silver nitrate which also breaks down on heating to silver, oxygen and nitrogen dioxide, which is a toxic acidic gas.)

“Monsieur (Lavoisier)

I have received from Mr Wargentin a book which he says you were kind enough to give me. Although I have never met you I would like to thank you most humbly for this. Nothing would please me more than to convey my thanks.

For a long time I have wanted to be able to read a collection of all the experiments that have been done in England, France and Germany on types of air. You have not only satisfied this wish but you have also given scientists, by your new experiments, wonderful opportunities to examine fire and the calcinations of metals more successfully in the future. Over several years I have performed experiments on a number of types of air and I have spent a long time investigating the particular properties of fire, but I have never been able to make ordinary air from fixed air. Following advice from Mr Priestley, I have tried several times to produce ordinary air from fixed air by a mixture of iron filings, sulphur and water. However I have never succeeded because the fixed air has always joined the iron and rendered it soluble in water. Perhaps you don't have any means of doing this either.

Since I don't have a large burning glass would you please try with your lens in the following way. Dissolve some silver in nitric acid and form a precipitate by adding alkali of tartar. Wash this and dry it and reduce it by the lens in your apparatus. But because some of the air that is given off is such that animals die in it and part of this fixed air becomes separated from the silver during this operation, you need to put a bit of quicklime in the water (over which the glass container collects the gas) so that the fixed air joins to the lime more quickly. In this way I hope you will see how much air is produced during this process and whether a lighted candle could stay alight and animals live therein.

I would be very much obliged if you could let me know the result of this experiment. I have the honour to always hold you in high esteem.

Karl Scheele
Uppsala, 30 September 1774

(translated by Sue Beigel) ❞

Further work

1. Why was the delay in publication of Scheele's book significant?
2. Why was Scheele's discovery of a number of routes to fire air important?
3. What factors may have resulted in Scheele's work being largely ignored at the time?

Activity 32 *Oxygen men* (continued)

Now you know more about Scheele and his work, have another look at your notes on 'Oxygen men' and continue to prepare for the Retro-Nobel debate.

5.5 Lavoisier takes on phlogiston

Lavoisier's changing perceptions

We have seen that by 1778 Lavoisier had realised that 'respirable air', not phlogiston, was responsible for combustion and that in 1779 he started to use his new term, oxygen. At first, few scientists supported Lavoisier's new ideas. Priestley stuck with phlogiston. Like other supporters of the phlogiston theory, all his perceptions of chemical reactions were based on the viewpoint that a metal was a combination of calx and phlogiston and that everything followed from that. Lavoisier's idea turned that on its head. The effort to change viewpoints was too much for many chemists. It is like our perception of some optical illusions. Look at Figure 42. Do you see it as two faces in profile, or a vase? Whatever your initial perception, it can be quite hard to change.

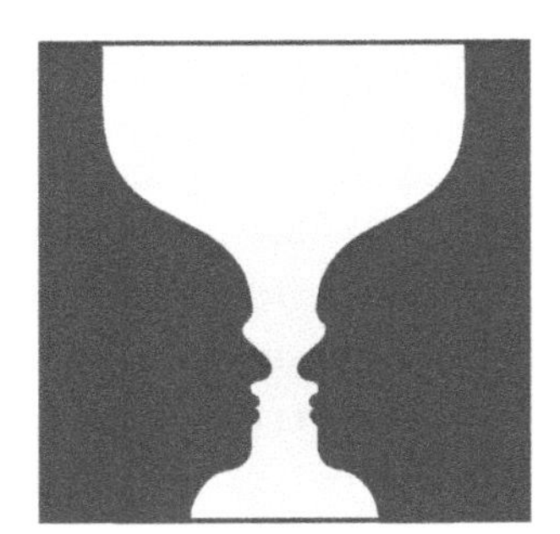

▲ ***Figure 42*** *Faces or a vase: which do you see?*

Other scientists made discoveries that, unknown to the discoverers, supported Lavoisier's position. One such example was Henry Cavendish (1731–1810), a rich English recluse who performed experiments in many areas of science. Cavendish exploded mixtures of flammable air (hydrogen) and dephlogisticated air (oxygen) and concluded that the liquid that was formed was water. Since the phlogistonists considered flammable air to be nearly pure phlogiston, Cavendish concluded that water was a compound of dephlogisticated air and phlogiston. Lavoisier, however, realised that Cavendish's experiment showed that water was a compound of hydrogen and oxygen.

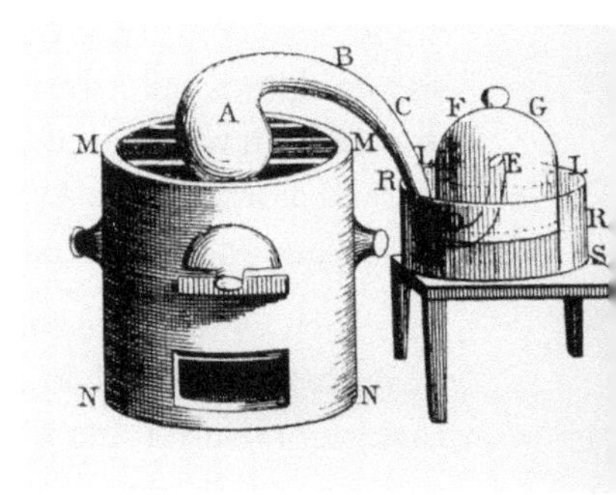

▲ ***Figure 43*** *Lavoisier's apparatus.*

In 1783 Lavoisier performed an experiment which was his response to the phlogistonists. The experiment was published first in his *Reflections on Phlogiston* of 1783 and then in his *Elements of Chemistry* (1789), which launched his new theory of chemistry.

Lavoisier's experiment involved the following steps using the apparatus shown in Figure 43.

1 Room temperature and atmospheric pressure recorded.
2 Volume of air in flask and bell jar measured.
3 Mercury heated in retort for 12 days. After this the apparatus was allowed to cool.
4 Formation of red calx of mercury in retort noted and weighed.
5 Decrease in volume in bell jar (approximately one-sixth) measured.
6 The air remaining was examined and found to be 'azotic' (unable to support life). Animals quickly died when introduced into this air.
7 The red calx of mercury was extracted and heated separately. The gas given off was collected and its volume measured.

Lavoisier found that, upon heating, the red calx of mercury turned to mercury and that an 'elastic fluid' or gas was given off. He found this gas to be the same as the 'dephlogisticated air' studied by Priestley, and that its volume, when adjusted to the correct temperature and pressure, was the same as that taken up by the mercury on its conversion into calx during the initial heating. The air remaining in the bell jar after this new gas had been removed was no longer respirable. Lavoisier argued that atmospheric air is therefore made up of two gases – oxygen and azote (nitrogen).

It may seem that Lavoisier merely repeated the experiment that Priestley and he did in 1774/5, but there are significant differences. First, he took very precise measurements at each stage of the experiment. Second, by starting with mercury, Lavoisier showed that oxygen is present in normal air and combines with the mercury to form a compound (mercury oxide, or mercury calx), and that the same amount of oxygen gas is released when the mercury oxide is re-heated.

The publication of Lavoisier's *Elements of Chemistry* caused a stir. It didn't convince staunch phlogistonists like Priestley, but others found the oxygen theory of combustion and the disappearance of imponderable phlogiston a great step forward. Within a decade, chemists such as Humphry Davy were using the new theory to make more discoveries in chemistry.

The role of Madame Lavoisier

▲ ***Figure 44*** *Madame Lavoisier with her first husband.*

Women are invisible in the publications of science in the eighteenth and nineteenth centuries. Women were not admitted to the scientific societies and could not publish scientific work in their own name. This does not mean that women were not interested in science or played no part in it. Women worked alongside husbands or brothers and contributed to discoveries that were claimed by their partners.

One such woman was Marie Anne Lavoisier. She married Lavoisier when she was just 14 years old, her father having been a close acquaintance of Lavoisier. Lavoisier ensured that his young wife was educated. She learned languages and translated work for him; she was taught to draw and paint and provided the illustrations for his books; she assisted him in the laboratory and recorded the measurements and observations. She must have developed a thorough understanding of chemical knowledge and of the new ideas. In discussion with her husband she may even have been the originator of some aspects of the theory and its experimental proof.

After Lavoisier's execution (see page 83), Marie continued to publicise his work and arranged for translations of his *Elements* to be published. Later, she married another well known scientist, Lord Rumford, the founder of the Royal Institution in London, but their marriage did not survive the fierce independence she had developed.

Activity 32 *Oxygen men* (continued)

Now you have learned more about the work of Priestley, Lavoisier and Scheele, you are in a position to prepare more of your presentation for the debate on the Retro-Nobel Prize. Draw together the information about the work that 'your' character did and build a case for awarding him the prize. Make sure you keep a careful note of the evidence that you will use.

Further work

1 Write word equations for the sequence of reactions that Lavoisier performed in 1783.

2 Why was Lavoisier's experiment important for the overthrow of the phlogiston theory?

3 Why were many scientists reluctant to accept Lavoisier's oxygen theory?

4 Find out more about the life of Marie Lavoisier. Do you think her role in the oxygen story is significant?

5.6 Decision time

Now the time has come to make your case for the Retro-Nobel Prize. Which of the three contenders, Antoine Laurent Lavoisier, Joseph Priestley or Karl Wilhelm Scheele, deserves the prize? What should it be awarded for – the discovery of a gas that became known as oxygen or a theory that used oxygen to overturn the phlogiston theory? It is up to the three groups of promoters to present their argument for their candidate and for the audience to make their decision.

Activity 39 *The Retro-Nobel debate*

Having prepared the case in support of one of the Retro-Nobel prize contenders, your team will have a maximum of 10 minutes to make a presentation, including time for questions. Some tips are given below.

After each team has made a presentation and responded to questions, decide which of the three should be awarded the Nobel Prize for discovering oxygen.

Tips for the Scheele group

You might like to stress the following facts in your case:

- Scheele actually generated the gas we call oxygen a number of times and using a number of methods between the years 1771–73, several years before Priestley and Lavoisier.
- Scheele correctly described the properties of this gas.
- Scheele wrote a letter to Lavoisier on 30 September 1774, before Priestley had met Lavoisier. The letter probably arrived in October 1774 just as Priestley was describing his work to Lavoisier. Lavoisier never replied to the letter. Perhaps he or his wife hoped to conceal Scheele's findings so that Lavoisier would get all the credit.
- Scheele also wrote his findings in a book, *On Air and Fire*, which was ready by December 1775 but was delayed at the printers so that it was not published until 1777.

Tips for the Priestley group

- Priestley told Lavoisier of his work with calx of mercury.
- Priestley actually published his results before Scheele or Lavoisier in the form of a paper read to the Royal Society on 23 March 1775. In science it is publication that counts.
- If the objection is made that he did not understand what he discovered then neither did Columbus when he discovered America (he thought he had found islands off the coast of India).

Tips for the Lavoisier group

- Neither Scheele nor Priestley knew what oxygen was. They both interpreted it in terms of an outmoded theory of phlogiston.
- It was Lavoisier who gave the gas its name and realised that phlogiston did not exist.
- If we give an award to the first person to make oxygen then perhaps it should go to an outsider: English plant physiologist, Stephen Hales (1677–1761), who probably generated this gas when he heated all manner of substances to collect the gases driven off.

The last days of Lavoisier, Priestley and Scheele

In 1775 Scheele moved to Koping to open a pharmacist's shop. He continued to make remarkable discoveries of new substances such as chlorine, manganese and citric acid. Although scientists across Europe knew of his work and he received offers of academic positions in Germany and England, he never published another book and remained at home. He died in 1786.

In 1780 Priestley settled in Birmingham where, with the financial help of Josiah Wedgwood, he set up a large personal laboratory. Priestley expressed radical political opinions such as approval of the early days of the French Revolution. On 14 July 1791 a dinner was held in Birmingham to celebrate the second anniversary of the fall of the Bastille. Although Priestley had nothing to do with the event, his house was pillaged by a Tory mob that ran amok in Birmingham. Priestley was not at home when they wrecked his house but he watched from a distance.

Priestley and the meeting house had been targeted because for years the Anglican clergy had inflamed public opinion against the Dissenters. As an activist pursuing civil and religious liberty, Priestley was especially loathed. He had openly sided with the American colonists in their fight for independence and had just been made a citizen of the French Republic for his bitter reply to Burke's attack on the French Revolution.

Priestley was not the only Dissenter to be targeted and the government was content to let the persecution continue. Tired of these setbacks, Priestley and his wife set sail for America aboard the ship *Sansom* on 7 April 1794. His journey across the Atlantic took eight weeks and Priestley (now 62 years old) was sick for most of the time. In New York he was welcomed as a hero.

Despite being encouraged by inventor Benjamin Franklin to settle in Philadelphia, Priestley preferred to be near where his three sons and other English immigrants had helped to found a settlement for the 'friends of liberty'. He settled in the small town of Northumberland in Pennsylvania. Here Priestley continued his scientific correspondence with men in England and influenced the subsequent researches of both Dalton and Davy. Priestley's last published work on chemistry was printed in America and called *The Doctrine of Phlogiston Established and that of the Composition of Water Refuted* (1800). He died in 1804, still a phlogistonist.

Lavoisier never read Priestley's final defence of phlogiston; like Priestley, his fate was sealed by political forces outside his control. In 1780 Lavoisier had made an enemy of a young journalist called Jean-Paul Marat (1743–93) by declaring a paper he had written as being 'without merit'. Marat became a leader of the Revolution in France and denounced Lavoisier. For many years Lavoisier had raised the money to support his scientific work (Figure 45) by being a member of a 'tax farm' that collected taxes. The tax farmers were detested by the revolutionaries. Lavoisier was arrested on 28 November 1793 while he was carrying out an experiment on respiration, recorded in a picture

▲ ***Figure 45*** *The laboratory of Lavoisier.*

sketched by his wife which shows his colleague Seguin seated in the mask while Madame Lavoisier sits at the table taking notes.

Ironically, Marat was never able to witness his revenge – he was assassinated in his bath in July 1793. On 8 May 1794, Lavoisier was put on trial and found guilty. The sentence was death by guillotine the same day. On the day Lavoisier was beheaded, Priestley was crossing the Atlantic. He only heard of the fellow chemist's execution after he landed in America.

PART 2

DISCUSSING ETHICAL ISSUES IN SCIENCE

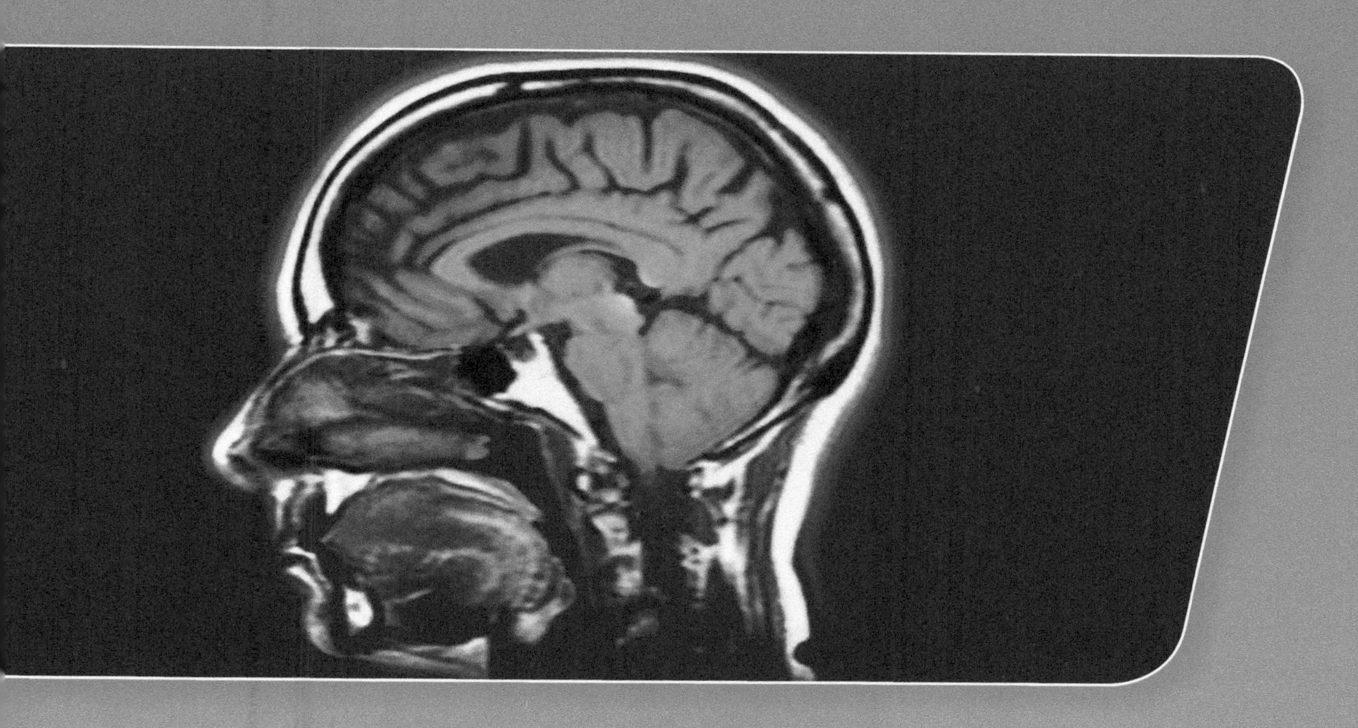

1 Introduction to discussing ethical issues in science

1.1 Right and wrong

What is right and what is wrong?

Ethics is an intellectual discipline, just as subjects such as mathematics, music, history and science are. Each of these intellectual disciplines has its own ways of working. By and large, the ways of working that are appropriate to one discipline can't simply be transferred to another. For instance, the laws of mathematics can help us to prove that the number of prime numbers is infinite and that the square root of two is irrational, but they can't help us to decide whether Beethoven's Ninth is his greatest symphony. And the scientific way of working that helps us to determine the factors that affect the boiling point of water (pressure and impurities in the water) doesn't really help us to understand why Harold lost the Battle of Hastings.

The discipline of **ethics** is all about deciding what is morally right and what is morally wrong and why. **Morals** are beliefs about whether things are right or wrong. For example, is it right or wrong to eat meat, to have sex before you are 16 years old, or sometimes to tell lies? Ethics has its own ways of working. Fortunately, while some of us are hopeless at mathematics and others of us are tone deaf or have no interest in history, just about all of us spend quite a bit of our time reasoning ethically. So, you almost certainly already have quite a bit of knowledge to help you understand ethics.

In this course we are particularly concerned with ethical questions in science. For example, is it acceptable to use animals in medical experiments, to undertake human reproductive cloning or to develop nuclear bombs? However, the reasoning that is used to answer such questions follows the same rules and procedures as the reasoning to answer any ethical question. We will start, therefore, with an apparently simple everyday question, 'Why is it wrong to steal?' (Figure 1).

▲ ***Figure 1*** *Stealing is generally regarded as wrong.*

Activity 1 What is wrong with stealing?

In pairs or small groups, spend 5 minutes thinking of as many possible different reasons why it might be wrong to steal. At this stage, don't start arguing about whether each reason is valid or not – just generate a number of possible reasons and write them down.

Activity 2 Exploring your reasons

After spending 5 minutes or so on Activity 1, start trying to explore the reasons a bit further. Think of their implications. For example, suppose one of your reasons for believing that stealing is wrong is that in the absence of this widely-held view people would be very afraid that their property would be forcibly taken from them. One implication is that we might expect people with lots of personal property to feel more strongly that stealing is wrong than people with little personal property. Do you think this is the case?

Thinking carefully, as in Activity 2, should help you to refine your reasons so that, even if you don't believe all of them, you can mount an intellectual defence of each of them. Of course, if you don't believe one of the reasons in your pair or small group, try arguing with whoever proposed it to see if you can validly change his or her mind. At the same time, you need to be open to the possibility that this person is right and that you will have to change your mind.

Activity 3 Categorising reasons

Try to put your reasons from Activities 1 and 2 into categories. For example, if you believe that the reason why it is wrong to steal is that having this prohibition is the best policy for the majority of society, this is an example of utilitarian thinking.

We shall have more to say about **utilitarianism** in the next lesson but suffice to say that utilitarians think that things are right in the world if they maximise the amount of happiness and wrong if they lead to more unhappiness. So a utilitarian would favour a law 'Don't steal' if, overall, this led to greater happiness than allowing a free-for-all.

Another category – though one that fewer people use nowadays than in the past – is that of **divine command**. If you feel that stealing is wrong because it breaks one of the Ten Commandments or is forbidden in the Qur'an, for example, then you presumably have a strong religious faith and believe that the scriptures of your faith help you decide what is right and what is wrong.

Another category might be that people have certain rights, and these include the right to retain your own property. In everyday language we might say that it isn't fair to steal from someone. But try thinking about whether it makes a difference how the person acquired whatever it is that someone else wants to steal. For example, is stealing from someone who has worked hard to acquire property worse than stealing from someone who has won it on the lottery or inherited it from their parents?

Activity 4 *What is theft?*

Explore precisely what is meant by theft. For example, suppose I have a girlfriend/boyfriend and you don't, and you attempt to entice my girlfriend/boyfriend away from me. Is this theft? If you think it is, explain why. If you think it isn't, explain why it isn't. Is it theft when a government requires its citizens to pay taxes? And what about the fact that tax rates are nearly always higher for people with greater incomes – is this stealing? Are there any distinctions that can be drawn between income tax and inheritance tax? Quickly jot down your ideas, then spend about 10 minutes discussing them with other people.

Further work

1 *Find out about the land distribution programme in Zimbabwe instituted by Robert Mugabe's government. Discuss whether this is an example of theft and therefore unethical, or an example of reducing indefensible inequalities and so ethical.*

2 *Consider why theft seems to be almost universal in human societies even though nearly everyone thinks it is wrong.*

1.2 Introducing ethical frameworks

Ethical frameworks

There is no one universally agreed way of deciding what is right and what is wrong. Instead there are a number of **ethical frameworks** that can be used. Quite often the same answers to ethical questions are reached whichever framework is used, but sometimes the different frameworks generate very different answers. Most people don't fully appreciate the reasons why they hold the ethical views that they do. Appreciating the range of different ethical frameworks should help you to sharpen your ethical thinking and evaluate ethical arguments used by others.

What are the consequences?

The simplest approach to deciding whether an action would be right or wrong is to look at what its consequences would be. No one supposes that we can ignore the consequences of an action before deciding whether or not it is right. The deeper question is whether that is all that we need to do. Are there certain actions – such as telling the truth – that are morally required whatever their consequences? Are there other actions – such as betraying confidences – that are wrong whatever their consequences?

Those who believe that consequences alone are sufficient to let a person decide the rightness or otherwise of a course of action are called consequentialists. The most widespread form of **consequentialism** is known as **utilitarianism**. Utilitarianism itself takes various forms, but it begins with the assumption that most actions lead to pleasure and/or suffering. In a situation in which there are alternative courses of action, the right action is the one which leads to the greatest net increase in pleasure.

Consider the question as to whether we should tell the truth. A utilitarian would hesitate to provide an unqualified 'yes' as a universal answer. Utilitarians have no moral absolutes beyond the maximisation of the pleasure principle. It would be necessary for a utilitarian to look in some detail at particular cases and see in each of them whether telling the truth would indeed lead to the greatest net increase in pleasure.

Activity 5 *A utilitarian approach*

Jot down a list of the sort of information that a utilitarian would need in order to decide whether factory farming should be permitted.

Divine command

People with religious faith or who were brought up in a religious family often attach great significance to the teachings of their religion in ethical matters. Right conduct is seen as fulfilling what is required by **divine command**. In some religious traditions, what is of paramount importance is what is contained in sacred scriptures; in other religious traditions such writings are interpreted to the community by a specialised group of people, such as priests.

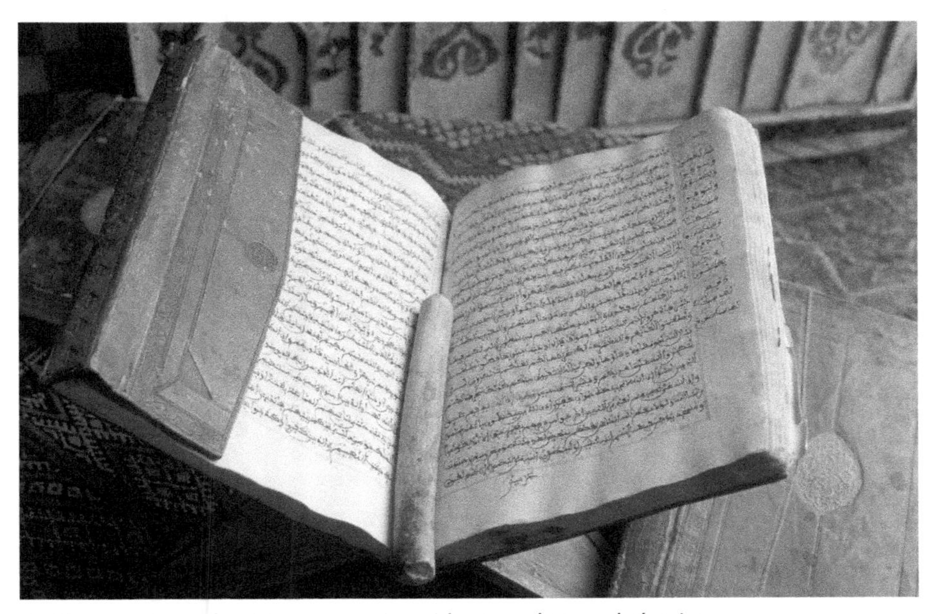

▲ **Figure 2** *Sacred scriptures contain guidance on human behaviour.*

The scriptures of the world's great religions (Figure 2) have a great deal to say about such human matters as ownership, warfare, sexuality, hospitality, honesty and selfishness. However, they have rather less to say about science. Nevertheless, people with a strong religious faith often have very firm views about ethical issues in science – such as abortion, the use of animals in medical experiments and genetic engineering.

Activity 6 *Considering faith-based views*

What consideration should be given to the ethical views of those with strong religious faith? Discuss your opinions. Try to think of examples of situations where religious views are either taken into account or ignored.

1.3 Further ethical frameworks

Rights and duties

A further ethical framework starts from the notion of **rights**. Not all philosophers accept that rights exist but the notion of rights has been of great political value. They are enshrined in a number of constitutions, for example the Constitution of the USA (Figure 3) holds the rights of life, liberty and the pursuit of happiness to be inalienable. More recently, rights have been extended to children in the 1989 United Nations Convention on the Rights of the Child, while some argue that animals (non-human animals) have certain rights too.

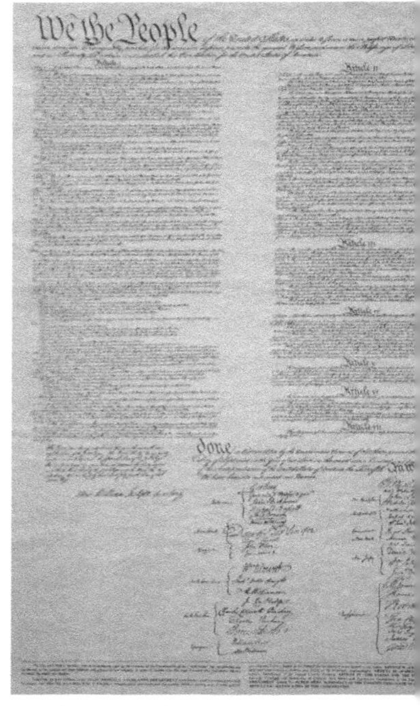

▲ **Figure 3** *The Constitution of the USA.*

Rights are accompanied by **duties**, but the relationship between rights and duties is often misunderstood. It is typically supposed that if you have rights then you also have duties – as in the political slogan that rights need to be accompanied by responsibilities. To see the logical error in this, consider a newborn baby (Figure 4). It is hard to argue that anything is more deserving of rights than a newborn baby. Presumably the child has the right to be fed, kept warm, protected and loved. But what duties does he or she have? Surely none. A newborn baby is simply too young to have duties, and is not yet responsible for his or her actions. However, others have duties to the child – namely, to feed, clothe, protect and love the child. Normally such duties are fulfilled by the child's parent(s), but if neither parent is able to undertake these duties, for whatever reason, the duties pass to others, for example other relatives, adoptive parents or social services. In general, if A has a right, there is a B who has a duty to ensure that A's rights are met.

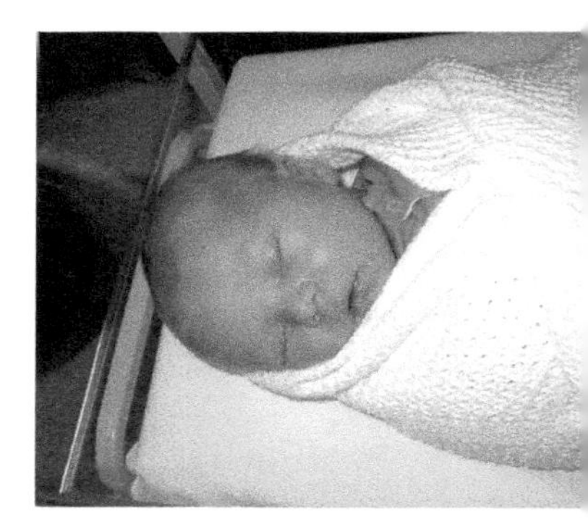

▲ **Figure 4** *A newborn baby.*

One of the rights that we normally presume people have is the right to make their own decisions in life. We believe that we should respect people's **autonomy**. In medicine, for example, we are less likely than people were 30 years ago to assume that we should do what a doctor tells us to do simply because he or she has told us to do it. We expect to be notified about the implications of any possible alternative courses of action and then to give our informed consent to one of them.

Activity 7 *What rights do you have?*

Write down a list of rights that you believe you have now, and a second list of additional rights that you expect to have within a few years' time.

Virtue ethics

A rather different approach to the whole issue of ethics is provided by **virtue ethics**. Instead of starting from particular actions and trying to decide whether they maximise the amount of happiness in the world, are divinely forbidden or infringe someone's rights, virtue ethics focuses on the characteristics of good people. For example, think about a good teacher. What characteristics might you expect him or her to have? You might want a teacher to know his or her subject, to treat all students fairly, to be able to maintain order in the classroom, to maximise your chances of doing well in any examinations, to be able to communicate clearly, to have a sense of humour and so on. Some of these are skills – for example, the ability to maintain order – but some are personality traits that we call virtues – notably treating all students fairly, rather than, for example, favouring males, Asians, high-attaining students or Chelsea supporters.

Activity 8 *Virtues*

Spend about 5 minutes discussing the following:

- What characteristics might you hope to find in a lifelong partner? Which of these are virtues?
- Suppose you have to spend a week in hospital. What characteristics might you hope to find in the nursing staff? Which of these are virtues?

Absolutism and relativism

A final point to consider is whether ethical judgements are absolute or relative. Both these words are used in a variety of ways but **absolutism** presumes the existence of an objective reason for a statement. Thus, someone might argue that it is absolutely wrong to torture people because such behaviour is forbidden in scripture, is inherently disrespectful to people, contravenes their rights or always leads to unhappiness. On the other hand, a position that derives from **relativism** may be just as much against torturing people but argue that torture is wrong because we decide it is rather than for any other absolute reason.

Many people don't like the idea of relativism in ethics, realising that it means that there are no absolute rights or wrongs. In different circumstances (including in different places and at different times) relativists may come up with a different list of what is right and what is wrong.

Relativists respond to such accusations in various ways. First of all they point to the lessons of history. In the past, for example, slavery was routinely used in many countries. Does that mean that such people were necessarily bad in the way that someone who kept slaves in Surrey would be today? Or consider votes for women. At one point no country had such a thing. Nowadays practically every democracy does. The lesson of history is that what is right and what is wrong depends, at least to some extent, on the circumstances.

Secondly, relativists ask where absolute knowledge about ethics comes from. As we saw earlier, some people believe it has divine authority. But many people argue that what is right and what is wrong is worked out in debate between people. On this view, ethics is all about learning how to get on adequately with your neighbour so that society can function reasonably well.

Activity 9 *Absolutism or relativism?*

Do you believe in absolutism or relativism? Defend your answer.

Further work

Using two of the ethical frameworks that you have studied, discuss whether or not stealing is wrong. (About 400 words should be ample for a written answer.)

1.4 Dealing with inequality

Distributive justice

One important ethical consideration is justice. There are several sorts of justice of which perhaps the most important for ethics is **distributive justice**. This means that scarce resources should be allocated among people in a way that is fair. For example, your chances of getting a fair trial should not depend on how much money you have. This is the basis of legal aid. If you have little money, the State pays someone to represent you in court. Of course, things are never as straightforward as this, and if you are wealthy you will almost certainly be able to obtain better legal representation.

The following extract describes two **thought experiments** on this theme. The intended reader is an academic in the USA.

> "***The Shallow Pond***
>
> The path from the library at your university to the humanities lecture hall passes a shallow ornamental pond. On your way to give a lecture, you notice that a small child has fallen in and is in danger of drowning. If you wade in and pull the child out, it will mean getting your clothes muddy and either cancelling the lecture or delaying it until you can find something clean and dry

to wear. If you pass by the child, then, while you'll give your lecture on time, the child will die straightaway. You pass by and, as expected, the child dies.

The Envelope

In your mailbox, there's something from [the US Committee for] UNICEF. After reading it through, you correctly believe that, unless you soon send in a cheque for $100, then, instead of each living many more years, over thirty more children will die soon. But, you throw the material in your trash basket, including the convenient return envelope provided, you send nothing, and, instead of living many more years, over thirty more children die sooner than would have had you sent in the requested $100.

Unger, P. (1996) Living High & Letting Die: Our Illusion of Innocence, *Oxford University Press, p. 9.* By permission of Oxford University Press Inc. ❞

Activity 10 *Behaving badly?*

What would you think of someone who behaved as the academic did in the 'Shallow Pond' situation? What would you think of someone who behaved as the person did in the 'Envelope' situation? If you feel that one of these two people has behaved morally worse than the other, why do you feel this way? Do you think you should feel this way? Talk to other people and compare your views with theirs.

Activity 11 *Life expectancy*

The following extract (page 94) is on the same general theme of d stributive justice. Read it and study the graph below then discuss whether you think it is acceptable that there are considerable health inequalities in England and Wales.

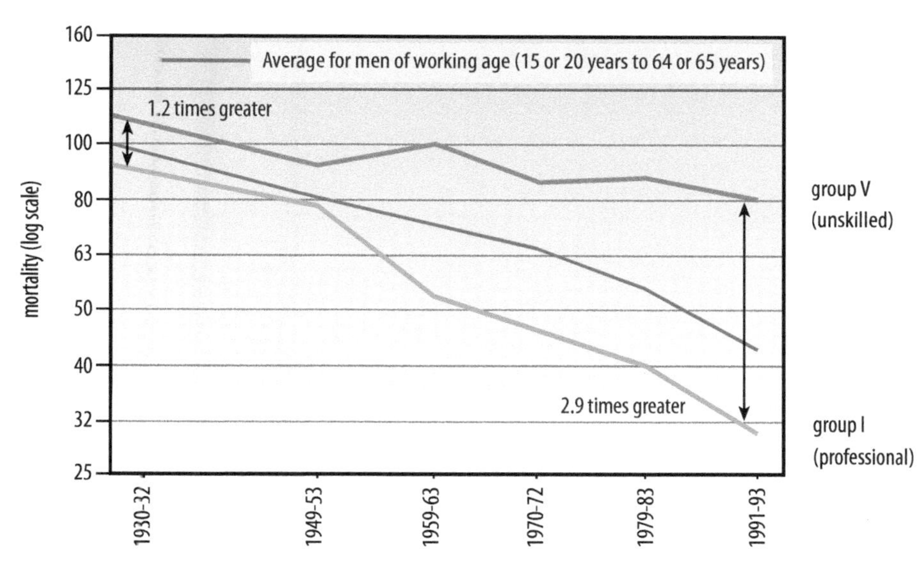

▲ ***Figure 5*** *Life expectancy showing the mortality gap between socioeconomic groups I and V in England and Wales. Reproduced ith permission from BMJ publishing group.*

Gap between classes in life expectancy is widening

Healthcare providers, local authorities, schools, employers, and the voluntary sector need to work together more closely to narrow the gap between different parts of the country and between different social groups, the health secretary said last week. [See Figure 5.]

Despite some improvements, the health gap between the top and bottom classes of the social scale remains large and is getting wider in some areas. Between 1930 and 1990 the gap between mortality among professional men and that among men in unskilled manual jobs increased almost two and half times. The difference can mean an extra 10 or more years of life for wealthier people.

In his document the health secretary, John Reid, sets out a three year plan to cut inequalities in health. He also spells out the actions that are needed to achieve the 2010 targets of reducing infant mortality by 10% across social groups and raising by 10% life expectancy in the most disadvantaged areas of the country, compared with the population as a whole.

'For too long we have been prepared to tolerate glaring differences in health between different parts of our country and different groups within it. Why should we accept that a man born in Manchester can expect to live, on average, ten years less than one born in Dorset and that a woman in Manchester is likely to live seven years less than a woman born in Somerset? And why should we accept that manual workers and some ethnic minorities appear condemned to suffer worse health?'

Kmietowicz, Z. British Medical Journal, ***327***, *12 July 2003, p. 68.*
Reproduced with permission from the BMJ publishing group.

Further work

Should private schools be allowed? Should parents be banned from paying for their children to receive music or tennis lessons? Discuss your ideas and try to justify them within one or more ethical frameworks.

2 Human life

2.1 Sperm idol reality TV show

Evaluating good and bad

One of the features of modern science, especially in the biological sciences, is that it seems to throw up ethical challenges faster than most of us have time to think about them carefully. What happens then is that people react with gut feelings rather than by using reasoned argument. There is nothing wrong with gut feelings – indeed many ethicists would argue that it is always worth carefully analysing one's initial reactions (positive or negative) to a new proposal – but on their own they are rarely enough to help us reach valid ethical conclusions.

Resource link

BioNews is a weekly news digest of stories in assisted reproduction and human genetics, published by Progress Educational Trust. It provides plenty of material for ethical debate.

Activity 12 *Sperm idol*

Here you are presented with a report of a possible ethical issue that has resulted from recent advances in biology. You are expected to explore within a range of ethical frameworks whether or not the proposal should be permitted.

Read the article below and use the points that follow to help frame your discussion.

"*Sperm Idol reality TV show?*

An independent television production company, based in the UK, has announced that it is in the process of developing a reality television programme in which men compete in a 'sperm race' to get a childless woman pregnant. The company – Brighter Pictures – is owned by Endemol, the company that produces *Big Brother*, and may offer the show to television stations in the UK and US.

In the six episodes of *Make Me a Mum*, a woman will take fertility drugs to increase her egg production and 1000 male volunteers will compete for the privilege of having their sperm used to fertilise her. Two men will get to be finalists – one will be selected by the mother-to-be on the basis of his 'sex-appeal', intelligence, personality, wealth and fitness, and the other will be chosen by experts, based on his genetic compatibility with the woman and the quality of his sperm.

The show plans to film the actual moment of fertilisation using 'new German technology', and feature the moment live on television – when the winner can be announced.

The television company's plan has come under much criticism and has been branded the 'sickest ever reality show'. A spokesperson for pro-life group Life said the whole thing sounded 'like prostitution', adding 'if the child learns that he or she was fathered not out of love but for the purposes of a TV programme, that's extremely psychologically damaging'. But Remy Blumenfeld, the creative director of the programme, has defended the idea. 'There's a tremendous amount of science to this show', he said, adding 'It's fascinating – it's much more about the rules of the science than the rules of attraction. It's about what we don't know, what we can't see'. But television watchdog Mediawatch UK condemned the plan as 'absolutely scandalous'.

BioNews ***268***, 27 July 2004 ”

- Within a framework of rights and duties, try to decide whether or not the show should be permitted.
- Within a utilitarian framework, try to decide whether or not the show should be permitted. You need to think about the consequences of **a** permitting the show and **b** forbidding it for all the relevant individuals – including those who would appear in the show, those who are involved in making it, the viewing public, the non-viewing public and any child(ren) that resulted from the show.
- Can divine command tell us anything useful in trying to decide whether or not to allow the show to go ahead?
- Does a perspective based on virtue ethics cast any new light on the question?
- Does it make a difference to your answers if you are male or female?

Project hint

When you do your Research project, look for opportunities to use ethical frameworks in this way to analyse controversial situations.

Further work

1 From the description in the above passage, the process to be used to produce a fertilised egg is *in vitro* fertilisation (IVF). From advanced level biology textbooks or other sources, find out:

a what it is like for a woman undergoing IVF

b what the approximate chances are of a fertilised egg that results from IVF developing into a newborn baby.

2 Do you think the show should be allowed to proceed? Draw on the discussions of this lesson to produce a reasoned case supporting your own point of view.

2.2 The beginning of human life

From conception to birth

One of the oldest of all questions in medical ethics is 'When does human life begin?' The answer has implications for a range of controversial practices, some long established (e.g. abortion) and some more recent (e.g. embryonic stem cell research). It is relatively easy to outline the biological **facts** relating to conception and birth, and we do this in the next few paragraphs. But in order to say when life begins, we also need to consider **values** – the ethical significance attached to the facts.

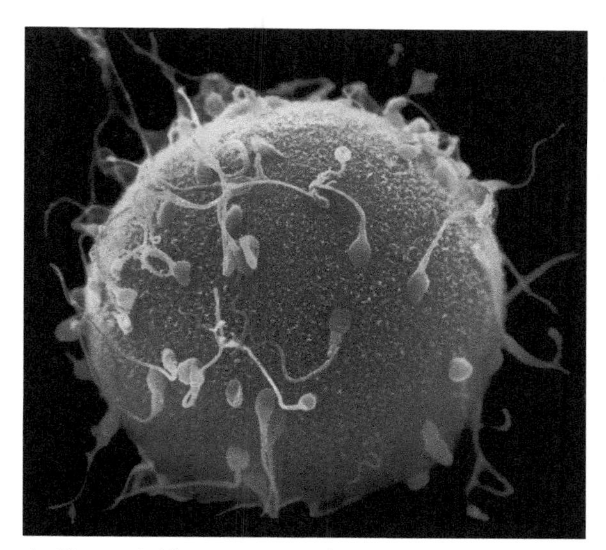

Figure 6 A human egg and sperm.

Conception occurs when an egg from the biological mother fuses with a sperm from the biological father (Figure 6). If all goes well, this fertilised cell begins to divide and about five days after conception (also called fertilisation) begins to implant in the wall of the mother's uterus (womb). Until about 14 days post-fertilisation there is still the possibility that the tiny bundle of cells will split into two (or very rarely more). When such a split does happen, genetically identical multiple births (usually twins) result.

Even in the absence of abortion (the deliberate premature ending of pregnancy) only about one in four fertilised cells survives to the end of pregnancy. The remainder are mostly lost as miscarriages in the first three months of pregnancy. A high proportion (possibly half or more) of those that do not survive are believed to have serious genetic abnormalities.

A normal pregnancy lasts about 38 weeks from conception (40 weeks from the end of the previous period – the time, traditionally, from when pregnancy is counted). Premature babies can nowadays survive, given intensive care, from about 30 weeks, occasionally even as early as 24 weeks (Figure 7). However, a high proportion of babies born before 30 weeks have serious health complications for the rest of their life.

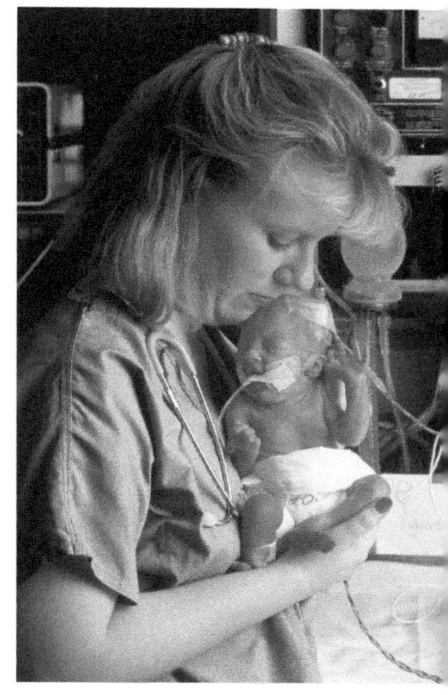

Figure 7 A premature baby in intensive care.

Activity 13 When does life begin?

Listed below are some possibilities for when human life begins. Evaluate them, thinking about the language of ethics. What rights do the various entities have at various ages and what related duties do we have to them? What religious teaching is there that is relevant? What contribution does a utilitarian perspective make? What would be the virtuous thing to do? Are there absolute answers or is everything relative?

Life begins:

- at the moment of fertilisation (conception)
- at implantation
- at 14 days
- somewhere between 24 and 30+ weeks
- at birth
- at some point in the first 18 months of life when a baby becomes aware of him or herself
- 'at 40'.
- There is no single point at which human life begins – we gradually develop into a human being.
- Sperm and eggs are alive and members of the species *Homo sapiens* just as we are, so human life has no beginning.

Activity 14 *Abortion*

Under what, if any, circumstances is abortion permissible? Discuss your views and try to justify them in terms of the ethical frameworks you have met in this course. Write a short essay (a few hundred words) setting out the arguments in support of your views.

Below is a famous metaphor, written by a feminist author, which sets out to defend abortion. You may find that it offers a different perspective for your views.

“You wake up in the morning and find yourself back to back in bed with an unconscious violinist. A famous unconscious violinist. He has been found to have a fatal kidney ailment, and the Society of Music Lovers has canvassed all the available medical records and found that you alone have the right blood type to help. They have therefore kidnapped you, and last night the violinist's circulatory system was plugged into yours, so that your kidneys can be used to extract poisons from his blood as well as your own. The director of the hospital now tells you, 'Look, we're sorry the Society of Music Lovers did this to you, we would never have permitted it if we had known. But still, they did it, and the violinist now is plugged into you. To unplug you would be to kill him. But never mind, it's only for nine months. By then he will have recovered from his ailment, and can safely be unplugged from you.' Is it morally incumbent on you to accede to this situation? No doubt it would be very nice of you if you did, a great kindness. But do you have to accede to it?

Thomson, J. J. (1971) A defense of abortion, Philosophy & Public Affairs, **1 (1)**, *pp. 47–66*”

Further work

Imagine that you were given the responsibility (e.g. by the government) of chairing a well funded committee to redraft the current abortion laws. Suggest how you might go about forming the committee and collecting evidence. (What sorts of people should be on the committee? How would you select them? Would you consult the general public? If so, how? Should the committee members visit particular organisations, particular countries? Which ones – and why? What processes of drafting, consultation and redrafting would you expect to go through?)

2.3 The end of human life

Ending life

Questions to do with what is a good way to die and whether human life can be ended intentionally have been at the heart of medical ethics since the discipline began. Here we start by examining the circumstances, if any, under which euthanasia is permissible. We then look briefly at what a good death might consist of.

Euthanasia is the deliberate causing of death of someone, motivated solely by considerations for the best interests of the person to be killed. Voluntary euthanasia occurs when the person consents; non-voluntary euthanasia occurs when the person does not give his or her consent. Active euthanasia involves doing something that will result in a person's death; giving a lethal injection, for example. Passive euthanasia involves not doing something, the absence of which results in the person's death; not giving antibiotics, for example.

Activity 15 *Euthanasia*

Discuss the main arguments for and against voluntary euthanasia. Make two lists headed 'for' and 'against' and write a list of bullet points under each.

Under what circumstances might there be arguments in favour of non-voluntary euthanasia? Try to think of one specific example (which can be hypothetical) and write down all the possible arguments you can think of, even if you disagree with them.

Is the distinction between active and passive euthanasia morally relevant? Write a few sentences to support your view.

Resource link

The British Social Attitudes Survey gives statistics on support for euthanasia.

Project hint

In your Research project, listing arguments for and against an action can help you clarify your own ideas about whether it is right or wrong.

Activity 16 *A perfect death*

Read the following passage and then discuss how you might like to die.

“*A perfect death*

My mother was 85 years old. She had just returned from her biennial 'long trip' adventure. This time she had travelled alone across the United States visiting friends. She was proud of having boarded 24 planes and of having seen the 'grassy knoll' in Dallas from which John Kennedy had been shot. She had lost weight through, and she looked very pale. 'Sit down,' she said when I next telephoned. I sat down. 'I am dying. I have cancer of the pancreas. It has gone to the liver. They say it will be three to six months, but I know it won't be that long.'

She told me that she wanted to say goodbye to her many friends. Refusing all help, she set herself a schedule of inviting them to her house – cooking meals for them, telling them her diagnosis, comforting them, and returning any gifts they had ever given her. She said that she saw such gifts as lifelong loans and that the time had now come to repay them.

Her strength was ebbing, but she seemed ever more focused and determined. She was referred to her local palliative care team and was delighted at their positive and unpatronising attitude. She rather

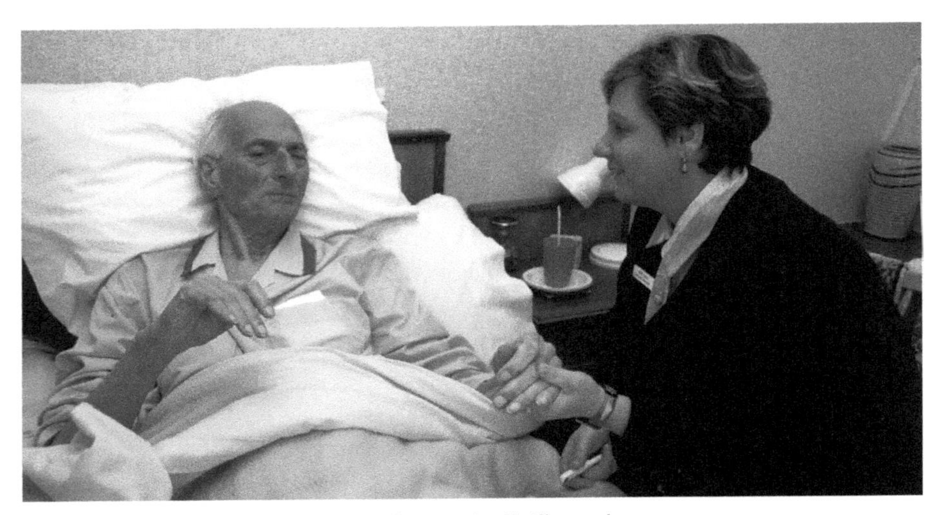

▲ *Figure 8 A hospice provides care for terminally ill people.*

reluctantly accepted a blood transfusion but said that she was sure it would not relieve her exhaustion. She was right.

Within a month of her diagnosis, she was too tired and breathless to walk across her living room. She was admitted to the local hospice, where she seemed to rally. Friends poured in and she 'held court' as she had always loved to do. 'It's so unfair,' she said in mock complaint. 'All my life I've entertained my friends. Now you should be entertaining me, but I am still the one telling the stories.'

The next day, a Sunday, she was much weaker. 'I've had enough,' she said. 'No more transfusions. No more drugs. I want it to be over. They say it's a matter or weeks, but I don't think so.'

On Monday I had to work all morning and did not get to the hospice until mid-afternoon. I was told that she was no longer taking telephone calls or seeing visitors but that she wanted to see me. As I walked in she looked at me, her gaze as piercing as if I was still her naughty child. 'Sit down,' she said. I sat down. She died.

I am grateful that she had waited for me. I have also learnt that the 'good death' that is the aim of modern palliative case is about much more than symptom control. It is, or should be, about enabling people to retain their dignity, to exercise choice, and above all to stay in control until (as in my mother's case) their last moment.

Katona, C. British Medical Journal, ***328***, *24 January 2004, p. 202. Reproduced with permission from the BMJ publishing group.* ”

Further work

An advance directive is a document that states in advance the treatments that a person wants or does not want if they are incompetent (i.e. unable to make informed decisions) when medical courses of action are decided. Research advance directives and discuss whether or not they are desirable.

2.4 Transplantation

Organ transplants

You may or may not know someone who has had a transplant – or who needs one. This lesson is about the shortage of organs for transplants.

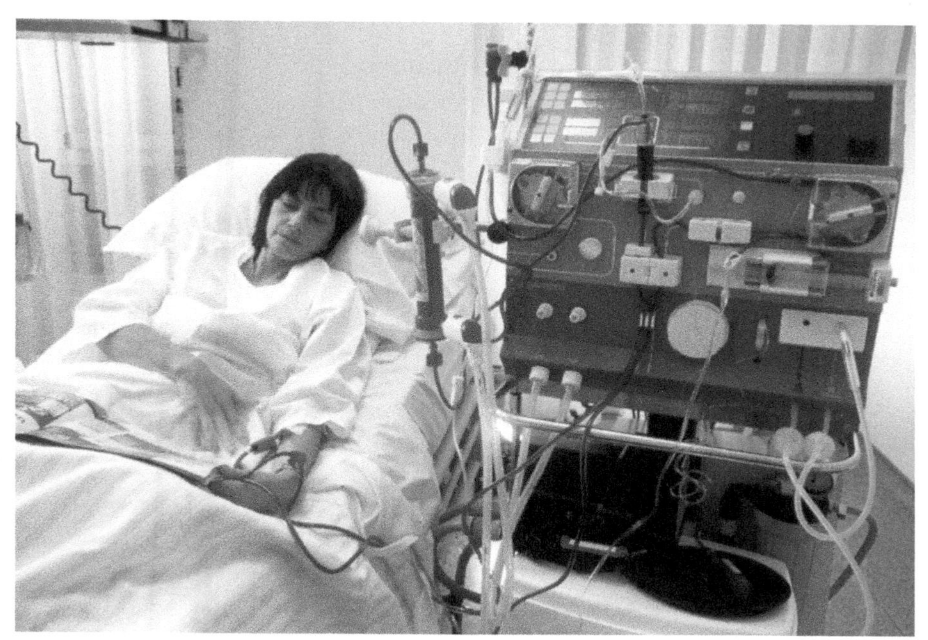

▲ ***Figure 9*** *A person undergoing kidney dialysis.*

Worldwide there are approximately 150,000 people waiting for an organ transplant. Each year many thousands of people have their life saved as a result of human-to-human transplants. However, each year many thousands of people die who would have lived had they received a transplant. Indeed, the majority of people waiting for a transplant never receive one; they die first. The purchase of human organs – a market-led 'solution' to the shortage – is, by-and-large, illegal. (The qualification 'by-and-large' is necessary as some countries permit the sale of human eggs, sperm and blood.) None, though, allows the purchase of organs for transplants. Nevertheless, there are not infrequent reports in the media of organs being offered for sale and/or bought for transplants. In one case, US$5.7 million was reportedly bid during an online auction of a human kidney before the auction was halted. The original advertisement read:

> “You can choose either kidney ... Buyer pays all transplant and medical costs. Of course only one for sale, as I need the other one to live. Serious bids only.”

The reason why most people waiting for an organ transplant never receive one is simply that there aren't enough human organs to go around. There are three main reasons for this:

1 The number of people who would benefit from a transplant continues to rise. In part this is because of advances in transplant surgery which mean that more organs (e.g. lungs) can now be transplanted than used to be the case. In part, too, this is because a greater range of medical conditions can now be treated by transplantation than were previously.

2 Only a very small proportion of deaths result in organs that are suitable for transplants. Deaths from motor vehicle accidents provide a high proportion of suitable organs. However, thanks to improvements in road safety (seat belts, improved car design, better road layouts, greater use of motorcycle helmets), the number of people killed in such accidents is reducing in those countries where transplant surgery is numerically significant.

3 Many countries have some sort of 'opt in' rather than 'opt out' system for organ donation. This can mean that for a transplant organ to become available:
   - **a** the dead person needs previously to have expressed a wish for his or her organs to be used for transplantation
   - **b** a doctor must ask relatives to consent to this
   - **c** no close relative must object to the transplant.

Activity 17 *Wants and needs*

Consider the distinction between 'wants' and 'needs'.

Activity 18 *Opt in or opt out?*

There is little doubt that the adoption of an 'opt out' rather than an 'opt in' system for organ donation would significantly increase (probably by a factor of more than two) the number of lives saved each year through organ donation. Discuss whether such an 'opt out' system should be introduced in the UK. Jot down a list of bullet points in favour of such a system, and a list of points against.

Xenotransplantation

Xenotransplantation entails moving (i.e. transplanting) cells or organs (e.g. pancreatic cells, a heart or a kidney) from an individual of one species into an individual of another species. Xenotransplantation has been proposed as a possible radical new solution to the problem of the shortage of human organs for transplantation. Since the 1980s a number of research groups have been attempting to genetically engineer domestic pigs so that their organs may be given to humans.

A number of national and international ethical committees as well as individual scientists have looked at the question of xenotransplantation. One of the particular matters of concern has been the issue of safety. We know that pigs carry what are called porcine endogenous retroviruses (engagingly abbreviated as PERVS). In the light of CJD and AIDS it is unsurprising that there is tremendous hesitancy in allowing any scientific/technological procedure to go ahead that might lead to new human infections.

Project hint

A question relating to xenotransplantation could form the basis for a Research project.

The current position in the UK is that if (and it is a big 'if') xenotransplants are allowed, the safety requirements will be stringent. In particular, there is a great deal of work going on to reduce to near-zero levels the chance of any infectious agents, such as viruses, passing as a result of transplants from pigs to humans. The United Kingdom Xenotransplantation Interim Regulatory Authority is proposing that anyone receiving a xenotransplant must agree to lifelong post-operative compliance with a whole set of conditions including:

- use of barrier contraception
- refraining from pregnancy or fathering a child
- allowing the relevant health authorities to be notified when moving abroad.

In addition, all household members and sexual partners will need to be seen pre-xenotransplantation to ensure they are informed about possible risks and how to minimise them, and to have baseline blood samples taken for indefinite archiving.

Activity 19 *Ethics of xenotransplantation*

The above passage concentrates on some of the safety issues raised by the possibility of xenotransplantation. Discuss other ethical issues xenotransplantation would raise. Choose one ethical framework and write a paragraph to explain how it leads to arguments for and against xenotransplantation.

Further work

Do you intend to carry a donor card once you are allowed to (at 18 years of age in the UK)? Discuss your reasons and compare views with other students.

3 Animals

3.1 Bugged-off students down their insect nets

Recent decades have shown an increasing awareness of the consequences of human actions for non-human animals (hereafter referred to as 'animals' – though it is always important to keep in mind whether humans are simply animals or more than animals). This lesson looks at a possibly unlikely candidate for such concern – insects (Figure 10).

▲ ***Figure 10*** *Insect specimens collected for study.*

Activity 20 Bugged off

Read the newspaper extract on the next page then carry out the activities below.

1 Identify the arguments provided by the students at Linkoping University as to why they should not have to kill the insects.

2 Evaluate the arguments provided by the students at Linkoping University as to why they should not have to kill the insects.

3 Assuming what most biologists would accept – namely that insects are not capable of suffering (they simply haven't a sufficiently complicated nervous system) – propose other arguments in support of the views of Maria Grankvist and her like-minded fellow students.

4 Have you ever been required in your science courses to undertake activities that you have felt were objectionable? If so, describe them briefly and try to explain why you felt the way you did.

“Bugged-off students down their insect nets

Biology students at a Swedish university are refusing to kill insects on ethical grounds.

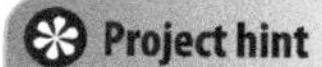

Project hint

A question relating to the use of animals in education could form the basis for a Research project.

They argue that the university should encourage future ecologists to show more respect for nature.

Maria Grankvist, an undergraduate at Linkoping University, said: ‘We’re expected to go out with nets and kill insects. Then we categorise them according to species. The trouble is it works only with fully grown insects so that many young specimens are thrown away.’

The students maintain that they should only have to categorise insects, not collect and kill them.

‘It’s about respecting the environment,’ said Ms Grankvist, who, along with two other students, is refusing to do the assignment.

Ms Grankvist and her fellow students have suggested that the university should place more emphasis on observing, identifying and studying living creatures within their natural habitat. Jan Landin, a senior lecturer at Linkoping who specialises in ecological microbiology, said he understood the students’ positions, but said: ‘The problem is that it would require more teaching resources than we’ve got. Since the 1990s, our funding has shrunk by 50 per cent per student.’

Dr Landin said that if students did not have experience of collecting insects, they would struggle with insect inventories at a later stage of their training.

But if changes are not made, students may well decide to study elsewhere. At Stockholm University, for example, biology students are not required to collect insects.

Bengt Karlsson, Director of Studies at the Department of Zoology, said: ‘In recent years we’ve allowed students to elect not to take this component on ethical grounds.’

At Linkoping, the message seems to be getting through. ‘We’re delighted the students are actively involved in curriculum issues,’ said Annalena Kindgren, a spokesperson for the faculty of science.

‘We’ll be looking at the possibility of making changes to this part of the curriculum.’

Buscall, J. Times Higher Education Supplement, *16 July 2004, p. 10*”

Further work

Imagine you are the head of the science faculty at Linkoping University. Draft a letter to the Times Higher Education Supplement (THES) *newspaper justifying the requirement for biology students to undertake the activity (i.e. collecting, killing and categorising insects).*

3.2 Animal rights

Animal rights

Recent years have seen a growing examination of how humans relate to and treat animals. The notion of animal rights has become prominent but is still controversial. What would it mean for non-human animals to have rights?

Activity 21 *Legal lions lie with lambs*

Read the following extract then discuss:

- whether or not non-human animals have moral rights
- how animals can have their interests considered even if they are not accorded rights.

“*Legal lions lie with lambs*

After encountering *Animal Liberation* by Australian philosopher Peter Singer in 1979, I learned that tens of billions of animals are annually killed for food. Many are raised in abhorrent conditions on factory farms. Hundreds of millions languish and die in biomedical research or testing facilities. Hundreds of millions more are hunted, trapped, skinned or dissected. I learned that, while humans are ‘legal persons’ with a vast number of legal rights, animals are ‘legal things’. Our personhood operates as legal armour that protects us, while the legal thinghood of animals allows us to do with them as we will.

▲ **Figure 11** *Chimpanzees in a zoo.*

Within the year, I began to shift my law practice towards animal protection and, throughout the next decade, steadily litigated in the interests of animals. Since then, I have argued that chimpanzees (Figure 11) and bonobos are entitled to basic legal rights. Take Jerom, for example. He was a chimpanzee whom US biomedical researchers injected with multiple strains of HIV viruses, beginning when he was just two years old. They were hoping to kill him. They imprisoned him, along with a dozen other chimpanzee youngsters, first in a small, windowless, cinder-block building, then in a large windowless grey concrete and steel box, 9 ft by 11 ft by 8.5 ft. After a decade, Jerom died a terrible and lingering death. The eminent Harvard constitutional law professor Laurence H. Tribe observed earlier this year that 'clearly Jerom was enslaved'.

In 1990, I received a call from the Vermont Law School. Its environmental law programme was so respected that it could chance offering a summer course in such a novel field as animal rights law. Would I teach a course? I would. I called it 'animal rights law'. We would discuss which, if any, animals might be suitable to hold basic legal rights and what it was about them that made them suitable.

I realised that, as with most lawyers, judges and law professors, most law students knew little about how animals came to be legal things, knew almost nothing about what legal rights were, or moral rights, either. Without such understandings it would be senseless to argue either that animals should or should not have the basic legal rights, so we added to the study of history of how and why we use animals, meditations on what legal rights are, where they come from, why humans have them, which humans have them, what happens when they do not, why non-humans lack them, how and why humans who once lacked them attained them, and the suitability of the common law as a vehicle for attaining basic legal rights for at least some animals.

Today, law journals publish animal rights articles. When I appear in court, judges may ask if I am there on an animal rights case. Some even want to chat about animal rights law. But when invited to speak about legal careers at law schools, I am invariably placed on the environmental law panel. I want to sit with the civil rights advocates. I belong there because animal rights law draws from the same well of liberty and equality as does human rights.

Wise, S. Times Higher Education Supplement, *12 May 2000, p. 17* ”

Further work

If animals have rights, do you believe this means that keeping pets is slavery and therefore wrong? Write a few sentences to explain your belief.

3.3 Animal experimentation

Ethical approaches to the use of animals

The use of animals (non-humans) in experiments is an issue on which opinions are often sharply polarised (Figure 12). The following is an extract from a Royal Society policy document on the use of animals in research.

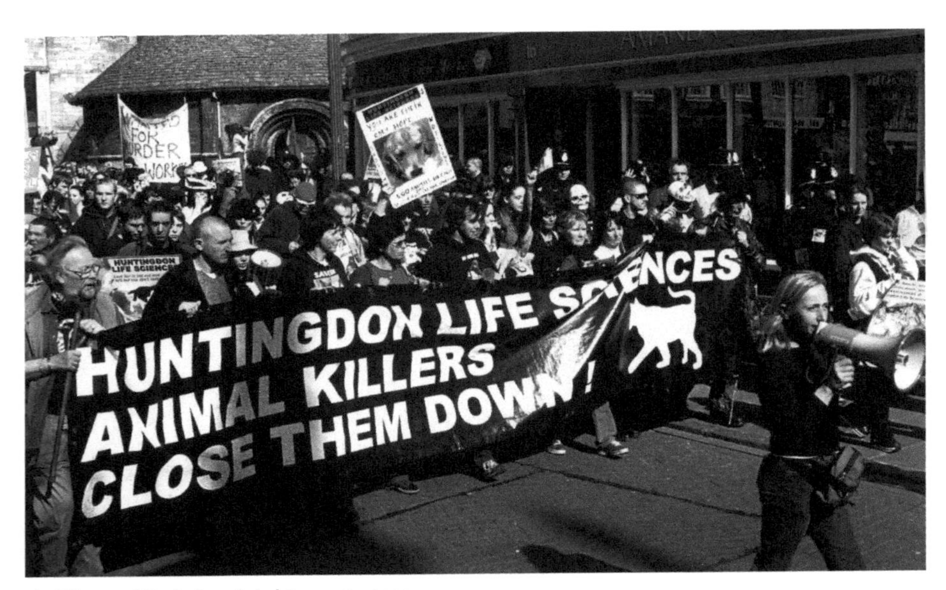

▲ ***Figure 12*** *Animal rights protesters.*

> “All those involved in the debate about the use of animals in research lay claim to one or other moral principle. In human and veterinary medicine, causing pain or suffering in a patient is considered unethical unless it is for the direct benefit of that patient. Those who favour work on animals may do so to alleviate the suffering of humans or other animals. Scientists in favour of this principle use their research to understand fundamental aspects of biology that in turn facilitate the development of therapeutic measures for both animals and humans. Those who oppose the use of animals in research may object to the means by which scientists attempt to achieve their goals.
>
> One view is that each animal has the right to life and humans should not take such a right away from it. It is not entirely clear whether the proponents of such a view would grant rights to every organism that showed signs of reacting to maltreatment. Nevertheless, they would argue that rights to good treatment, once granted, must be respected. Others would argue that while granting rights to animals is inappropriate because human rights are firmly embedded in a social context, humans have responsibilities for animals in their care and should ensure that their welfare is good. Both the rights and the responsibilities arguments are sometimes taken as absolutes, over-riding all other moral claims.

However, this could also be the case for the moral argument for supporting animal experiments because of their potential medical benefit. The alternative to such absolutism is to respect the range of views by attempting to both minimise the suffering inflicted on animals used in research while maximising the scientific and medical gain, which is consistent with the Royal Society's position on this issue. Indeed, this is the position enshrined in UK law governing the use of animals in research. Balancing between these positions required by law is not an exact process since the assessment of scientific and medical benefit and that of animal suffering are both difficult to quantify and are not expressed in the same terms. The assessments are incommensurate and, therefore, referring to the judgement as cost-benefit analysis is misleading. So the degree of suffering might be expressed as low, medium or high and the likely scientific and medical benefit might be similarly classified. Research that involves low suffering to the animals and was likely to be highly beneficial would generally be regarded as acceptable. Research that involves medium suffering but only a medium chance of generating a beneficial outcome would probably be deemed as unacceptable – but clearly this judgement will depend on a consensus view derived from a judgement by those bodies responsible for granting approval to research projects.

Criticism of the use of animals in research sometimes arises when there appears to be no immediate tangible health benefit of the research. An inability to quantify the benefits of a research project can be seen to imply that it is frivolous or wasteful and therefore unethical. This is an invalid assumption, however, as research studies that do not have direct benefit to humans or other animals can instead provide a vital contribution to fundamental scientific understanding that may provide benefit in the future. Individual experiments are similar to the individual bricks in a building, with knowledge being built up over a long period of time and with the benefits perhaps only being realised when the building or the research is completed. On the other hand, the benefits of applied research may be easier to quantify. For example, in drug development, many thousands of compounds may need to be tested in order to develop a new drug. This means that in some cases the research may not be successful, and may seem futile, whereas in fact such work is essential in refining knowledge. It is therefore important when considering the ethical justification of the use of animals in research to realise that the development of a successful drug such as insulin or the antibiotics may result in saving many millions of human and animal lives.

Current UK law encapsulates the middle ground thinking. Animal research is allowed, but only by qualified people with the appropriate licences issued by the Home Office, and under tightly controlled conditions. Projects are independently assessed for scientific validity and subjected to ethical review. As far as possible the potential benefits are judged in relation to likely pain and suffering. Animals must be maintained in good environmental conditions and protected from disease. In the UK, Home Office inspectors can visit premises at any time, without prior notice. The law protects all vertebrates, but the use of more complex animals and especially primates is even more strictly controlled. The use of animals is not permitted where a replacement alternative is available. Where no replacement alternative is available, then experimental protocols should be refined in such a way as to reduce any pain or suffering to a minimum, using for example, analgesics and human end-points. Finally, the number of animals used should be reduced to the minimum consistent with achieving the scientific objectives of the study.

Royal Society (2004) The Use of Non-human Animals in Research: A Guide for Scientists, *pp. 10–11* ”

Activity 22 *Arguments for and against using animals in research*

Based both on the above extract and on your own thinking, summarise:

1 arguments in favour of using non-human animals for scientific research

2 arguments against using non-human animals for scientific research.

List the arguments as bullet points in two columns headed 'for' and 'against'.

Snowflake the rescued rabbit

The following article appeared in a magazine published by Animal Aid.

“ ***Sarah from York tells the story of her adopted male bunny***

When Regal Rabbits – a company which bred animals for vivisection – closed down in 2000, we were lucky enough to be able to offer one of the unwanted animals a home. We already had one neutered female bunny, Thumper, so we jumped at the chance to adopt a male to keep her company. We later named him Snowflake.

We couldn't believe how gigantic Snowflake was when he arrived. It turned out that he had been used as a breeding male, so he must have been imprisoned at Regal for several years. We still don't know how old he was, but he was clearly more scared of people than the baby bunnies adopted by some of our friends. In fact, when he came to live with us he used to cower under the coffee table, running from left to right if anybody went too close to him. The saddest thing of all was that he would wet himself if you did actually manage to get right up to him – he was so scared we didn't think he would ever trust us. To make matters worse, Thumper refused to accept him, and bit him at every opportunity! He, on the other hand, desperately wanted to be friends and used to sneak into her house. Somehow he conquered all the barriers we had put up after being advised to separate the garden until they were used to

▲ ***Figure 13*** *Rabbits like this are used in animal testing.*

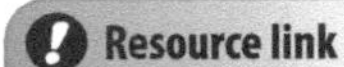

Resource link

Animal Aid campaigns peacefully against all animal abuse and promotes a cruelty-free lifestyle.

each other. We would be woken at four in the morning by scrabbling and stomping; he'd not only managed to get into her half of the garden, but had gone all the way up to her bedroom at the top of the hutch!

Remarkably, Snowflake accepted me within two weeks, but it took my partner, Darren, over a year to earn his trust fully. It seemed he was scared of male voices, so I can only assume most of the workers at Regal farm had been men. As for Thumper, she finally made her peace with him after a couple of months. One day when we were out, the two rabbits somehow managed to lock themselves out of their houses and drift into the same side of the garden. We came home to find them cuddled up together like old friends. They were happy together from then on.

Outrage ***135***, *Summer 2004, p. 24* ”

Activity 23 *Styles of writing*

Discuss whether you prefer the style of writing in the Royal Society or the Animal Aid extract and why.

Further work

Research the issue of the use of animals in scientific experiments in more detail. Your teacher may provide some useful references.

Project hint

When you are consulting source materials for your Research project, notice the various writing styles you encounter and think about their effectiveness. When writing your own report, think about your own writing style and how you might use different styles to convey information and to persuade readers by your arguments.

Resource link

The Research Defence Society works to promote good practice in laboratory animal welfare and to develop non-animal replacement research methods.

4.1 Genetic testing

Genetic testing: friend or foe?

The science of genetics has given rise to a plethora of new technologies, many of which have developed very rapidly and which give rise to ethical issues that people have not previously needed to consider.

Genetic testing involves using the DNA of a human (or other organism) to draw conclusions about its past or make predictions about its future. It can be undertaken at any stage of the life cycle, for example (in humans) before implantation, during pregnancy, shortly after birth, during childhood or in adulthood. In this section we concentrate on the genetic testing of adults and newborn babies, but similar ethical issues are raised in the other cases. The term 'genetic screening' is sometimes interchangeable with 'genetic testing' and sometimes distinguished from it; here no distinction is made. The following article describes a recent case involving genetic testing.

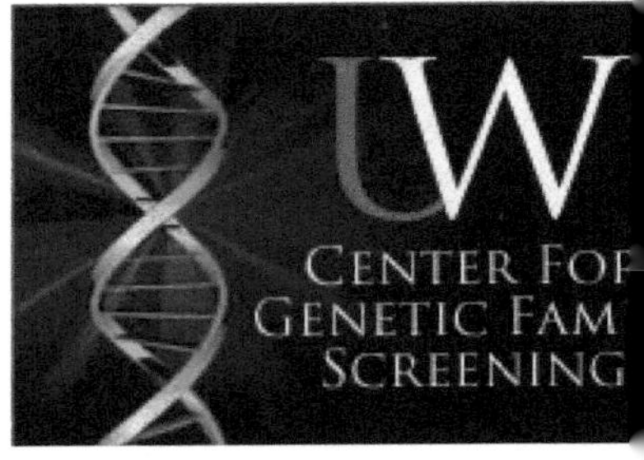

▲ ***Figure 14*** *Genetic screening is now widely available.*

" US employer agrees to stop genetic testing

A US freight railway company has agreed to stop requiring the genetic testing of employees who file claims for a wrist condition called the carpal tunnel syndrome. The US Equal Employment Opportunity Commission had filed a lawsuit against Burlington Northern Santa Fe alleging that the policy violated the Americans with Disabilities Act.

A railway worker who refused to provide a blood sample after filing an injury claim was threatened with dismissal, the commission said, in its first legal challenge against genetic testing by employers. A spokesperson for Burlington Northern, Richard Russack, told the US federal court that it would stop the testing for 60 days 'to evaluate the situation'.

The debate over biological screening in the workplace has intensified as scientists unravel the human genetic code, but the controversy has largely been theoretical so far. As a result of the lawsuit filed by the employment commission, Burlington Northern has become one of the first companies to acknowledge having used genetic testing on its employees, according to the commission's lawyers.

Concern that such tests could be used to weed out workers on the basis of their genetic predispositions to injury or disease has led 22 states to ban the use of genetic screening for making employment-related decisions, according to a survey by the *Washington Post*.

The commission alleged that the blood sample that employees were asked to submit was used to identify a genetic defect on chromosome 17, which some experts believe could predispose a person to forms of the carpal tunnel syndrome. The syndrome causes numbness and weakness in the wrist.

The commission also alleged that employees were not informed of the genetic test or asked to give their consent.

Mr Russack said that his company in some instances requested employees to undergo genetic tests 'because there could be a predisposition within the body chemistry of the individual' to develop the carpal tunnel syndrome 'that had nothing to do with work'. But he said that such tests were not required and there had been no disciplinary action or threat of such action against any worker who refused the tests.

Reliance on such tests is controversial, and the law governing their use is unsettled. There are worries that workers subjected to such tests will face illegal discrimination and invasions of privacy.

Gottlieb, S. British Medical Journal, ***322****, 24 February 2001, p. 449. Reproduced with permission from the BMJ publishing group.* ”

Activity 24 *Screening for deafness?*

Suppose that it is possible to use genetic screening for a common form of early-onset loss of hearing in which a person develops extremely poor hearing in their late 40s to early 50s. Discuss whether employers of teachers (e.g. Local Education Authorities, the governing bodies of independent schools) should be allowed to require new teachers to be genetically screened for the condition.

Activity 25 *Screening for heart attack?*

Suppose that it is possible to use genetic screening to see if someone is likely to have a sudden heart attack during middle age. Should airline companies be permitted to require such testing of prospective pilots?

Project hint

A question relating to genetic screening could form the basis for a Research project.

Activity 26 *Screening for PKN*

The genetic disorder phenylketonuria (PKN) can be detected using the Guthrie test as described below. The test has never been controversial. Why do you think this is the case even though newborn babies cannot give their consent?

Detecting phenylketonuria

Phenylketonuria is a hereditary disease caused by a non-sex-linked recessive allele: the liver fails to produce an enzyme (phenylalanine hydroxylase), with the result that the amino acid phenylalanine accumulates in the bloodstream instead of being converted to another amino acid, tyrosine. This causes severe damage to the brain of the developing child leading to mental retardation. Until the 1950s, adults with phenylketonuria were frequently institutionalised. Nowadays, though, in a large number of countries all newborn babies are tested by the Guthrie test to see if they have raised levels of phenylalanine in their blood. (Note that this is not a genetic test.) Phenylalanine occurs naturally in most diets, so if tested babies do have raised levels, they are put on a diet that is low in phenylalanine. Although these diets are quite expensive, and extremely boring for those who have to live on them throughout their childhood, they do allow normal brain development to take place.

Further work

View the film GATTACA *(1997) and discuss the issues it raises.*

4.2 Human reproductive cloning

What is cloning?

Ever since the arrival of Dolly the sheep in 1997, the possibility of human reproductive cloning has been in the air. This lesson clarifies what is meant by human reproductive cloning and helps you to examine arguments for and against it.

Cloning refers to reproduction without sexual fertilisation. Human reproductive cloning has not yet (Winter 2006) been achieved. In principle, there are two main ways in which it might. The first would be by embryo splitting. This method has been used in cattle for many years. It occurs when a single embryo resulting from fertilisation outside the cow (using the procedures of *in vitro* fertilisation) is then split in two and both are put into the cow's uterus. Identical twins result.

▲ ***Figure 15*** *Cloning is central to the plot of the film* The Boys from Brazil *(1978).*

The second way in which human reproductive cloning might take place would be by what is sometimes called cell nuclear replacement. Here you would first obtain a human egg and remove its nucleus (resulting in an enucleated egg). Separately you would obtain the nucleus of any ordinary cell such as a skin cell from the person you wish to clone. The nucleus from this cell would then be placed in the enucleated egg which would then be implanted into a woman (either the one who produced the egg or another one) and allowed to develop for the nine months of pregnancy.

Deserving cases?

The following passage identifies some cases in which there might be an argument for human reproductive cloning.

A question relating to human reproductive cloning could form the basis for a Research project.

> “ 1 A couple in their forties who have been trying to have a child for a number of years. All attempts, including assisted reproduction, have failed. At last IVF has given them a single healthy embryo. If they implant this embryo, the chances of it surviving are small and with it will perish their last chance to have their own child. However, if they clone the embryo say ten times they can implant two embryos and freeze eight. If they are successful first time – great! If not, they can thaw out two more embryos and try again, and so on until they achieve the child they seek. If both implanted embryos survive they will achieve identical twins.
>
> 2 A couple in which the male partner is infertile. They want a child genetically related to them both. Rather than opt for donated sperm they prefer to clone the male partner knowing that from him they will get 46 chromosomes, and that from the female partner, who supplies the egg, there will be mitochondrial DNA. Although in this case the male genetic contribution will be much the greater, both will feel, justifiably, that they have made a genetic contribution to their child. They argue that for them, this is the only acceptable way of having children of ‘their own’.
>
> 3 A couple in which neither partner has usable gametes, although the woman could gestate. For the woman to bear the child she desires they would have to use either embryo donation or an egg cloned with the DNA of one of them. Again they argue that they want a child genetically related to one of them and that it's that or nothing. The mother in this case will have the satisfaction of knowing she has contributed not only her uterine environment but nourishment and will contribute subsequent nurture; and the father, his genes.
>
> 4 A single woman wants a child. She prefers the idea of using all her own DNA to the idea of accepting 50% from a stranger. She does not want to be forced to accept DNA from a stranger and mother ‘his child’ rather than her own.

5 A couple have only one child and they have been told that they are unable to have further children. Their baby is dying. They want to de-nucleate one of her cells so that they can have another child of their own.

6 A woman has a severe inheritable genetic disease. She wants her own child and wishes to use her partner's genome combined with her own egg.

Harris, J. (2004) On Cloning, *Routledge, London, pp. 31–3* ”

Activity 27 *To clone or not to clone?*

Based on the text above, and on your own thinking, write down at least three arguments against human reproductive cloning. Then for each argument, write down a counter-argument (a 'but'). For example, the first cloned babies would come under intense media interest *but* this is true of the children of royalty, sporting stars, politicians and so on.

Project hint

In your Research project, matching arguments with counter-arguments can help you clarify your own ideas and make a case in support of your point of view.

Further work

Watch the film Blade Runner *(1982), preferably the* Director's Cut. *What difference, if any, would it make if the androids were human clones?*

4.3 Embryonic stem cell research

Therapeutic cloning

Since Dolly the sheep there has been an explosion of medical interest in the possibility of using cloning techniques on human embryos. The main reason for this is because such research holds out the hope of tremendous medical benefits. Many people have tissues or organs that don't function effectively, particularly as they get older. Treatments based on stem cells may allow such conditions as Parkinson's disease, Alzheimer's disease, insulin-dependent diabetes and spinal cord injuries to be treated.

The following two passages describe what's involved in embryonic stem cell research and raise some ethical issues.

“ ***Early embryonic development – stem cells***

By five days after conception, a hollow ball of cells has resulted. The outer cell layer goes on to form the placenta. The inner cell mass of 50 or so cells goes on to form the tissues of the developing embryo.

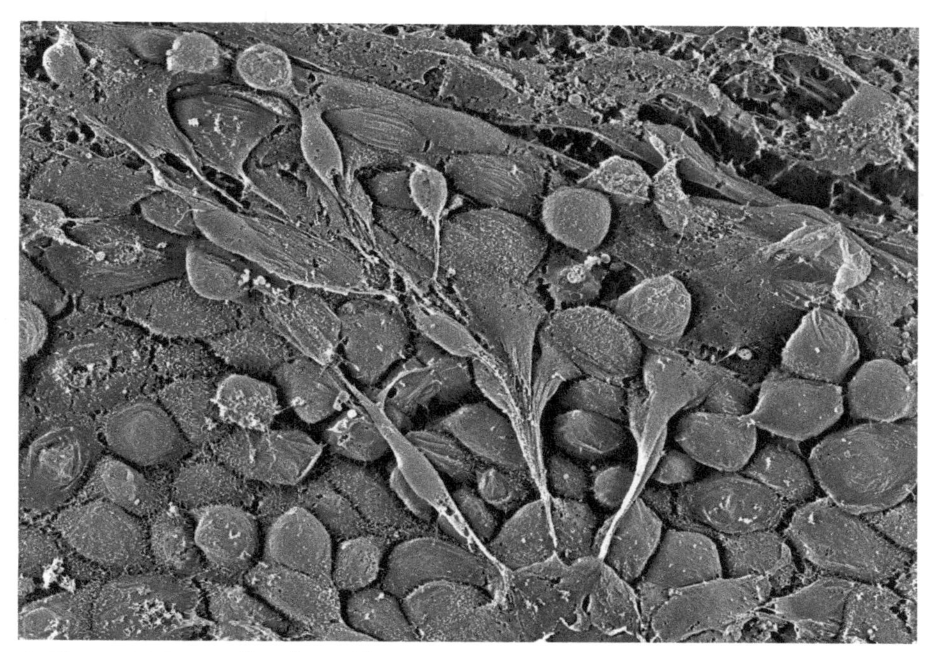

▲ ***Figure 16*** *Stem cells collected for transplant.*

These 50 cells are embryonic stem cells. Each of these cells can potentially give rise to most of the 216 different cell types found in an adult.

Stem cells offer great hope to medicine. They may one day produce new cells, tissues or organs for treatment and repair by transplantation [Figure 16]. Embryonic stem cells may be the most suitable type of stem cell for this sort of treatment, unlike adult stem cells which are committed to developing only into certain cell types.

In therapeutic cloning a patient needing a transplant would have one of their ordinary cells removed – this could simply be a cell from the base of a hair or any other suitable tissue. This cell, or its nucleus, would then be fused with an egg cell from which the nucleus had been removed. The resulting cell would then be stimulated to divide in the same way that the cell that gave rise to Dolly the cloned sheep was.

If all went to plan, after about five days a mass of cells would have resulted and stem cells could be isolated and encouraged to develop into tissues. These tissues would be genetically identical to the person needing a transplant. This would mean that there should be no problems with rejection.

Salters-Nuffield Advanced Biology (2002) AS Student Book 2 – Pilot edition, *Heinemann, Oxford, pp. 22–5* ”

“ ***Therapeutic cloning***

The main objection to therapeutic cloning is the suggestion that it is immoral to create life to be used as a means to an end and then discarded. With therapeutic cloning embryos will be created in order that their stem cells can be harvested and used in an attempt to heal patients with disease, disability and trauma. After these embryos have served their purpose they will be discarded. This kind of claim is often reinforced by appeal to the principle expressed by Immanuel Kant, which demands that a human individual should never be thought of solely as a means but always also as an end. It has been argued, therefore, that '[creating] human life for the sole purpose of preparing therapeutic material would clearly not be for the dignity of the life created'.

In opposition to this view it has been argued that the Kantian principle, invoked without any qualification or gloss, is seldom helpful in medical or bioscientific contexts. The argument is that this principle, especially in its simplistic form, would surely outlaw other established medical procedures normally considered ethically unproblematic. Blood transfusions, for instance, involve using the donor as a means to an end with respect to the recipient. Similarly, an abortion performed exclusively to save the life of the mother would also, presumably, be outlawed by this principle. It can therefore be argued that while Kant's principle does have powerful intuitive force, it is so vague and open to selective interpretation, and its scope for application is consequently so limited, that its utility as one of the fundamental principles of modern ethical thought is virtually zero.

For example, we often use others as a means to an end. It may be that doing so is only wrong when that person's autonomy is infringed by this action. If a blood donor consents or even volunteers to give blood then it is not clear that using him as a means to an end is morally suspect. Similarly, it could be argued that using an embryo is equally morally unproblematic, as to do so does not undermine any person's autonomy. This views the embryo as not being capable of autonomous choice, and thus using that being as a means to another's end does not wrong the embryo and, because it benefits another, it should be welcomed. Embryos are constantly created and die in normal sexual reproduction; it is estimated that five embryos are created for every live birth that occurs. It is difficult, therefore, to object in principle to the creation of embryos for a significant moral purpose.

Bennett, R. & Harris, J. (2003) Pursuing a rational analysis of cloning, in Levinson, R. & Reiss, M. J. (Eds) Key Issues in Bioethics: A Guide for Teachers, *RoutledgeFalmer, London, pp. 55–6* ”

Activity 28 *Medical uses of stem cells*

Discuss whether or not it is ethically acceptable to use embryonic stem cells for research and medical treatments. Use the ethical frameworks introduced earlier in this course. For each framework in turn, write brief notes on arguments for and against using stem cells for this purpose.

A question relating to the use of stem cells could form the basis for a Research project.

Further work

1. *Produce a simple fact sheet about stem cells and therapeutic cloning, suitable for a member of the general public. (Hint: Think about designing this for someone with a reading age of a typical 14-year-old and make sure it can be read in just 5 minutes.)*
2. *Show this fact sheet to your teacher/lecturer and, once he/she has approved it, make 20 photocopies.*
3. *Produce a short interview schedule with just five questions about people's attitudes towards the use of human embryos for medical research. (Hint: Include some questions that can be answered 'yes' or 'no', e.g. 'Do you think the government should permit the use of human embryos for medical research if it was likely that this would save some people's lives?' Also include some 'open' questions that cannot be answered in this way, e.g. 'How would you feel if you heard that human embryos were being used for medical research?' If you give multiple-choice answers to such questions, this makes the results easier to collate at the end. However, if you do this, make sure you give sensible choices and a wide range. Sometimes it is useful to leave a couple of lines for comments following multiple-choice answers.)*
4. *Show this interview schedule to your teacher/lecturer and, once he/she has approved it, make 20 photocopies.*
5. *Lend the 20 photocopies of your fact sheet to 20 people who fall into two different categories, e.g. 10 adult women and 10 adult men, or 10 advanced level science students and 10 advanced level English students. Tell them that the next day you would like to carry out a 5-minute interview with them about their attitudes towards the use of human embryos for medical research (not their knowledge of the science).*
6. *The next day, carry out the interview with these 20 people. (Hint: Practise a couple of interviews with your friends first. Ensure you can write down what is said and ensure you have more than enough copies of your interview schedule.)*
7. *Analyse your findings to see if there are interesting similarities or differences between your two different categories of people.*

4.4 GM crops

GM maize

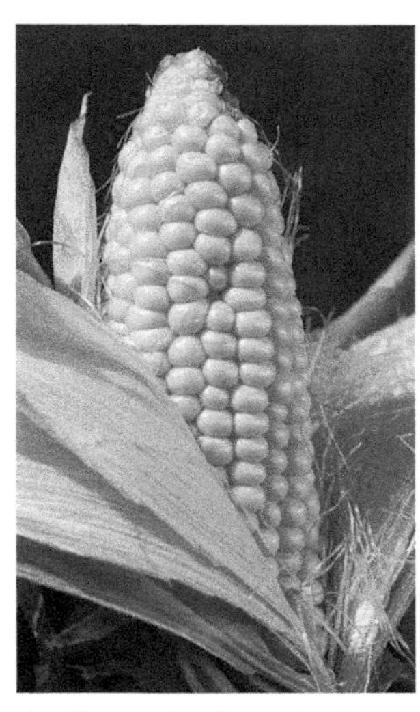

▲ ***Figure 17*** *Genetically modified maize.*

GM (genetically modified) crops have caused huge controversy, especially in Europe. Here we start by looking at one particular GM crop species, maize, and examining the arguments for and against its use.

Maize (corn) is a very important crop with an annual worldwide yield similar to that of rice or wheat. Transgenic (i.e. genetically modified) maize is being developed for a number of reasons, the two most important current ones being resistance to insect attack and herbicide resistance.

Insect attack

Some 7 per cent of potential world maize production is lost to a moth called the European corn borer. This equates to 40 million tonnes of maize a year, worth approximately US$2 billion. Of the order of US$40 million worth of conventional pesticides are currently used each year to stop the pest doing even more damage. However, losses are difficult to eliminate by the use of such pesticides largely because the larvae live inside the maize stalks. Biological control (e.g. through the use of parasites or predators of the moth) has not been very successful.

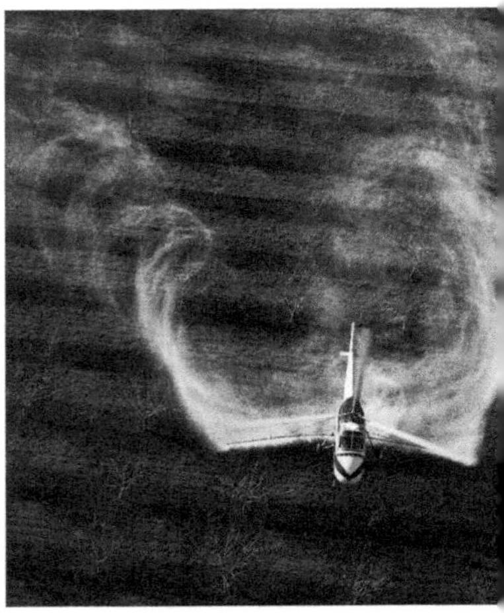

Maize has been genetically engineered by a number of companies so that it produces a protein of a soil bacterium. When the European corn borer larvae eat this protein, their intestinal walls are damaged, causing them to die from starvation.

▲ **Figure 18** *Crop spraying.*

Herbicide resistance

Herbicide-resistant maize has been bred to make it easier to deal with the problem of weeds. There are many reasons why weeds are considered undesirable. The most obvious is that they compete with a food crop for nutrients, water or space. Weeds can be dealt with in a number of ways; where labour is cheap they can be removed by hand, for example. In many countries, though, herbicides are extensively used to control weeds (Figure 18). Indeed, approximately 90–95 per cent of the area of land used to grow crops in Europe and the USA is treated with herbicides each year.

At present a large number of different herbicides are available commercially. These differ considerably in their environmental impact, i.e. their biodegradability and effects on non-target species such as insects, birds and mammals. An argument from those who favour the widespread use of genetically engineered herbicide-tolerant crops is that by genetically engineering the crop to be resistant to environmentally acceptable herbicides, the overall impact of herbicide use on the environment will be lessened. Two of the most suitable herbicides are glyphosate and glufosinate. Transgenic varieties of maize have been developed that are resistant to each of these herbicides.

Benefits of herbicide resistance

Benefits from herbicide-tolerant crops have been suggested for the farmer, the environment and the consumer. The farmer is predicted to benefit for a number of reasons. First of all, glyphosate and glufosinate are less expensive to purchase and easier to apply than some alternatives. Secondly, inducing herbicide tolerance in a crop may increase a farmer's flexibility because it may mean that an extra herbicide is available. Any existing herbicides can still be used because the fact that a crop has been genetically engineered to be tolerant to a particular herbicide does not mean that that herbicide – or indeed any herbicide – has to be used. Thirdly, herbicides such as glyphosate are particularly effective. Their use should, therefore, lead to a greater range of weeds being controlled, resulting in higher crop yields.

Benefits to the environment have been suggested because the herbicides to which crop tolerance is being developed generally break down faster to non-toxic products in the soil and are less likely to leach (dissolve) into groundwater. In addition, they are often active in smaller amounts meaning that the total mass of chemicals applied to a crop should be less. Finally, some of these herbicides reduce the need for pre-emergence application (when the herbicide is applied before the seed germinates). The advantage of this is that post-emergence application can reduce the risk of erosion of fragile soils.

Benefits to the consumer have been suggested on two fronts. First of all the technology, through increasing crop yields and requiring farmers to spend less on herbicides, may make food prices slightly lower. Secondly, the technology should lead to lower rates of herbicide application, the use of less toxic chemicals and a decreased risk to domestic water supplies.

Opposition to GM maize

A frequently voiced objection to genetic engineering of any form is that it is 'unnatural'. This argument cannot be dismissed out of hand but is difficult to defend when the specific instance of maize is being considered. Maize has already been subject to some 8000 years of selective breeding and various grass species, including a different genus (namely *Tripsacum*), have been crossed to produce it. In other words, conventional maize is itself hardly 'natural'.

How safe is GM maize? Nothing in life is totally safe. Equally, not everything that is safe is good. However, we rightly forbid many actions because we consider the likelihood of their being unsafe too great for any benefits they might bring. So the question is: 'Is GM maize safe enough?' The various regulatory authorities the world over have considered this question carefully.

Expert opinion

Most experts agree that the various transgenic maizes are safe for animal (including human) consumption, being neither toxic nor allergenic. That is why they have been approved by a raft of regulatory authorities in the EU, USA, Japan, Canada and elsewhere. However, some transgenic maizes have an antibiotic-resistant marker gene. The reason for this is that it makes it easier in the laboratory to see whether the genetic engineering has worked. The possibility has been raised that when large amounts of foods containing these antibiotic-resistant marker genes begin to be consumed (whether by farm animals or humans), the gene might move to disease-causing micro-organisms in the gut and so make them resistant to the antibiotic too.

Most experts suspect that the chances of this happening are not great. Nevertheless, the existence of a finite risk slowed the regulatory approval of transgenic maize in the EU. In the long run, the most likely solution is for companies to use other, less controversial markers.

The case against GM maize

Two common arguments against the genetic engineering of herbicide-resistant crops are that this increases the chances of the crop invading and then damaging natural ecosystems, and that it increases the chance of genes inserted into the crop escaping into weeds, wild relatives of the crop or other plants.

The argument that herbicide-resistant crops (whether genetically engineered or not) are more likely to invade natural ecosystems needs to be considered carefully; it may be important for a number of European crops, for example oil seed rape. It is, however, very difficult to imagine transgenic or conventional maize invading natural ecosystems, as today's maize does not spread like a weed. The fear that transgenic genes might pass from maize to other plants is more significant. Wild relatives of maize are found in Mexico and Guatemala. In Europe and North America, though, it is very difficult to believe that genes from transgenic maize could pass to other plants.

The consequences of pest-resistant maize are less clear. In laboratory experiments, lacewings (*Chrysopa carnea*) have shown reduced survival when fed on prey reared on transgenic maize. However, recent farm-scale trials in the UK suggest that transgenic maize is unlikely to be any more harmful to the environment than conventional maize treated with pesticides.

▲ **Figure 19** *GM crop protesters.*

Consumer choice

Considering now the acceptability of GM crops to the public, there was a widespread perception among consumers in Europe in the late 1990s that foods containing products made from some genetically modified crops (notably soya and maize) were being forced on the general public. This was largely because the US FDA (Food and Drug Administration) labelling policy, announced in 1992, was based entirely on safety considerations rather than on enabling people to choose what sorts of products they wish to purchase.

(The above account of GM crops is based on Reiss, M. J. (1999) Genetically modified foods: ethical issues, *Journal of Commercial Biotechnology* **6**, pp. 139–45.)

Activity 29 Should we have GM crops?

Discuss whether you think GM crops should be allowed.

Activity 30 Genetic engineering in medicine

The use of genetic engineering in medicine, for example to produce genetically engineered insulin for use by people with insulin-dependent diabetes, has been far less controversial than GM crops have. Suggest why this might be the case.

Further work

Research other possible uses of GM crops and evaluate them from an ethical perspective.

Project hint

A question relating to GM crops or medicines could form the basis for a Research project.

Resource link

Trials of a vaccine against AIDS derived from GM plants are due to start in 2009.

GM plants are being developed to produce mammalian proteins and plastics.

For details visit the website via the Hotlinks page.

4.5 Improving people through genetic modification

Improving athletes

▲ ***Figure 20*** *Athletes in competition.*

Most people are deeply against the idea of genetically modifying people. The arguments in favour of such genetic modification seem strongest when it would be for medical reasons, for example to allow someone who would otherwise have a life-threatening genetic condition to lead a normal life. Here an apparently trivial use of genetic modification in humans – its use to 'improve' athletes (Figure 20) – is presented for you to examine critically.

> **"*Why I believe genetic modification could be good for sport and society***
>
> In the past year, the World Anti-Doping Agency has battled with scandal after scandal. Gene doping, as it is known, compromises the success of the WADA project considerably. The reaction to GM athletes has been rapid. Just this year, WADA included a prohibition of gene doping in the anti-doping code.
>
> Yet what might intuitively seem a straightforward ban on another form of 'cheating' hides a more complex problem that has not been addressed. Two years ago the US President's Council on Bioethics met to discuss genetic enhancement in sport, during which it recognised that sports authorities might not be best placed to rule on GM athletes. Its debates acknowledged the broader context of gene doping and questioned whether the practice would actually be bad for the sport.
>
> Academics are in the thick of this debate. One view is that genetic enhancement could yield far safer enhancements than current synthetic drugs. Moreover, gene doping might actually be impossible to detect.
>
> Many scientists have recognised that the only way it might be possible to find out whether somebody has gene doped would be to conduct a muscle biopsy. But few ethical committees or, indeed, athletes, would be happy to endorse such a request just for the sake of some contested notion of 'fair play'.
>
> In fact, gene doping might promote fair play. Currently, athletes are genetically diverse, which is an irrelevant inequality in sport. It would be far better – and in the spirit of sport – to use genetic modification to eliminate genetic differences between athletes or, at least, allow all athletes to use it in a way that is most useful to them.
>
> The medical and scientific response to such proposals reflects the standard response to any form of genetic enhancement: we do not yet know if it is safe, so it is unethical (and illegal) to make such alterations. But this should not be the end of the debate. Gene doping is a good

example of the kind of ethical discussions triggered by technological developments.

The press coverage that has plagued the 'new genetics' and concerns about drug use in sport have prejudiced the evaluation of gene doping. The public perception of human cloning has taken a similar turn. Gene doping would not create superhumans but could help to overcome the considerable harm caused by current forms of doping in sport.

There are many serious ethical issues arising from the non-therapeutic application of genetics that demand our attention. For example, what would be the appropriate use of genetic information to 'select' the next generation of elite athletes?

The Human Fertilisation and Embryology Authority's recent decision to permit the selection of an embryo to save the life of a sibling alerts us to the complexity and profundity of these matters. But the language used to describe these 'designer' or 'spare-part' babies has made the public less likely to accept such decisions. The case of the Frankenstein runner is comparable.

Governments must recognise why decisions on this technology should not simply be left to the world of sport. The fair-play argument might be a sport-related one, but if genetic modification is legalised and used in medicine, then surely it would be unreasonable to prohibit GM athletes from sport and mistaken to call them 'cheats'.

Miah, A., Times Higher Education Supplement, *13 August 2004, p. 14* ”

Project hint

A question relating to the enhancement of sporting performance, by drugs or GM, could form the basis for a Research project.

Activity 31 *Better athletes?*

List Miah's arguments in favour of genetically modifying athletes.

Evaluate his arguments critically. What information is provided (or could be found out) in support of each argument? What are the counter-arguments?

Activity 32 *More intelligent people?*

Suppose that it becomes possible to enhance people genetically so that they are more intelligent. Discuss whether this would be a good idea.

Further work

*Review the medical circumstances under which it is **a** legally and **b** morally acceptable, in your judgement, for so-called 'designer babies' to be produced.*

5 Science and scientists

5.1 Facts and values in science

Facts and values

This lesson looks at what, if any, is the relationship between facts in science and the values we place on these facts. For example, does the fact that a piece of knowledge might be used to harm people mean that scientists should not seek to acquire such knowledge? More generally, are there certain sorts of research that scientists should not undertake because it would not be morally right to undertake them? Conversely, do scientists have a duty to undertake certain sorts of research?

It was David Hume (1711–76, Figure 21) who first pointed out that there is no logical connection between what is and what ought to be. In other words, there is a fact/value distinction. The contradiction in this idea of Hume's has since become known as the naturalistic fallacy. So the essence of the argument that there is a clear divide between ethics and science can be stated like this: science concerns itself with matters of fact, with what is, whereas ethics concerns itself with what people ought to do.

▲ ***Figure 21** The Scottish philosopher David Hume.*

In other words, the two disciplines of science and ethics occupy separate spheres of knowledge. In claiming that science should concern itself with ethics one might as well claim that scientists should get involved professionally in disputes over aesthetics. The job of a physicist, this line of reasoning goes, is to explain why we get rainbows, not to wonder whether they are beautiful or to advocate what we should do when we see one. Put simply, scientists should provide society with information about the possible factual consequences of the development and use of new technologies such as vaccinations, nuclear fission, genetic engineering and nanotechnology. It is then up to all of us as citizens, often via our elected representatives, to decide what we should do with these new technologies.

This line of argument is expressed particularly well by Eric Hall:

> “Science is a discipline concerned exclusively with the reliability that can be attributed to factual ('is') statements as a result of empirical investigation. It is widely recognised that 'is' statements in science cannot be turned into the 'ought' statements of moral discourse.
> For example, science can fairly accurately judge the consequences of bringing together a number of sub-critical masses of U235 above a densely populated geographical area. It can say absolutely nothing, however, about whether such an action would be right or wrong.

The answer to the latter question lies outside the domain of science, but within the remit of moral discourse. The domains of scientific and moral discourse are fundamentally different; they have different core concepts (space, time, energy and good, right, ought), different procedural ground rules and different tests for truth.

Hall, E. G. (1999) Science education and social responsibility, School Science Review, ***81 (295)****, pp. 14–16* ”

The interrelationship of facts and values in science

However, it can be argued that the relationship between **facts and values** in science is much closer than indicated above. Even if we accept a characterisation of science as open minded, universalist, disinterested and communal, all scientific knowledge is arrived at within particular social contexts. At the very least this means that the topics on which scientists work – and so the subject matter of science itself – to some extent reflect the interests, motivations and aspirations both of the scientists that carry out such work and of those who fund them.

There is no doubt that the majority, almost certainly the great majority, of the funding provided for scientists, both currently and for some considerable time past, has been provided with the hope/expectation that particular applied ends will be met. These might be the production of a new vaccine, the development of a new variety of crop, the synthesis of a new chemical dye, the construction of a better missile-detection system, and so on.

It can be argued that ethics is inevitably conflated with science in most cases. Both the scientists and those who fund them hope that production of a new vaccine will lead to more lives being saved (presumed to be a good thing), that the development of a new variety of crop will lead to increased food yields (presumed to be a good thing), that the synthesis of a new chemical dye will lead to greater cash flows, increased profits, improved customer satisfaction or increased employment (all presumed to be good things) and that the construction of a better missile-detection system will lead to increased military security (presumed to be a good thing).

In each of these cases, the science is carried out for a purpose. Purposes can be judged morally; that is, they may be good or bad. Indeed, just beginning to spell out some of the intended or presumed ends of scientific research (increased crop yields, increased military security, etc.) alerts us to the fact that perhaps there are other ways of meeting these ends. Indeed, perhaps these ends are not as desirable as may have been assumed.

Activity 33 *Facts and values in scientific work*

Discuss the relationship between facts and values in science. Do you think science is value free? Should scientists deal only in facts?

Activity 34 *Ethical implications of scientific work*

With reference to either animal experimentation or genetic engineering, discuss the extent to which scientists should consider the ethical implications of their work.

Further work

Is it acceptable for scientists' religious faith to affect their work?

5.2 Ethical values in the practice of science

Codes of ethics

Surveys show that most members of the public trust scientists – though government scientists are trusted less than university scientists. This lesson looks at how scientists should behave professionally. It starts by considering the Hippocratic oath for doctors and goes on to examine what scientists might need to do to be ethical in their work.

The Hippocratic oath, which dates back some two and a half thousand years, is perhaps the oldest code of ethics. It is as follows:

> “I swear by Apollo the physician, and Aesculapius, and Health, and All-heal, and all the gods and goddesses, that according to my ability and judgement, I will keep this Oath and this stipulation – to reckon him who taught me this Art equally dear to me as parents, to share my substance with him, and relieve his necessities if required: to look upon his offering on the same footing as my own brothers, and to teach them this art, if they shall wish to learn it, without fee or stipulation; and that by precept, lecture, and every other mode of instruction, I will impart a knowledge of the Art to my own sons, and those of my teachers, and to disciples bound by a stipulation and oath according to the law of medicine, but to none others. I will follow that system or regimen which, according to my ability and judgement, I consider for the benefit of my patients, and abstain from whatever is deleterious and mischievous. I will give no deadly medicine to any one if asked, nor suggest any such counsel; and in like manner I will not give to a woman a pessary to produce abortion. With purity and with holiness I will pass my life and practise my Art. I will not cut persons labouring under the stone, but will leave this to be done by men who are practitioners of this work.
>
> Into whatever houses I enter, I will go into them for the benefit of the sick, and will abstain from every voluntary act of mischief and corruption; and,

▲ ***Figure 22** Hippocrates (460–377 BC), Greek physician and the founder of modern medicine.*

further, from the seduction of females or males, of freemen and slaves. Whatever, in connection with my professional practice or in connection with it, I see or hear in the life of men, which ought not to be spoken of abroad, I will not divulge, as reckoning that all such should be kept secret. While I continue to keep this Oath unviolated, may it be granted to me to enjoy life and the practice of the Art, respected by all men, in all times! But should I trespass and violate this Oath, may the reverse be my lot!

Hippocrates, c.400 BC ”

Activity 35 *The Hippocratic oath*

Discuss the extent to which you think the Hippocratic oath is still applicable today.

Internal and external ethical values

One distinction that can be drawn is between internal ethical values and external ethical values in the practice of science (Figure 23). Internal ethical values are those that are intrinsic to the scientific way of arriving at knowledge. They include such things as:

- accurate recording of data
- honest reporting of findings
- acknowledgement (e.g. through the citing of references) of those whose work has been relevant.

External ethical values include such things as:

- undertaking work intended to benefit humanity, for example through the satisfaction of consumer preferences
- undertaking work intended to enhance animal welfare or the conservation of endangered species
- undertaking work aiming to reduce pollution or inequalities between people.

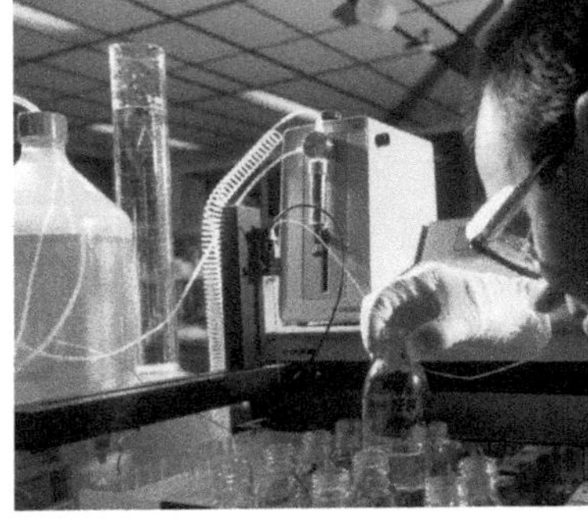

▲ ***Figure 23*** *A scientist working in a lab that makes pesticides.*

Project hint

When carrying out your Research project, you might find it helpful to consider the ethical behaviour of scientists in relation to your research question.

Activity 36 *Internal and external ethical values*

Is it possible for work to satisfy external ethical values but contravene internal ethical values? Conversely, is it possible for work to satisfy internal ethical values but contravene external ethical values?

Activity 37 *Code of ethics for today*

Draw up a code of ethics for today's scientists.

Further work

Did your science studies at GCSE encourage you to develop ethical values? Discuss your experiences with other students.

Resource link

There are over 850 codes of professional ethics listed at the Center for the Study of Ethics in the Professions, University of Illinois.

Another useful website for science and engineering codes is the Online Ethics Center for Engineering and Science.

5.3 Weapons development

The scientist's dilemma

It is rarely appreciated how much of the world's scientific research budget is devoted to military applications. It has been suggested that the figure is possibly as high as 50 per cent, though reliable data is not easy to obtain. This lesson looks at what responsibility, if any, scientists have for modern warfare (Figure 24).

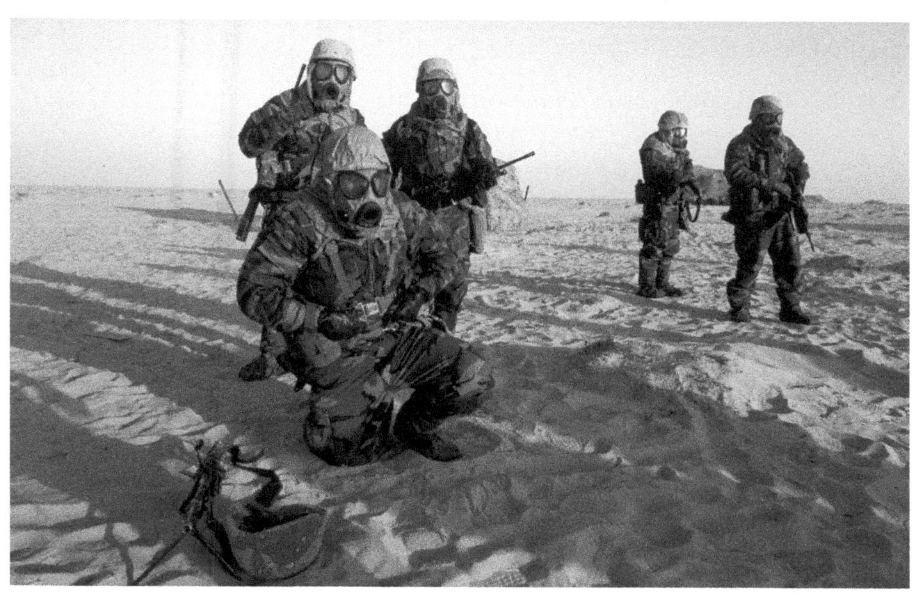

▲ ***Figure 24*** *Soldiers equipped for chemical warfare.*

> ***"Science for evil: the scientist's dilemma***
>
> You are a scientist. You see your science being put to evil purposes, with disaster looming ahead. What do you do? This was the dilemma that confronted nuclear physicists in 1945 after the atomic bomb had been exploded over Japan. The search to understand the ultimate nature of matter, driven by intellectual curiosity and carried out in an abstruse mathematical framework, had produced the ultimate weapon of war.
>
> Whether the development and use of these first atomic bombs was morally justified is today deeply disputed, but the problem that confronted the scientists at the end of the war was how to control the genie that had escaped from the bottle. They had produced a weapon that threatened the future of humankind. Their collective responsibility (or guilt) was unambiguous, but what should they do?
>
> This was the genesis of the Pugwash organisation, an informal group of scientists who saw it as their responsibility to prevent the catastrophe of nuclear war in the future. From the beginning they were international, including, crucially, scientists from both sides of the Iron Curtain; they

were experts, in both scientific and military spheres; and they conducted their discussions out of the limelight. The aim was to bring calm academic thinking to the complex scientific, military and political issues involved.

Different sciences, similar problems

The participants in the Pugwash conferences were often people of influence and importance in their own national hierarchies. They knew the facts and they could feed ideas back into their national policy circles. Since ignorance, misinformation and fear are the source of many of our troubles, Pugwash helped to preserve some degree of rationality in the era of MAD – 'mutually assured destruction.'

▲ ***Figure 25*** *Joseph Rotblat.*

As the decades passed the focus shifted from arms limitation to arms control and then to arms reduction. At each step there were important scientific issues to be considered. Could you, for example, detect an explosion of a certain size? Could antiballistic missiles provide a secure defensive shield? What were the probabilities of computer error leading to false alarms? It was at this level of assessing complex scientific-military questions that Pugwash played its crucial role.

Though vast stockpiles of nuclear weapons still exist and much remains to be done, a future without nuclear catastrophe is no longer an impossible dream. ... Certainly the award of the Nobel peace prize in 1995 to Pugwash and its President Joseph Rotblat (and the award of the same prize to International Physicians for the Prevention of Nuclear War in 1985) suggests that claims on behalf of the scientific and medical community have been taken seriously.

Chemical and biological weapons

If nuclear weapons came to haunt physicists, so chemical and biological weapons have come to haunt chemists and biologists. Chemical and biological weapons were on the verge of being used in the last world war and have developed apace with the discoveries in the corresponding basic sciences. The chemists have perfected nerve gases of deadly efficiency which, in the hands of an extremist sect, have already been used on the citizens of Tokyo. Similar weapons have been used against ethnic minorities in Iraq and elsewhere. The progress in molecular biology could also lead to lethal ways of targeting populations.

Pugwash has likewise turned its attention to this new use of science for warlike purposes. It has been actively involved in the various treaties and conventions that, in principle, prohibit the use of chemical or biological weapons (see below).

The difficulties here lie largely in monitoring, as in Iraq. The line between civilian and military laboratories is difficult to draw – as the attack last year by the United States on a pharmaceutical factory in the Sudan illustrated. There is substantial disagreement over the status of this factory, and the evidence that it manufactured chemical weapons is at best doubtful. The problem, of course, is that many peaceful uses require chemical and biological research (and production), and many of the materials and methods are similar to those used in military applications. Moreover, the scale of operations can be modest and easily disguised. All this is very different from nuclear weapons, where the production of atomic bombs is easily distinguished from an atomic power station and hard to hide.

Major conventions on chemical and biological war

1925 Geneva Protocol (Protocol for the Prohibition of the Use in War of Asphyxiating, Poisonous or Other Gases, and of Bacteriological Methods of Warfare)

Bans manufacture, use or import of poisonous gases and extends this to prohibition of bacteriological weapons.

1972 Biological Weapons Convention

Bans development, production, stockpiling, acquisition, transfer and use of biological weapons. Verification mechanisms under development by ad hoc group of governmental experts.

1997 Chemical Weapons Convention

Bans development, production, stockpiling, acquisition, transfer and use of chemical weapons; requires the elimination of all chemical weapons and their production facilities by 2007; creates an Organisation for the Prohibition of Chemical Weapons in The Hague to conduct routine and unannounced inspections to verify the convention.

Atiyah, M., President of Pugwash British Medical Journal, ***319***, *14 August 1999, pp. 448–9. Reproduced with permission from BMJ publishing group.* ”

Project hint

A question relating to weapons development could form the basis for a Research project.

Resource link

There is more information on the Pugwash website.

Activity 38 *Science for evil?*

Discuss your general feelings having read the extract 'Science for evil: the scientist's dilemma'.

Activity 39 *A just war?*

Under what circumstances, if any, do you think war might be justified? Write a short essay (about 500 words) in support of your views.

Further work

Research the issue of landmines. Should they be banned?

PART 3

THINKING PHILOSOPHICALLY ABOUT SCIENCE

1 Introduction to thinking philosophically about science

1.1 Processes of science

What is philosophy?

Philosophy is the name we give to the study of the most fundamental questions in life. Philosophers consider such questions as: where did the universe come from? Does science remove any place for God? Can we know anything for certain? What is science? What is truth? What is the human mind? Is there life elsewhere in the universe? Do our genes determine our actions? Am I the same person today as I was yesterday? Might there one day be intelligent machines?

As soon as you begin to think about these questions seriously, you are doing philosophy. It is quite likely that you have already been doing some philosophical thinking but without realising that is what you are doing. If, for example, you have discussed with a friend a question such as whether the universe began with the Big Bang, or whether there is a soul (and if so how it is related to the brain), or whether a machine could think, then you have already started doing philosophy.

The way that philosophy is done is by argument. Someone puts forward a philosophical **point of view** (a **proposition**) and other people challenge this person to explain it clearly and give his/her reasons for believing it. Much of your time in this part of the course will be spent in arguments like this.

As well as being intrinsically fun and interesting, the skills you will develop here – skills in explaining ideas clearly and thinking logically – will be useful to you in the other subjects you study, and indeed in any situation in life where you are called on to explain the reasons for your point of view.

Reading about philosophy

For a good introduction to philosophy see Professor Simon Blackburn's book *Think* (Oxford University Press).

Another good introduction is the book by Jenny Teichman and Katherine Evans called *Philosophy: A Beginner's Guide* (Blackwell Publishing).

A book which covers many of the themes explored in this part of the course is *Philosophy Matters* by Roger Trigg (Blackwell Publishing).

The Philosophers' Magazine contains many excellent, accessible articles of philosophical interest. The magazine contains sections dedicated to science and ethics, and interviews with leading thinkers. There are also some philosophical games to enjoy.

Resource link

By far the best site from which to begin researching philosophical ideas is Epistemelinks. This site is a dedicated philosophy search engine. The sites to which you are then linked are reputable sources of information.
The Philosophers' Magazine website is a good general source.

The editor of *The Philosophers' Magazine*, Julian Baggini, has also published a good primer for philosophical arguments, *The Pig that Wants to be Eaten and 99 other Thought Experiments* (Granta) as well as *Making Sense: Philosophy Behind the Headlines* (Oxford University Press) which introduces philosophical issues behind questions in the news.

A collection of thought-provoking philosophical questions is Stephen Law's *The Philosophy Files* (Orion books).

Nigel Warburton's book *Philosophy – The Basics* (Routledge) provides a helpful guide to some key theories in philosophy.

Finally, *Bad Thoughts*, by Jamie Whyte (Corvo Books) entertainingly exposes the flaws in many commonly used arguments.

What is science?

One way to begin thinking about this philosophical question is by thinking about how science operates. The ways in which science operates can be illustrated by various games. Two such games are described in the next activities. As you play the games, think about how they illustrate how science is done.

Activity 1 *Eleusis*

Play the card game Eleusis (see below and overleaf). The game involves trying to discover a rule that someone has invented but has not told you. In some ways, this is similar to scientists trying to discover natural laws. After playing a few rounds of the game, discuss the processes by which you tried to discover the rule.

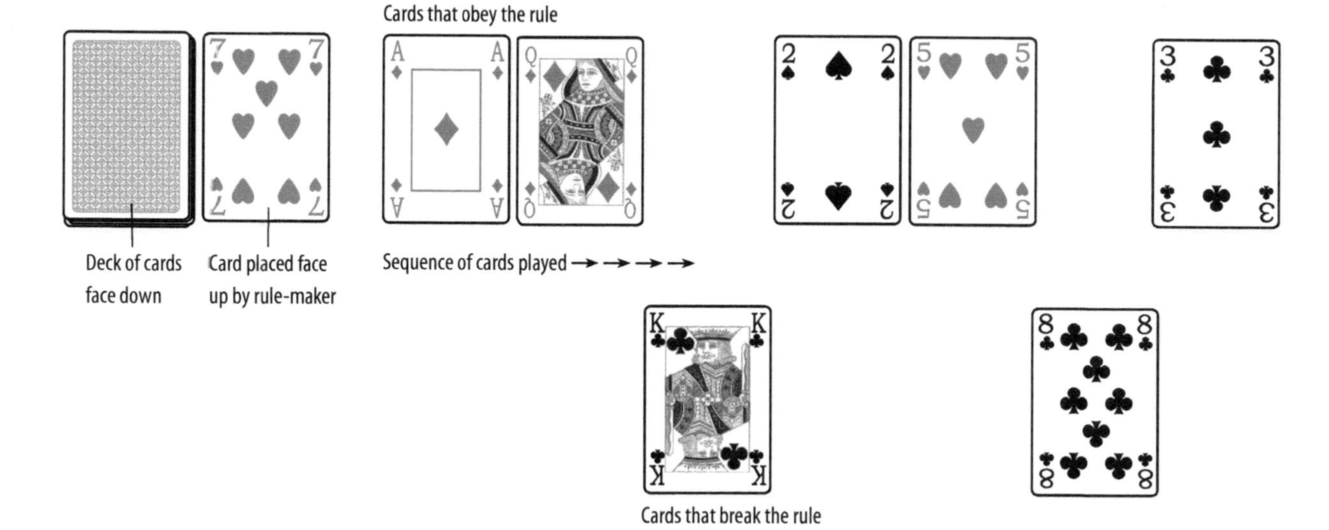

▲ **Figure 1** *Playing Eleusis.*

Eleusis

Eleusis is played in groups of four or five people. One person is the rule-maker. The other three or four players are each dealt 10 cards. It is the task of the rule-maker to invent a rule that determines how the cards are to be played, and it is the task of the other players to discover what the rule is.

Rules can be very simple (e.g. always play a red card after a black card) or more complex (e.g. the sum of the last three cards played has to equal 10 with picture cards counting as 1). To start with, the rule-maker should try to think of quite a simple rule.

The game starts when the rule-maker turns over a card from the unused pile. The person on the rule-maker's left then places a card from his/her hand next to the upturned card. The rule-maker then says 'yes' or 'no' depending on whether the played card follows the rule that has been chosen. If it obeys the rule, then the card is kept in place. If it does not obey the rule, then it should be moved down to form another line as shown in Figure 1. Play then proceeds round the group in this manner. As play continues, two lines of cards should be built up – one being the sequence of correct cards and the other the rejects. In this manner, all players should be able to see the sequence of correct and incorrect plays.

After placing a card a player has the chance to declare what he or she thinks the rule is. The rule-maker then has to say if the player is correct or not. A correct guess ends the round and the person guessing right has won.

If all 10 cards from each hand have been played and the rule has not been guessed, then the rule-maker has 'won' and has to declare what the rule was.

Activity 2 *Twenty questions*

One player (the experimenter) is sent out of the room temporarily while the rest decide between them which object in the room is to be the target. When the experimenter comes back into the room, he/she is allowed to ask 20 questions in order to identify the target object – but each question must only be answered 'yes' or 'no'. The experimenter must identify the object after 20 questions or lose the game.

Play this game and discuss how it illustrates processes in science.

Processes of science

The formulation of questions in Twenty questions is a similar process to the design of experiments. In Eleusis, an 'experiment' is carried out by playing a card and seeing whether the outcome is as predicted. Just watching the game without being able to decide which cards are played is similar to the process of making observations in science (as in astronomy, for example).

The terms **hypothesis** and **model** are often used to describe processes in science – and can be applied to these games. When a player has an idea about what he or she thinks the rule/object is, then he/she is making a model. In order to find out whether or not the model is correct, the player makes and tests a hypothesis (an assumption or guess). The player chooses some aspect of his/her model that enables him/her to make a prediction of the sort: 'assuming xx is allowed by the rule, then playing this card will get the answer yes'. If the hypothesis survives the test, the model is used to predict the outcome of future tests. As more tests are carried out, the model might receive further support or might be shown to be incorrect. This is analogous to the scientific process of making a prediction that is then tested by experiment.

The term **theory** is used in science to mean an underlying framework of rules, often relating to a particular model. This is unlike common everyday usage where the term is often used to mean a guess.

The process of arriving at a model from experiment and observation can involve both **induction** and **deduction**. Induction means 'generalising from experience'. When scientists use induction, they form a theory that goes beyond what they observe. If, for example, I observe 1000 white swans, I may use induction to form the theory that 'all swans are white' (Figure 2). I have evidence for this theory, but I have not proved it true (there may be non-white swans I have not observed). Deduction means using logic to prove something. Suppose that all swans are indeed white. Then I can deduce that the next swan I see will be white. Here, the conclusion follows logically from the starting point of the argument. In the Eleusis game, *induction* is used to work out what the rules are. Once the rules are known, you can *deduce* what cards are allowed.

▲ ***Figure 2*** *White swans.*

Further work

Make notes to summarise the main points that Eleusis and Twenty questions illustrate about the processes of science. Write a paragraph setting out your thoughts about what science is.

1.2 Science and pseudo-science

Science or pseudo-science?

▲ ***Figure 3*** *Are horoscopes scientific?*

There is a range of writings and activities that we come across in our daily lives that have the appearance of being based on science, but do not work in ways that can genuinely be regarded as scientific. As an example, consider the horoscopes that appear in newspapers (Figure 3) or the huge number of diet books that are published each year. **Pseudo-science** is the name given to activities that superficially appear scientific but do not genuinely belong to science.

Project hint

For your Research project, it might be interesting to explore the scientific basis for a pseudo-science and to discuss the ethical and philosophical implications of promoting a pseudo-science as if it were scientific.

Activity 3 Pseudo-science

List three reasons why it is important to be able to tell the difference between science and pseudo-science.

Activity 4 Is it science?

Here is a list of various activities. Say whether each is (in your view) a science (S), pseudo-science (P) or neither (N).

- aromatherapy
- astrology
- astronomy
- biology
- economics
- engineering
- geography
- horticulture
- mathematics
- medicine
- memetics
- meteorology
- phrenology
- physics
- psychology
- social science
- theology

Activity 5 Characterising science

Various characteristics are listed here, that might or might not be associated with those activities that you have described as being scientific. Indicate whether you think each is irrelevant, fairly important, very important or essential to an activity being a science.

- doing calculations
- carrying out experiments
- making observations
- making measurements
- writing reports
- doing a degree in the subject
- holding conferences
- writing books
- making predictions
- checking the work of others
- solving problems
- using factual evidence
- showing curiosity

Activity 6 A science decision tree

One way of sorting a list of items into categories is to follow a decision tree. You may have come across a similar idea in biology; part of such a tree is illustrated in Figure 4.

Construct a decision tree to enable someone to tell a science from a pseudo-science.

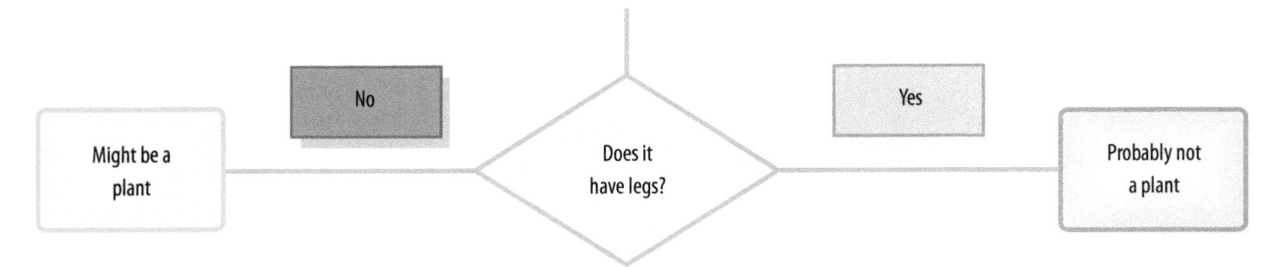

▲ ***Figure 4*** *Part of a biology classification decision tree.*

Further work

Look through some newspapers or magazines and find an article that contains science or pseudo-science. Write a short comment on the article, indicating the manner in which it uses scientific information or the way in which the information may appear to be scientific.

1.3 Homeopathy: a little of what you fancy

Alternatively speaking

Where should you turn when you are ill? Nowadays, alongside mainstream 'scientific' medicine, there is a wide range of 'complementary' therapies, based on different principles. The debate about the validity of these forms of medicine raises questions about what counts as a scientific approach to illness and whether non-scientific (or pseudo-scientific) approaches have any validity.

Homeopathy is a theory of medicine developed by the German physician Samuel Hahnemann (1755–1843, Figure 5). He believed in using extremely dilute substances to cure illnesses. According to his theory, the more a substance is diluted, the more potent it becomes. A homeopathic doctor may recommend a '30X' dose, which means a dose that has been diluted by a factor of 10, 30 times over. This means that it will be 10^{30} times weaker than the original sample. A '30C' dose means it is diluted by 100, 30 times over, so it will be 10^{60} times weaker. In chemical terms, this is so weak that it may mean that no molecules of the original sample are present following dilution.

▲ ***Figure 5*** *Samuel Hahnemann.*

The main argument used by supporters of homeopathy is that it works. They claim that the majority of people who use it are satisfied with the results. The fact that it does not operate according to any known scientific principles should not be held against it – after all, drugs such as aspirin were used for many years before we found a scientific explanation for their effects.

Critics of homeopathy respond that it is not a proper science at all – it is at best a pseudo-science without any proper scientific evidence for its effects. The fact that people believe it helps them does not count as evidence. They may well have recovered from their illness anyway. Also, the placebo effect has to be considered. Perhaps what is helping people is the belief that they are receiving a remedy, a belief which may improve their condition even if it is false.

Though homeopathy is rejected by the vast majority of the medical profession, it continues to thrive as an 'alternative' or 'complementary' therapy. It is quite widely practised in the USA and in Western Europe. In Belgium, medical insurers recently decided to offer policies that cover up to 10 per cent of the costs of homeopathic treatment. A group of sceptical Belgian scientists and philosophers decided to stage a 'homeopathic suicide' in response to this. In the following article, Belgian author Luc Bonneux explains what happened.

> **Resource link**
> The full text of the Belgian skeptics article is available online.

"Belgian Skeptics Commit Mass Suicide

The Belgian skeptics … resigned themselves to committing mass suicide by drinking a lethal dose of terribly toxic and dangerous drugs: snake poison, Belladonna or deadly nightshade, arsenic, dog's milk, petrol, and cockroach. Dog's milk does not sound that dangerous, but try milking a pit bull terrier.

To assure immediate death, these powerful drugs were immensely dynamized: the daring skeptics selected the over-the-counter 30C homeopathic solutions (reimbursed by the health insurance, if prescribed by a certified quack). A dynamization of 30C means the poison is diluted 10 to the 60th times. That is a one followed by sixty zeros. The whole earth (estimated at 10^{50} molecules) is way too small to hold a single molecule in that dilution. That is, in homeopathic terms, an awfully powerful dilution. The immensely "dynamized" spirits of arsenic and snake poison (not to mention the pit bull milk) will rise from the liquid, and kill the skeptic on the spot.

All important newspapers and TV stations were recruited to witness the terrible extermination of these dangerous minds. It would be a great loss to Belgian academia, a terrible blow to all these narrow-minded people that do not understand the miracles of homeopathy. Among the twenty-three suicidals were a hoard of professors from medical and other faculties, a rightly famous publicist and television program maker, and even a few normal people armed with nothing but common sense …

The skeptics on death row solemnly queued to personally select their own toxin. In front of the assembled national press they filled their chalices and drained their drinks, fully expecting to meet their Maker (if He existed). The skeptics didn't succeed in their suicide attempt, however. All of them survived. Those who had come by car had to wait before returning home, a bit dizzy from the alcohol on their empty stomachs. Indeed, homeopathy in alcohol at the liberal dose of a bottle a day might decrease your cardiovascular risk (but a good Bordeaux is still a lot cheaper and infinitely better).

Bonneux, L., Belgian skeptics commit mass suicide, The Skeptical Inquirer, *May 2004"*

Activity 7 Discussing homeopathy

Use the article 'Belgian skeptics commit mass suicide' as a basis to begin discussing the arguments for and against homeopathy. The questions that follow may help guide your discussion.

1 Would you make use of homeopathy? If you would, under what conditions? If not, why not?

2 Evaluate the arguments for and against homeopathy described in the text above.

3 Would you class homeopathy as a science, pseudo-science or something else?

4 What is it that makes homeopathic remedies attractive to people?

5 Should homeopathic treatments be available on the NHS?

Fair testing?

To test homeopathic claims rigorously, scientists use a technique known as the clinical trial, which is commonly used in conventional medicine. Clinical trials are conducted using large, randomly selected samples of people. Some of the sample group receive the treatment while others form a control group who receive either dummy treatments or no treatment at all. By comparing the response of the groups it is possible to tell whether the remedy is effective, whether the placebo effect is operating (so that people improve simply because they *believe* the remedy is medically effective) or whether recovery is simply due to natural processes.

Occasionally, some of the tests of homeopathy indicate some beneficial effects, but the majority show that the treatment has no effect whatsoever. Tests which have indicated beneficial effects have been controversial and in at least one case, that of Jacques Benveniste, the scientist who published the work was subsequently heavily criticised, leading to his suspension. The Benveniste case is interesting for another reason, namely that his research was in fact subsidised by a homeopathic company.

Activity 8 *Fair testing*

Discuss whether the fact that a scientist is employed by a homeopathic company invalidates the research findings on homeopathic medicine. Write a paragraph explaining your point of view.

1.4 The nature of science?

A simple picture of science

One simple picture of the scientific process is shown in Figure 6. Scientists operate by making some experimental findings, forming a theory, deducing some predictions then testing them.

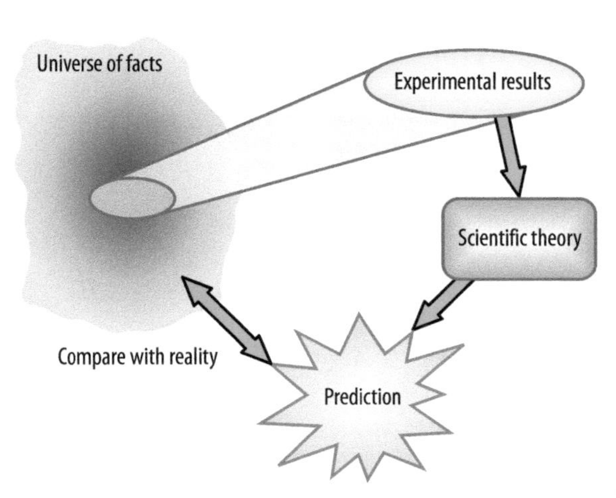

▲ ***Figure 6*** *A simple picture of science.*

Many people would agree that science operates in this manner, and this might be what you have been taught. However, other philosophers of science have criticised this picture as overly simple. It may capture some elements of scientific activity, but it leaves out a great deal.

One central question is the link between theory and observation. A general theory (which covers all actual and possible observations we can make) can never be proved by any finite set of observations. For example, take a simple theory such as 'all swans are white'. No matter how many white swans you observe, you have never proven this theory, since it remains possible that there are non-white swans that you have not yet observed. Scientific theories face the same problem: they make claims about things we have not observed, so it would seem that we can never strictly deduce that a scientific theory is certainly true, no matter how many observations we make to support it. Yet science relies on forming universal theories on the basis of limited observations. The problem of how we can be justified in believing theories which go beyond the available data is called the **problem of induction**.

Activity 9 *A simple picture of science*

Discuss the picture of science represented by Figure 6. How satisfactory a picture of science is this? What aspects of scientific activity does it seem to apply to? What else would you add in order to make a more adequate picture of science? To help you answer the questions, think about one or more actual examples of scientific work such as those you studied in the *History of science* part of this course.

Falsificationism

The Austrian philosopher of science Karl Popper (1902–94, Figure 7) thought that the problem of induction posed a serious threat to science. How could science be seen as a rational process if we could never prove scientific theories true? Popper reasoned that what makes science distinctive is not that good theories can be proved but that bad ones can be eliminated. If the predictions made by a scientific theory can be shown to be wrong then the bad theory will be weeded out. It only takes the observation of one black swan to disprove (falsify) the statement 'all swans are white' (Figure 8).

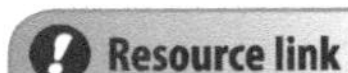

For more on Popper see the Karl Popper website.

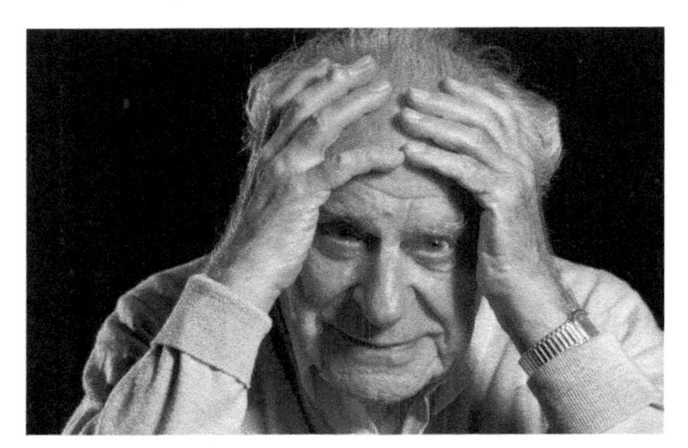

▲ **Figure 7** *Karl Popper.*

▲ **Figure 8** *Swans.*

For Popper, the crucial thing about scientific statements is that they should be testable by experiment. It is the fact that a statement can be falsified (disproved) in an experimental test that makes it scientific, a view known as **falsificationism**.

Falsifiability, for Popper, provides a test for distinguishing between science and pseudo-science. A statement such as 'Gold is insoluble in 0.1 M hydrochloric acid' can be tested by an experiment. On the other hand, a statement such as 'A low-fat diet is healthier' is too vague to be testable – what does 'low-fat' mean, and what comparison is being made when we refer to 'healthier'? In Popper's view, scientific statements are distinct from non-scientific statements because they can be tested, and scientists are prepared to reject them if they fail the test.

Popper argued that scientists should constantly be seeking to falsify their theories. He thought of science as an activity of 'bold conjecture and attempted refutation', meaning that the work of scientists is to think up radical theories then try to disprove them. However, there are problems with this picture of science.

How scientists actually work

Popper's description is not an accurate reflection of what scientists do. While testing theories is important, it is not the only aspect of the scientist's task. Often, particularly with theories which have stood up well to testing in the past, scientists are more concerned to apply the theory to solve problems. For example, the effort of genetic biologists today is not focused on trying to disprove Watson and Crick's discoveries concerning the DNA molecule but on using them to solve puzzles such as the human genetic code. This sort of puzzle-solving activity is characteristic of much science. It means relying on theories in order to find the best explanation, rather than constantly trying to overturn them.

The criterion of falsifiability

There are also questions about the **criterion of falsifiability**. Science is not always a simple matter of making a prediction, testing it against observation then rejecting the theory if the prediction is false. Take, for example, Newton's laws. When scientists in the mid-nineteenth century tried to explain the orbit of the planet Uranus, they were unable to do so. The planet's orbit did not follow the pattern they predicted. Yet they did not conclude that Newton's laws had been falsified. After all, his theory had stood up to many previous tests and proved highly useful. Instead, they modified their hypothesis. They reasoned that if there was another planet orbiting outside Uranus, its gravitational effect could explain why their predictions of the orbit of Uranus were false. This hypothesis used Newton's laws to predict the position of the other planet, which was confirmed when Neptune was discovered.

The scientists who did this work were not following the rule of strict falsificationism. They did not abandon a theory which had been highly successful in the face of a single failed prediction. This is in line with how scientists often

▲ ***Figure 9*** *Solar system planets.*

have to work. Few successful theories fit with every experimental result (not least because experiments themselves can be mistaken).

Positive points from Popper

This example does not mean that we abandon entirely to the idea that testability is an important feature of scientific theories. It does, however, mean that the story is more complicated than simple falsificationism suggests (as Popper himself would have admitted).

When a theory faces problems, much depends on whether there is another theory which can solve them. If there is, then scientists may decide that the old theory should be abandoned. As you will see in Lesson 1.5, one way in which this may happen was described by Thomas Kuhn with his theory of scientific revolutions.

Activity 10 *Falsificationism and cold fusion*

Analyse the cold fusion debate using falsificationism as a framework. (See Section 2 of the *History of science* part of this course.) Consider the questions listed in this activity and write a few sentences in answer to each.

1 What theories were developed?

2 Were these theories testable?

3 Were scientists willing to persevere with a theory which had made false predictions or was it considered to be falsified?

4 Is a falsificationist point of view accurate in this case?

Project hint

You might find it useful to try answering these questions about the 'science story' behind your Research topic.

1.5 Paradigms and revolutions

▲ **Figure 10** *Thomas Kuhn.*

An alternative to Popper

American historian and philosopher of science Thomas Kuhn (1922–96, Figure 10) proposed an alternative to Popper's falsificationist picture of science.

Normal science

Scientists do not operate in isolation. Normally, they are guided in their scientific work by a framework of theories, ideas and rules that they share with other scientists. Kuhn called this framework a **paradigm**. The paradigm is what binds scientists together. It is the framework which they have learned to accept and within which they do their scientific work.

An example is the Newtonian paradigm in physics. Newton formulated his laws of motion in the late seventeenth century and these laws provided the guiding idea in physics throughout the eighteenth and nineteenth centuries. The Newtonian paradigm acted as an example for other scientists to be guided by. Solutions to other problems were modelled on the approach used by Newton. Newton had formulated an 'inverse square' law for the gravitational force, and Coulomb, working 100 years later, used the same approach to formulate an inverse square law for the electrostatic force. In biology, the tremendous success of Darwin's theory of natural selection meant that this theory became the dominant paradigm. Subsequent generations of biologists tried to solve new problems in the same way that Darwin had.

Scientific revolutions

This is all very well, provided that the paradigm itself works. Sometimes, however, scientists find that the problems they are working on cannot be solved in the ways that their paradigm suggests. If the problem cannot be solved, even by the leading scientists in the field, then that branch of science enters a crisis. This is a stage at which the paradigm itself is called into question. There is now no longer the widespread agreement which exists during normal scientific work. People propose different modifications to the paradigm. This happened to the Newtonian paradigm around the turn of the twentieth century, when problems that it could not solve could no longer be ignored.

At this stage, it is possible that a new paradigm may emerge. It may be that a large number of scientists are unhappy with the existing paradigm and transfer their support to the new one. This is a process that Kuhn called a **scientific revolution**.

In Kuhn's view, a scientific revolution occurred when the Newtonian paradigm was rejected in favour of Einstein's theory of relativity. Most scientists would

Project hint

If you are exploring a topic within the general area of scientific revolutions, Popper's and Kuhn's theories about the nature of science are particularly relevant.

Resource link

For more about Kuhn see the Emory University website.

argue that the new theory did not really displace the old, but rather modified it for cases of things travelling at high speeds (close to the speed of light). But Kuhn pointed to the way in which the new theory introduced revolutionary ways of thinking about energy, mass, space and time. The theory redefined these fundamental categories, so much so that Kuhn claimed there could be no neutral way of experimentally testing one theory against another.

Social influences on science

Kuhn's work drew attention to an important aspect of science which other thinkers had neglected: science is a social activity. Scientists do not work in isolation from each other; they are bound together by the paradigms they share. Nor are they insulated from the society of which they are a part. Social forces play a role in shaping the way scientists act. In particular, Kuhn argued that they have an influence during scientific revolutions, so that the very direction in which a scientific field develops is, to some extent, affected by social forces.

The extent of the influence which society has on science is a matter of ongoing debate amongst historians and philosophers of science. Yet there can be no doubt that it is useful to examine the scientific process from a social perspective, since scientists are human beings and humans are social animals.

Activity 11 *Science, society and Darwinian evolution*

Look back at your earlier work concerning Darwinian evolution (Section 4 in the *History of science* part of this course). Discuss the context for this scientific work and the ways in which it was influenced by society. You may also want to bring this discussion up to date by thinking about how evolutionary science is under pressure from some societies for religious reasons. Factors to consider include:

- the topics scientists choose to work on
- the way in which they publish their results
- the opposition they face on particular questions
- the ethical ideas associated with the theory.

1.6 The truth about truth

The debate about the concept of truth is a lively one in philosophy and it has very direct implications for science. Roughly speaking, philosophers divide into two categories: **realists**, who believe in an objective reality which we try to describe with our theories, and **relativists**, who believe that truth depends on one's point of view. For relativists, there is no such thing as absolute truth; everything is only ever true from a certain point of view.

Truth in science

A recent example of how the debate about the concept of truth is relevant to science comes from the 'discovery' of a new planet. On 5 January 2005, astronomer Mike Brown and his colleagues at the California Institute of Technology found what seemed to be a tenth planet in the Solar System. 2003 UB313 lies in the far part of the Solar System known as the Kuiper belt (Figure 11), a region which also contains Pluto. UB313 is in fact larger than Pluto.

▲ ***Figure 11*** *Artist's impression of some Kuiper belt objects.*

Is it correct, though, to say (as many newspapers did), that a new planet has been discovered? Is it an objective fact that there are in fact at least 10 planets in the Solar System? This is the language of scientific realism; planets exist out there independently of us, and hopefully we will find them if we look in the right place. The number of planets in the Solar System is a solid, objective fact that in no way depends upon our beliefs or decisions.

Needless to say, though, this simple account of the events conceals some tricky questions, not least of which is, what is a planet? How do we tell the difference between a planet and an asteroid? There are at least nine other objects similar to UB313 and Pluto in the Kuiper belt. Should we count all these as planets or leave them to be called asteroids? It is very hard to see how the realist could justify a statement that Pluto and the newly discovered 'tenth planet' (which still lacks a catchy name) are definitely, as a matter of objective fact, planets, whilst these other objects are definitely not.

At this point, the relativist point of view comes into play. It seems as though society played a role in deciding that we should count Pluto as a planet. It is very much up to us to make a decision about whether to count the newly discovered body as a planet too. In which case, the newspaper headlines about the 'discovery' of a tenth planet are over-simplifications, to say the least. The realist idea that the number of planets is an objective fact is vulnerable to a relativist counter-argument that stresses the role of our human point of view in making decisions about how to apply concepts such as that of a planet.

Resource link

For a fairly 'realist' announcement of UB313 see the BBC website.

In summer 2006, as this book was going to press, the International Astronomical Union (IAU) tightened up its official definition of the term 'planet' in such a way as to exclude both UB313 and Pluto. So the official result of the discovery is that there are now only eight planets in the solar system.

Activity 12 *What is truth?*

Discuss your initial thoughts about realism and relativism. What would your definition of truth be?

Are your sympathies with realism, relativism, neither or both?

What is truth?

Scientific realism

The view that we can reasonably believe our best scientific theories to be true is called **scientific realism**. Realists believe in science. They claim that its laws have been confirmed by experimental testing and that the unobservable entities which scientific theories refer to actually exist. Scientific realism is often said to be the working hypothesis which scientists themselves accept. They believe that the purpose of science is to discover truth, and that there has been considerable success in this enterprise.

Realists usually accept the following:

- True statements are those which correspond with the facts.
- Facts are states of affairs which exist independently of the human mind.
- Truth is not dependent upon human beings and their methods of enquiry.
- Truth is objective.

For scientific realists, science is a matter of trying to establish an objectively true picture of the world. Science makes progress towards the truth. It may not yet have given us a completely true picture of the world but it is moving closer to truth. This truth is something which exists independently of us. It is not relative in any sense. We cannot define truth in human terms, either as what we all agree upon or as what we are personally convinced of.

▲ **Figure 12** *Without reliable scientific knowledge, could we make and use these devices?*

The most powerful realist argument is based on the success of science. Science gives us reliable knowledge enabling us to control nature and predict what will happen (Figure 12). How is it that science has been so successful, unless it contains some truth? Relativists wish to argue that all world-views are equally valid – but some just don't seem to work.

Relativism and paradigms

Relativists claim that truth depends upon human beings. Reality is not something that exists independently of human minds. It is something which human minds help to create. Just because a belief is true for one person, this does not make it true for someone else. Each person, or each community, has their own truth. Relativists dislike the idea that any one individual or group of people can claim to be in possession of a universal truth. They associate this claim with an unpleasant tendency to impose that truth on others.

Relativists usually accept the following:

- Statements are not true or false absolutely.
- When someone calls a statement true, he or she means that it is true for him/her.
- Just because a statement is true for one person, this does not mean it is true for someone else.
- Truth is not objective but depends upon human beings.
- Facts are shaped by language.

Activity 13 *Relativism and the discovery of oxygen*

Review Section 5 of the *History of science* part of this course about the discovery of oxygen. Do you think a relativist or realist interpretation of this revolution is more plausible? Write a paragraph explaining your point of view.

1.7 Growing your own philosophy of science

Perspectives on science

Having learned something about some of the central ideas and questions within the philosophy of science, you are now in a position to evaluate the viewpoints of some scientists who were asked to describe how they viewed science. The aim here is to use these ideas as a springboard to develop and support your own thinking. You should not assume that the ideas presented here are correct. They are intended to provide a starting point for discussion.

▲ ***Figure 13*** *Rodin's sculpture* The Thinker.

Activity 14 *What do they think they are doing?*

The three viewpoints below are from a Spiked Online survey of 250 scientists. They were asked: 'If you could teach the world one thing about science, what would it be?' Read then evaluate the viewpoints of the authors. One way into this is to consider whether each author can be classified as a falsificationist, a realist or a relativist. Make brief notes summarising what each person has to say about central philosophical questions, such as the following:

- In science, do we get to have certain knowledge or something else (if so, what else?)
- How is science different from non-science?
- What method or methods do scientists work by?

Project hint

When carrying out research for your project, look for examples of people saying how the relevant scientific discoveries were made. Make a note of anything that they say which indicates a particular philosophical viewpoint.

“If I could teach the world just one thing about science, it would be that *the ideas you have in mind, and that seem so certain to you, might be wrong*. Science is based upon questioning received ideas, discussing them, and always searching for novel and more effective ways of thinking about the world.

Science is not about certainty; it is about doubt. It is certainty that makes us blind and stupid. The worst moments in the history of civilisation are the ones when somebody has power, and is totally certain that they have the Truth, the only and final Truth.

Carlo Rovelli, Professor of Physics at the University of the Mediterranee in Marseille”

Resource link

Other scientists' views are available at Spiked Online.

“A couple of decades ago, the public felt that scientists provide absolute and objective truths about the material world. Today, we realise that scientists are only human, and so even scientific truths are fallible.

However, *the scientific method is still the best path to learning about the material world*.

▲ ***Figure 14*** *Simon Singh.*

Scientists might sometimes misinterpret their observations. But ultimately, there is a way for them to check their theories, which is simply to compare theory with reality. A scientific theory can be checked, challenged, tested and probed. And if the theory stands up to all of its critics, then it is probably correct. But if the theory fails any test, then it has to be discarded, regardless of the seniority of its supporters or the beauty of the theory. As the nineteenth-century British biologist Thomas Henry Huxley put it, 'the tragedy of science is the slaying of a beautiful hypothesis by an ugly fact'.

Simon Singh, science writer and broadcaster ”

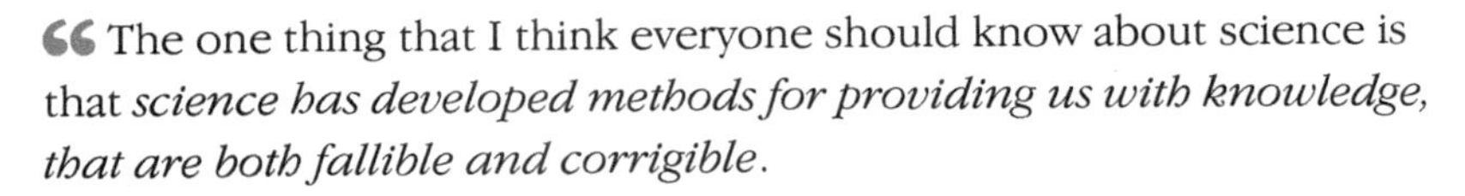

“ The one thing that I think everyone should know about science is that *science has developed methods for providing us with knowledge, that are both fallible and corrigible*.

It is important to know that scientific knowledge is fallible – is always subject to challenge and refutation – because this saves us from dogmatism, and makes us sceptical of all claims to infallible knowledge. It is important to know that scientific knowledge is corrigible – when errors are found, there are techniques for improving the erroneous knowledge – because this saves us from radical scepticism, and from the argument that scientific knowledge has no better claim to acceptance than any old belief or prejudice. One such argument is that creationism and evolutionism are just alternate beliefs, and that both should be taught, leaving it up to the individual to decide what they want to believe.

The metaphor for science that I like goes back to the Greeks. We are in the position of sailors, navigating a ship at sea. If the ship develops a problem, then we cannot put into drydock to fix it. We must carry out the repairs while still navigating towards our goal, as best we can.

John Stachel, Emeritus Professor of Physics at Boston University, and Director of the Centre of Einstein Studies ”

Activity 15 *Speak for yourself*

You will now have spent a number of lessons thinking about what science is. Having outlined one of the author's answers in Activity 14, use the discussion as a springboard to develop your own philosophy of science. Take a few minutes to review how you thought about science before you began this section of the course (look back at your notes from Lesson 1.1 of this part of the course). How has your view of science changed as a result of studying this section?

2 Thinking skills

2.1 Reasons and points of view

Be reasonable

Much of philosophy is concerned with reasons and arguments. There are many questions which cannot be settled simply by finding out the relevant facts. These are questions which concern fundamental ideas – questions about what is truly real and what we can really know. On philosophical questions like these, different people form different **points of view**.

A point of view is a belief in a **proposition** (a statement of a judgement). Some people, for example, take the point of view that the physical world is all that there is (a point of view known as **materialism**). Others take the point of view that there is a god beyond the universe (a point of view known as **theism**).

Throughout the history of human thought, different people have held different fundamental philosophical beliefs. One of the most regrettable aspects of the history of ideas is that these differences have often led to one group of people imposing their philosophical point of view on others, often using the threat of violence to do so. This is the exact opposite of a properly philosophical approach, which is based on using reasoned persuasion, not intimidation. The aim in philosophical discussion is to identify and evaluate the strength of the **reasons** that can be given in support of a point of view.

The word **argument** is often used to mean 'quarrel'. When used in philosophy, however, it has a different meaning. A philosophical argument is used to persuade someone to accept a proposition (a statement of a point of view) by showing how it follows logically as a **conclusion** from reasonable assumptions. These assumptions are called the **premises** of the argument.

It is a good first step, when reading a philosophical argument, to ask yourself what the argument is seeking to prove (what the conclusion is) and what premises it begins from. The following points will help in laying out the structure of someone's reasoning:

- Useful clues in identifying the conclusion of an argument are phrases such as 'I take the view that …', 'Therefore …', or 'It follows that …'.
- The conclusion is not necessarily the last sentence in the argument. Often, the conclusion is stated at the start of the argument or even mid-way through.

Project hint

A key aspect of your Research project is that you should state a point of view on a science-related issue and present arguments to persuade other people to your way of thinking.

Resource link

For a treasure trove of links and ideas for developing thinking skills, see the Austhink website.

Project hint

The skill of laying out arguments is an important one for your Research project. It will help you to present your own arguments clearly, and to analyse those put forward by other people.

- The author may present several different arguments for the same point of view. It is helpful to list each of the arguments separately and consider each on its own merits.
- People often argue for several different conclusions at once. You will have to think carefully to decide on the main point the person is seeking to establish.

Activity 16 *Laying out arguments*

The arguments that follow all refer to the existence or otherwise of 'aliens'. For each argument, identify the point of view which the author is seeking to support (the conclusion of the argument) and the reasons which are given to support it (the premises). Present your summary in a table with two columns headed 'premises' and 'conclusion', and one numbered row for each of the arguments. Write a sentence or two under each heading. Laying out the arguments in this way shows, in each case, how the premises lead to the conclusion.

Argument 1
There must be life on other planets. The universe is such a big place.

Argument 2
If there are aliens, they would have visited Earth by now. So there probably aren't any.

Argument 3
For complex life forms to evolve takes incredibly delicately balanced conditions. It therefore seems unlikely that alien life forms exist. After all, we only know that the right conditions exist on Earth.

Argument 4
I think that it all depends on how you define life. Simple organisms could well have evolved in many places in the universe, but the existence of complex life forms is much less likely.

▲ ***Figure 15*** *Aliens.*

Argument 5
If there are aliens, they would never be able to find us in such a big universe. Our best chance of finding them is by searching for radio messages.

Argument 6
It seems likely that we will eventually find out that life is not unique to Earth. If it was true that the Earth was the centre of the universe, it would be reasonable to assume that life was unique to the Earth. But science has shown that the Earth is not the centre of the universe. This conclusion is supported by the fact that we are discovering more and more planets which could contain life.

Valid and invalid reasons

Once you have identified the reasons someone gives for his or her point of view, you should evaluate whether they are good reasons. The terms 'valid' and 'invalid' are useful here.

When reasons support a point of view, we call them **valid**. Say, for example, that your point of view is that aliens might well exist, and your reason is that anything is possible in a large enough universe. This would be a valid reason for believing that aliens might exist, since if anything is possible, then aliens are possible. The reason you have given provides support for your point of view.

It is quite common for people to form points of view without valid supporting reasons. They might simply believe in aliens as a matter of faith. Or they might think that they have reasons, but they are not in fact valid. Consider someone who believes that aliens exist because he or she can't bear the thought that we are alone in the universe. In other words, the person believe in aliens as a result of wishful thinking. This is not a valid reason since the fact that someone wants a belief to be true does not make it likely to be true. In this case, we would say that his or her reasons are **invalid**.

Project hint

In your Research project, look for examples of valid and invalid reasons used in argument. Spotting an invalid reason will enable you to demolish an argument against your own point of view. When putting forward an argument to support your own viewpoint, think carefully about your reasons and make sure they are valid.

Further work

Making sense of SETI

There are many good and – at present – unanswered scientific questions about the possible or probable existence of extraterrestrial life. But there are also philosophical questions about the purpose of the quest and its implications for our concept of human beings and their place in the universe.

Read the extract on page 154 from an interview with Paul Davies then discuss your views about the Search for Extraterrestrial Intelligence (SETI) project (Figure 16). (Paul Davies is a professor of physics with a particular interest in the relationships between science and religion.) Why does Davies think SETI is a religious enterprise? Is he right about this in your view? Should SETI be seen as science, pseudo-science, a philosophy or a religion?

Project hint

An aspect of SETI might make an interesting topic for your Research project.

▲ ***Figure 16*** *The Arecibo radio telescope which is used in SETI.*

“Frank Drake, the grandfather of SETI, once said that the search for intelligent life elsewhere in the universe is really a search for ourselves. It is a search for who we are and what our place is in the great scheme of things. Whether SETI succeeds or not, it fosters interesting conversations. Like the world's great religions, it asks: What is a human being? What is intelligence? What kind of place is the universe? Different people derive comfort from different answers. Some like to think that we are in splendid isolation, while others – and I'm in this category – like to think we live in a bio-friendly universe in which the emergence of life and mind – consciousness – is built into the scheme of things in a deep way. Interestingly, people who engage in SETI seem to be atheists or even militant atheists. Jill Tarter, Director of the Center for SETI Research, has been very outspoken against religion, and yet I see SETI's quest as fundamentally religious.

Davies, P., The next philosophy [online interview] ”

2.2 Reasons and objections

Reasons, objections and replies

It is very rare indeed for a philosophical theory to be accepted by everyone. In almost all philosophical debates, there are reasons for and against a given point of view. If you are going to build a case for a particular point of view, you will need to identify and respond to the **objections** which can be raised against it.

Activity 17 *Reasons, objections and replies*

The following extract is taken from an article by Mick Hume in *The Times*. Read it then write a series of bullet points that summarise:

- the author's point of view
- the reasons he gives
- the objections he considers to his point of view
- the answers he gives to those objections.

“***A grisly theatre of death – not exactly an advertisement for a dignified end***

Dr Anne Turner, a 66-year-old retired GP suffering from progressive supranuclear palsy, went to Switzerland to kill herself with the help of *Dignitas*, a euthanasia clinic. Her adult children drank champagne with her, then watched as she died from a cocktail of barbiturates …

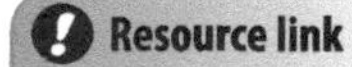

Resource link

For the full text of this article, see the *Times* archive online.

Campaigners argue that people should have choice and the right to die. In fact, everybody already has the 'freedom' to kill themselves and no law could stop a determined suicide. Somebody like Dr Turner, a medical professional in the early stages of degenerative disease, also had the knowledge and ability to do it. Instead, she chose to stage a grisly travelling theatre of death for the world media.

When personal tragedy is politicised in this way, it raises bigger questions about what attitude we as a society should take to life and death. Individuals may fear the future and see their situation as hopeless. But that is no reason for the rest of us to sanction their suicide wish in culture and law, in effect to say to the desperate person on the ledge: 'We feel your pain – go ahead and jump.'

The *Dignitas* clinic takes that attitude to its logical conclusion by helping to kill people such as a British couple who were depressed but not terminally ill. After all, once you claim assisted suicide as a human right, how do you deny it to anybody?

Like Dr Turner, I think of myself as a humanist. I have no truck with the religious 'pro-life' lobby and support legalised abortion just as I oppose legalised euthanasia. I hope that compassionate doctors will continue to make the end as painless as possible, as they have always done. But I also think that our society should make clear that we do not want to assist suicide or endorse euthanasia; that the law should not treat death as simply a lifestyle choice; that there must be more to human dignity than dying quietly at home.

Hume, M., Notebook, The Times, *27 January 2006* ”

Objecting to yourself

We are all very much inclined to believe that our beliefs are correct. Having confidence in your convictions is very proper. However, at the same time we cannot neglect the possibility that what seems to us to be true, might actually be false. In other words, forming a reasonable point of view means considering objections to your viewpoint.

It is much easier to think of objections to other people's point of view than it is to see objections to your own. It takes a deliberate effort of thought to ask, 'if I was arguing against what I actually believe, what would I say?' Many people are content to form their opinions and perhaps find some supporting reasons. It is rarer to find someone who thinks seriously about the **counter-arguments** to their viewpoint. But if you are going to form a really strong argument for your viewpoint, it is important to identify objections and to work out how you can respond to them.

Project hint

In your Research project, you can strengthen your argument in favour of your point of view by identifying some objections and responding to them.

Activity 18 *Objecting to yourself*

Consider the issue of voluntary euthanasia which Mick Hume discusses. What is your own point of view on this issue? What reasons would you give to support your viewpoint? What objections are there to your view? How would you respond to these objections? Write a few sentences on each of these questions.

2.3 Analysing the language of arguments

Minding your language

As well as looking at the form of arguments, philosophers pay a great deal of attention to how language is used. There is a good reason for this. A great many of the mistakes and confusions which people get into when they try to think about philosophical questions arise because they are unclear about the meaning of the words they are using.

For example, heated debates can be started by the question 'Does God exist?' People rarely step back and ask themselves what the word 'God' might mean. Yet we could hardly expect to be able to decide whether there is a God without first checking that we knew what the word meant. It is important, therefore, when reading a philosophical argument to think about the key words used in the argument and to ask yourself what they mean.

There are a number of things you can do to help answer this question.

Project hint

In the Introduction section of your Research project, you need to identify and define key words and phrases. Use these guidelines to help you do so.

Examples

Giving examples is a helpful first step towards working out a definition for a word. It is particularly worthwhile since a single word often has more than one meaning. It is easy to forget this and look for 'the' definition. By thinking of a few examples of the way in which the word is used, we can become aware of the different meanings it can have.

Contrasts

The meaning of a word often becomes clearer when it is contrasted with other words. For example, when thinking about the meaning of a word like 'theory', we might want to contrast it with words like 'fact' and compare it with similar words such as 'hypothesis' or 'law'.

Checking the dictionary definition

Using a dictionary (Figure 17) can be a helpful step in thinking clearly about concepts. Dictionaries record how words are actually used and they often indicate when the word has more than one meaning. Bear in mind, though, that many words cannot be given simple definitions. This is particularly true when dealing with philosophical and ethical concepts such as right and wrong, truth and falsity, life and death. A dictionary definition can be a helpful place to start when trying to explain what a word means, but it does not remove the need for some hard thinking of your own.

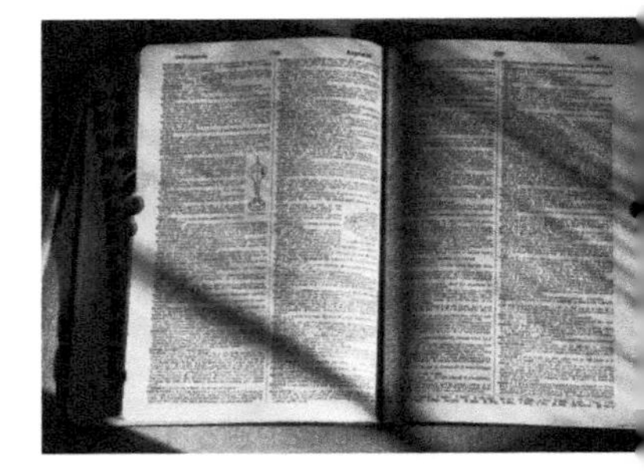

▲ ***Figure 17*** *Use a dictionary to help think about the key words in an argument.*

The point of a philosophical argument is to provide valid reasons for a point of view. This means adopting the skills of logical reasoning and taking care to use words clearly and precisely in explaining your viewpoint. However, in reality we are all prone to using language emotionally, and this can be particularly powerful in the course of an argument. Certainly someone who is good at using language to stir up feelings will be more likely to persuade others of his or her point of view (Figure 18).

Reason versus emotion

However, there is a big difference between being swayed by the emotional appeal of a speaker's words and being rationally convinced of the logic of his or her case. When you are analysing other people's arguments it is worth checking to see whether they are carrying you towards their conclusion by relying on logic – or simply on emotional appeal. The danger is that you might find you are being skilfully manipulated and your critical thinking faculties are being lulled into inactivity.

▲ ***Figure 18*** *Emotive language can be used to stir up feelings.*

Activity 19 *Language and the SETI debate*

Consider the way that language is used in the following argument about life on other planets. Identify key terms which are vague and need to be defined clearly. Use examples, contrasts and a dictionary then write a paragraph for each one giving a clear definition. Think too about the way in which the argument uses emotive language. What words are being used to stir up your feelings? Does the argument seem persuasive because of its logical validity, or is it relying too much on an appeal to emotion? Write a paragraph to sum up your thoughts.

> “There has to be someone out there. It is such a big universe. How can anyone believe that life exists only here on Earth? That's such an arrogant thing to think. It is just as stupid as believing that the Earth is the centre of the universe. There must be millions of other stars with planets which can support life. Surely intelligent life will have evolved on at least one of them.”

Resource link

For more on SETI visit the SETI website.

Activity 20 *Analysing key terms*

In the *History of science* part of this course, the reliability of sources was discussed using the categories of fact, subjective opinion and speculation.

Write a paragraph about the meaning of each of these terms. You may like to refer to a dictionary definition.

Include examples of how each term is used and a comparison of the meaning of each with the other two.

3 The universe, science and religion

3.1 Before the Big Bang

The Big Bang

One branch of science which has led some to believe that modern science gives support to religion is modern cosmology (the study of the whole universe). In the 1920s American astronomer Edwin Hubble's observations of the red shift of light from distant galaxies were interpreted to mean that the universe itself is expanding (Figure 19). Further support came with the discovery, in 1963, of the microwave background radiation spread through space, a cooled-down relic of the radiation produced in the Big Bang itself (Figure 20).

▲ ***Figure 19*** *Observations of light from distant galaxies indicate that the universe is expanding.*

Nowadays the accepted cosmological model is that of the Big Bang: the universe began in an explosive expansion some 13 billion years ago. This is held to be the moment at which matter, space and time came into existence. That makes it sound quite similar to how one would imagine the creation of the universe, a parallel which some theologians and Church leaders have been quick to exploit. In 1951 at a Vatican conference, Pope Pius XII hailed the emerging Big Bang theory as providing scientific proof of the religious doctrine of Creation.

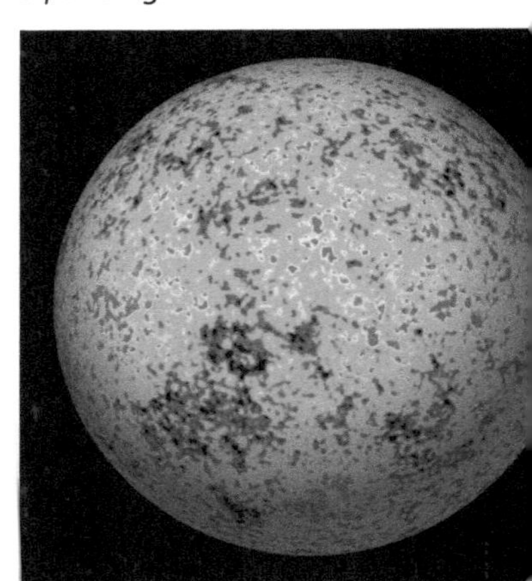

▲ ***Figure 20*** *An all-sky map of the microwave background radiation.*

▲ ***Figure 21*** *Fred Hoyle.*

The theological ideas associated with the Big Bang model also influenced its critics. The British cosmologist Fred Hoyle (Figure 21), one of the architects of the rival steady state theory, was motivated to find an alternative partly because he believed that the idea of a universe springing into being was a theological notion which had no place in science.

There is a long tradition of argument in philosophy about the origins of the universe. It is natural to wonder 'where did it all come from?' Those who look for an explanation of the universe's existence often draw the conclusion that the answer lies in the existence of a supernatural being beyond the physical universe, the so-called **first cause** of everything that exists.

Project hint

If you are exploring a topic within the general area of the origins of the universe, questions about the Big Bang and the notion of a 'first cause' are particularly relevant.

The first cause cosmological argument has been debated by philosophers for over 1000 years. While it seems intuitively forceful when first encountered, critics have been swift to point out that the matter is not at all clear cut. Can we draw firm conclusions about what may lie beyond the known universe? We have no experience of such a realm. Indeed, it is not clear that we can meaningfully talk about causes and beings outside the familiar world of space and time which we inhabit. There is also the nagging worry that if we postulate a supernatural being as the explanation for the existence of the universe, we are going to have to ask for an explanation of that being's existence (the 'who created God?' question).

In recent years the argument over a first cause has been given fresh life by connecting it with the Big Bang theory. The philosopher and religious apologist William Lane Craig has expounded a version of the first cause cosmological argument and defended it all over the world.

> "Since everything that begins to exist has a cause of its existence, and since the universe began to exist, we conclude, therefore, that the universe has a cause of its existence. We ought to ponder long and hard over this truly remarkable conclusion, for it means that transcending the entire universe there exists a cause which brought the universe into being *ex nihilo* ... we may plausibly argue that the cause of the universe is a personal being.
>
> *Lane Craig, W., in Smith, Q. and Lane Craig, W. (1993)* Theism, Atheism and Big Bang Cosmology, *Oxford University Press, pp. 63–4*"

Resource link

A detailed defence by William Lane Craig of the '*kalam*' first cause cosmological argument is available online.

Activity 21 God and the Big Bang

Discuss Lane Craig's argument with reference to the questions that follow (the argument uses the Latin phrase *ex nihilo*, which means 'from nothing at all', and 'transcending the entire universe' means 'outside or beyond the universe').

Write a list of bullet points in answer to each of these questions.

1 What point of view is Lane Craig arguing for?

2 What are his reasons?

3 Can you think of objections to his argument?

Project hint

Interviewing someone to elicit his or her point of view on a philosophical or ethical question is a good way to gather material for your Research project.

Activity 22 Beliefs about the Big Bang

Draw up a set of questions to find out someone's point of view and arguments about the Big Bang. Use your questions to interview a fellow student, a teacher, a religious leader or a scientist.

Your questions should aim to draw out what the person believes and to clarify his or her position. For example, you may want to know whether the person holds **theist**, **atheist** or **agnostic** beliefs. Also, you should try to find out the person's argument and (politely!) probe how he or she responds to counter-arguments.

(A theist is someone who believes in God. An atheist is someone who believes there is no god. An agnostic is someone who is not sure whether there is a god.)

Make a list of your questions in the order you intend to ask them. Leave a few lines after each question to jot down notes of the person's answers. In addition, you might want to tape-record the interview (first ask the interviewee whether he or she agrees to this).

After you have conducted your interview, produce a short report describing your interviewee's beliefs and arguments, and his or her response to counter-arguments.

3.2 Designer universe?

Science and design

Is there evidence of the work of a designer who planned and shaped the natural world (Figure 22)? If so, what sort of being might the designer be? Why, if the designer is perfect, is the design of the universe less than perfect? These questions have been debated by philosophers and theologians for thousands of years. In the past two centuries, as biological science has advanced in its explanation of the origins of life, scientists have found themselves caught up in arguments about design.

▲ ***Figure 22*** *God creates man (Adam), as painted by Michelangelo (1475–1564) on the Vatican's Sistine Chapel.*

Broadly speaking, scientists and religious believers adopt one of four positions on the question of design.

> **Project hint**
>
> Issues concerning creation/evolution can provide a fruitful question for study in a Research project. It is a very broad topic so try to identify a specific question to explore.

Relativist

Many scientists would regard the idea of an intelligent designer as a religious belief which is simply not one which science has to deal with. It is not the job of science to answer religious questions, or to provide arguments for or against what is principally a matter of personal faith. This is a relativist viewpoint: science and religion may both make true claims, but truth in science and religious truth do not overlap.

Naturalist

Some scientists go further and argue that the success of science in explaining the physical causes of events removes the need to believe in a divine designer. In this view, belief in God was a primitive explanation for the universe and the advance of science has meant that there are fewer and fewer unexplained mysteries to provide the basis for a design argument. Although science has not yet explained everything, it is reasonable to suppose that the remaining 'gaps' in its theories will be filled and the powerful advance of science removes the space for God. This view, which argues for natural processes instead of supernatural ones, is known as **naturalism**.

Theistic evolution

Some scientists are religious believers who argue that science indirectly supports the existence of God because God explains why the universe is regular and why the processes of scientific enquiry have been successful. It is a miracle that we are able to understand the world at all – why should our minds be so well adapted to understanding it? Why do the theories which have worked in the past continue to work? Science itself cannot explain where the laws of science came from in the first place. The most natural explanation of the lawfulness and intelligibility of the universe is that they are the work of a supernatural law-giver. This viewpoint is known as **theistic evolution**.

Intelligent design

Some religious believers think that scientific theories such as evolution contain serious weaknesses and, therefore, we need to accept the intelligent design hypothesis to achieve a full explanation. Evolution might have a role to play in explaining variation between species but it cannot fully explain where the species came from originally. This is called the **intelligent design theory** and is a modern-day version of the creationist criticisms which Darwin faced when he proposed evolution.

Activity 23 *Science and design*

For each of the four positions outlined above, discuss whether it can be considered 'scientific'. For example, is it falsifiable? (Can it make predictions that could, in principle, be found false by experiment or observation?) Look back at Section 1 for some guidance with this question.

Activity 24 Discussing design

Make a survey of a range of different viewpoints on the design question, then define your own viewpoint in relation to these, giving reasons for the choice you have made and considering objections to it. Use the quotations below as a guide. To start with, try to identify what type of viewpoint (relativist, naturalist, theistic evolutionary or intelligent design) each of these people holds. Be prepared to make a brief oral presentation of your argument to the rest of your class.

To help with your presentation, make brief notes summarising your point of view and the arguments you call upon to support it. Try to lay out your argument(s) in the form of premises … conclusion.

“A lot of people think there's an intrinsic conflict between Christianity and evolution, but there isn't. Religion is about ethics and values, and science is about facts. You need both of them, but they don't interact very much.

Manier, J., Stephen Jay Gould takes a new swing at explaining evolution, Chicago Tribune, *2 December 1996*”

▲ ***Figure 23*** *Steven Jay Gould (1941–2002).*

“Most religions offer a cosmology and a biology, a theory of life, a theory of origins, and reasons for existence. In doing so, they demonstrate that religion is, in a sense, science; it's just bad science. Don't fall for the argument that religion and science operate on separate dimensions and are concerned with quite separate sorts of questions. Religions have historically always attempted to answer the questions that properly belong to science. Thus religions should not be allowed now to retreat away from the ground upon which they have traditionally attempted to fight. They do offer both a cosmology and a biology; however, in both cases it is false.

Adapted from Dawkins' speech in acceptance of the 1996 Humanist of the Year Award from the American Humanist Association”

▲ ***Figure 24*** *Richard Dawkins.*

“We believe God has raised up ICR to spearhead Biblical Christianity's defense against the godless and compromising dogma of evolutionary humanism. Only by showing the scientific bankruptcy of evolution, while exalting Christ and the Bible, will Christians be successful in 'the pulling down of strongholds; casting down imaginations, and every high thing that exalteth itself against the knowledge of God, and bringing into captivity every thought to the obedience of Christ' (II Corinthians 10:4,5).

Institute for Creation Research *home page*”

Resource link

The Institution for Creation Research website gives a flavour of how creationists view things.

“I am a creationist and an evolutionist. Evolution is God's, or Nature's, method of creation. Creation is not an event that happened in 4004 BC; it is a process that began some 10 billion years ago and is still under way … Does the evolutionary doctrine clash with religious faith? It does not. It is a blunder to mistake the Holy Scriptures for elementary textbooks of astronomy, geology, biology, and anthropology. Only if symbols are

Resource link

The Wikipedia site contains the Dobzhansky quote and references to plenty more theistic evolutionists.

construed to mean what they are not intended to mean can there arise imaginary, insoluble conflicts ... the blunder leads to blasphemy: the Creator is accused of systematic deceitfulness.

Dobzhansky, T. (1973) Nothing in biology makes sense except in the light of evolution, American Biology Teacher, ***35**, pp. 125–9.* With permission from the National Association of Biology Teachers. ”

▲ **Figure 25** Theodosius Dobzhansky (1900–75).

Further work

In recent years in the USA, defenders of the intelligent design viewpoint have argued that this perspective is a valid alternative scientific theory, and that it should be taught in schools alongside the theory of evolution. One reason why they are keen to portray their viewpoint as a scientific theory is that the United States Constitution prohibits the teaching of religious beliefs in schools. It is therefore crucial to their case that the idea of intelligent design be seen as a genuinely scientific theory. Think about the concept of 'science' and 'theory' (you might like to revisit the work you did on science and pseudo-science). Is intelligent design best seen as a scientific theory or as a religious belief?

3.3 The limits of science

Beyond belief?

There is no doubting the extraordinary power that science has to explain events which were previously seen as mysterious. Only a few hundred years ago, people had no real idea what forces were at work in the world around them, even when it came to explaining something as common as the weather. Storms and earthquakes were seen as supernatural events – acts of God – before which we were powerless; they could only be explained as divine punishments. Yet nowadays, science gives us an explanation of these phenomena in terms of physical forces which are entirely natural – although, of course, not yet entirely predictable.

In the face of the huge advances made by science, should we then conclude that one day science will explain everything? Or will there always be events which lie beyond the domain of science? One focal point for this debate is the ongoing controversy about miracles. In ordinary terms, a miracle is a wondrous event which cannot be explained except by saying it happened due to the will of God (or the gods). It would seem to follow that if miracles occur, they are events which are forever beyond the reach of scientific explanation. Conversely, the advance of science seems to make the occurrence of miracles less probable.

Project hint

If you are exploring a topic within the general area of the mechanistic universe, questions relating to the intervention (or otherwise) of a divine creator are particularly relevant.

Surprisingly, though, there are scientists who still believe there is space in the world for the miraculous. In their view, science does not rule out the possibility of miracles. Needless to say, this viewpoint has been the subject

▲ ***Figure 26*** *Christ turning water into wine.*

of vigorous debate and it provides an excellent starting point when thinking about whether there are any events which are, as it were, 'off limits' for science.

The letter below was published in *The Times* at the time of the appointment of a Bishop of the Church of England (David Jenkins) who had publicly questioned whether Jesus Christ was raised from the dead. The letter was followed soon afterwards by an editorial column in the science journal *Nature* which sought to provide a refutation.

> "In view of the recent discussions about the views of Bishops on miracles we wish to make the following comments. It is not logically valid to use science as an argument against miracles. To believe that miracles cannot happen is as much an act of faith as to believe that they can happen. We gladly accept the Virgin Birth, the Gospel miracles, and the Resurrection of Christ as historical events. We know that we are representative of many other scientists who are also Christians standing in the historical tradition of the churches.
>
> Miracles are unprecedented events. Whatever the current fashions in philosophy or the revelations of the opinion polls may suggest it is important to affirm that science (based as it is upon the observation of precedents) can have nothing to say on the subject. Its 'laws' are only generalisations of our experience. Faith rests on other grounds.
>
> *Letter to* The Times, *13 July 1984, from Professor R. J. Berry FRSE, Sir Robert Boyd CBE FRS, Professor Martin Bott FRS, Professor Denis P. Burkitt FRS, Sir Clifford Butler FRS, Professor John T. Houghton FRS, Professor D. Tyrell FRS, Professor E. H. Andrews, Professor E. R. Dobbs, Professor J. B. Lloyd, Professor M. A. Jeeves, Professor C. A. Russell, Professor D. C. Spanner and Professor G .B. Wetherill*"

The editorial reply in *Nature* contains a summary of the letter's argument then continues as follows.

> ***Miracles do not happen***
>
> A group has invited trouble by claiming that science has nothing to say about miracles … Nobody can sensibly complain that scientists of various kinds are often religious people of one persuasion or another, or quarrel with the conclusion of Berry et al. that the 'laws' of science are 'only generalisations of our experience' and that 'faith rests on other grounds'. But it is a travesty to assert that science has 'nothing to say' about miracles.
>
> Take an uncontentious example, such as the turning of water into wine. This is said to have happened at a wedding feast, when the supply of wine was unexpectedly exhausted. The only published account has it that jars of drinking water were found to have been transformed into wine in the socially embarrassing circumstances that had arisen. The account is now firmly a part of the Christian legend, but that is not the same as saying it is the account of a phenomenon. Obvious alternative explanations abound. As scientists, the signatories would not have given a favourable referee's opinion of such an account for a scientific journal. And far from science having 'nothing to say' about miracles, the truth is quite the opposite. Miracles, which are inexplicable and irreproducible phenomena, do not occur – a definition by exclusion of the concept.
>
> Ordinarily, the point would not be worth making. The trouble with the publication from Berry et al. is that it provides a licence not merely for religious belief (which, on other grounds, is unexceptionable) but for the mischievous reports of all things paranormal, from ghosts to flying saucers.
>
> Nature, ***310***, *19 July 1984, p. 171. The editorial and letter are reproduced in Alexander, D. (2001)* Re-building the Matrix, *Lion Publishing, Oxford, Ch 13, which provides further commentary on the argument.*

Activity 25 *I believe in miracles . . .*

Consider each article above. You are going to use these articles as a springboard for developing your own viewpoint and a reasoned case to support it. First, for each article, identify the viewpoint being argued for, the reasons that are given, and the response to any objections. Then use these arguments to build a case for your own point of view on the question of miracles. Write a few paragraphs making your case. You should include a statement of your viewpoint and your reasons for it. Here you should think about what the word 'miracle' really means. Consider also objections to your viewpoint and your response to them. You should be aware that the subject is a sensitive one – so try in your argument to stick to reason and don't resort to personal attacks on those who oppose your views.

The prayer experiment

There have been various attempts to set religious belief on a scientific basis.

In April 2006, *New Scientist* magazine reported a prayer experiment with 1802 patients undergoing coronary bypass operations. There were two groups of patients in a double-blind trial: those in one group were prayed for by several Christian groups while those in the other group were not, and neither doctors nor patients knew who was in which group. A month after surgery, 52% of the prayed-for patients and 51% of the rest suffered further complications – the prayers had made no significant difference. A third group of patients were told they were being prayed for, and received the same prayers as the first. In this third group, significantly more patients (59%) suffered complications. Was it the prayers that made the difference, or did the knowledge they were being prayed for make the patients more anxious and hence prone to complications?

There are different viewpoints about this sort of 'experiment'. Some would say that it is foolish since science and religion are entirely separate things. Others would say that if God is real and prayer really does make a difference, then there should be evidence for it. Some believe that we do have such evidence, while others are sceptical.

Further work

Explain your viewpoint on the prayer experiment. As part of your answer, explain what you think about the relationship between science and religion.

4 All in the mind

4.1 Mind games

Few concepts are as puzzling as that of the mind. What sort of thing is the mind? Is it a physical thing (the brain, Figure 27) or is it something spiritual (more like the **soul**)? Is it a mistake to think of the mind as a thing at all? Should we think of it as more like a property of something else (like consciousness, perhaps)? Is having a mind a matter of acting in certain ways?

How does science help us here? Can science fully explain the mind, partly explain it, or not explain it at all? All of these points of view have been defended philosophically. A way into the discussion is to identify some of the main theories which philosophers have argued for and to locate yourself on the map of possible viewpoints.

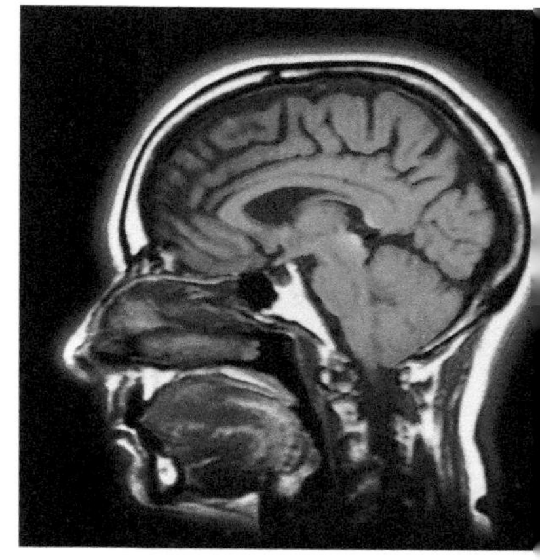

▲ ***Figure 27*** *Is the mind distinct from the brain?*

Activity 26 *Your own philosophy of mind*

For each of questions 1–7 below, choose one answer (a, b or c). The information following the questionnaire will help you work out where on the spectrum of philosophical theories of the mind your own viewpoint falls.

Project hint

If you are exploring a topic within the general area of the human mind, questions about the nature of the mind are particularly relevant.

1 A human being is:
- **a** made up of body and soul
- **b** composed of physical stuff but with mental and spiritual features
- **c** made only of atoms and molecules.

2 The mind will:
- **a** never be explained by science
- **b** be partly but not completely explained by science
- **c** be completely explained by science.

3 Our choices are caused by:
- **a** our soul alone
- **b** conscious processes which happen because of our brain
- **c** processes in our brain alone.

4 Consciousness is:
- **a** a miracle that God creates in us
- **b** a distinctive non-physical phenomenon caused by the brain
- **c** purely a brain process.

5 Intelligent machines:

a are impossible

b may be possible but will be completely different from today's machines

c are already possible.

6 Other people's minds:

a can never be known because you can't see into their soul

b can partly be known by observing their behaviour and/or their brain

c can be known for certain by looking at their brain and/or behaviour.

7 Animals are:

a completely different from us – they have no soul

b physically similar to us but with a different mental life

c just like us – we too are animals.

If most of your answers were a:

You are a **dualist**. This means that you think that the soul and the body are distinct things that could probably exist apart from each other. This is a view associated with the French philosopher René Descartes (1596–1650) and, in many people's view, is the traditional religious teaching.

Dualism seems like an intuitively satisfying viewpoint although it faces a serious difficulty. If the mind is completely distinct from the body and entirely non-physical, how can it affect the body or be affected by it? Is dualism consistent with what we know from science of the way in which changes in the brain can profoundly affect the mind? This is called the **interaction problem**.

If most of your answers were b:

You are a **materialist** but of a **non-reductionist** type. This means that you think that human beings are made up of physical stuff without a separate soul. The mind exists but it is best seen as an aspect of the body rather than something totally separate. The events which happen in the mind depend on what happens in the brain, but they are different from purely physical processes. The sensations and experiences which make up our conscious life have a distinctive quality which cannot be completely reduced to physical events in the brain.

Non-reductionism is an attractive idea but it needs careful thought. How do the mental aspects of a person relate to his or her physical aspects? Can our mind make a difference to our brain? If you say it can, you face the interaction problem (see above). If not, it seems that our idea of free will and human agency is under threat.

If most of your answers were c:

You are a **reductionist** – a materialist who thinks that everything is physical and that science will, in the end, explain every aspect of human life. Reductionists think of people as entirely subject to the laws of science. The idea of the soul is to be rejected as nothing more than a superstition.

Reductionism may seem scientific but can you really explain everything about people using science?

Activity 27 *What is in the mind?*

Having identified your point of view, form a group with others who share your viewpoint. Think about the arguments you can use in favour of your viewpoint and against the alternatives. One person from your group should then explain your arguments to the other groups.

Project hint

Discussing a shared point of view with others can help clarify your thinking. Look for ways in which you and other students can help one another in this way when working on your Research project.

Further work

Write up your discussion of the question: 'What is the mind?' Begin by outlining the different answers that people give to the question, then explain your own viewpoint, giving reasons as well as considering and replying to objections.

Resource link

The Wikipedia site gives an overview of different theories.

4.2 Do you believe in ghosts?

The biology of ghosts

According to the dualist theory, the mind is not a physical thing at all. It is not located in space as, for example, the brain is. Nor is it bound by the laws of physics. It is a non-physical entity, a centre of conscious spiritual or mental powers. This makes it sound similar to what people imagine a ghost or spirit to be.

The article 'Visions of the imagination – ghosts don't make biological sense' (below) explores the connection between ghosts and mind-body dualism and gives you an opportunity to explore arguments and counter-arguments about dualism.

Activity 28 *The biology of ghosts*

In the extract that follows on pages 170–1, Michael Whalley considers the debate between dualism and **monism**. When he uses the term monism, it means the same as the term materialism (which was explained in Lessons 2.1 and 4.1). Read through the article, making brief notes about the flow of the argument. Roughly speaking, you should end up with about half a page of notes which cover all the main arguments the author makes. In this case, the author has helpfully stated explicitly what some of the main arguments are, so you might choose to make use of his labels as headings in your notes. Your notes should cover:

- the author's point of view
- the reasons he gives for his point of view
- the objections he considers
- how he responds to these objections.

If you come across a choice phrase, there is nothing wrong with including a short direct quotation, so long as you make it clear that you are quoting the author directly (use quote marks and give a reference to the article).

Project hint

Activity 28 gives you practice in the useful skill of making a précis (summary) of an article. You will need to do this when researching source material for your project.

Forum: Visions of the imagination – ghosts don't make biological sense, argues Michael Whalley

I suspect that I am not alone in enjoying a good ghost story while remaining a complete sceptic about the existence of ghosts. There is nothing strange about this; it is merely another example of the well-known suspension of disbelief necessary for enjoying any good literary fantasy from H. G. Wells's *The Invisible Man* to Arthur Conan Doyle's *The Lost World*. But while scepticism about ghosts is perhaps the norm nowadays, a hard core of believers seems unmoved by the opposition.

▲ ***Figure 28*** *Ghosts: do you believe in them?*

There seem to be two forms of opposition to ghosts: the argument from doubtful evidence and the argument from gullibility. The first points out how shaky the evidence usually is, how it relies on personal anecdotes which cannot be confirmed by other observers, and how it is open to explanations of a non-supernatural kind. The second concentrates on how eager people are to believe almost anything exciting and out of the ordinary, and consequently how easily fooled they are and prone to jump to conclusions not warranted by the evidence. These are good, fighting moves, and they need to be made. But it is surprising how rarely you hear the scientific argument against ghosts, though it is surely pretty devastating.

We should note, as a preliminary, that belief in ghosts implies the acceptance of mind/body dualism. That is, the mental aspects of a person (the 'mind', 'soul' or 'spirit') are seen as a distinct, nonmaterial entity, capable of existing without the body. The alternative view is monism in which mental phenomena are traced to purely material causes in the central nervous system, and can no more exist separately from the body than a radio signal can exist apart from the wave that carries it. It does not follow that if you are a dualist you must believe in ghosts; you may think that the nonmaterial 'spirit' can exist only in conjunction with a material body. The main point in the present context is that if you do believe in ghosts you must be a dualist.

Dualism has taken some hard knocks in recent years from philosophy and neuro-biology but even without the esoteric arguments from these fields a little thought should show that nobody who accepts biological evolution can plausibly embrace mind/body dualism. The argument against ghosts from biology may be outlined so: If we suppose that both evolution and dualism are correct, at what point during the evolutionary history of humans did members of the species become endowed with a non-material spirit or soul? This must have been a unique occurrence – since the possession of a spirit (like being pregnant) is an all-or-nothing affair, not something that could develop gradually. Whatever the answer, the soul cannot be explained by natural selection; to suggest a gene for spirituality would contradict its nonmaterial nature. Dualists must therefore resort to divine intervention – which hardly helps, since God is even more difficult to explain than dualism.

The same kind of point can be made at the individual rather than the species level. At what stage in development does a person acquire a spirit? Does it happen at the moment of conception? How? Do individual ova and sperms have spirits? (Again, the notion of a 'semi-spirit' is nonsensical. Spiritual
meiosis?)

You may say that these difficulties do not demonstrate conclusively that dualism is false. They simply show that its origins have not been explained yet. And monism itself is faced with the problem of how consciousness can have a physical basis. But the monist can claim that while a clear explanation of consciousness is still wanting, it seems highly probable that it is related to brain function. And dualism, far from explaining anything, introduces overwhelming conceptual difficulties. So if dualists insist on the nonmateriality of the mind, they must refute the argument from biology.

None of this makes me one jot less appreciative of the wealth of ghostly literature and art. I will even go further and admit that there are certain ghost stories (*The Toll House* by W. W. Jacobs comes to mind) which I would be careful to avoid reading alone late at night. And if I were offered the chance to spend a night on my own in an allegedly haunted house, I might well claim more pressing business.

This does not mean I believe in ghosts. What it does show is how deeply ingrained are the fears and imaginings we are exposed to as children. And these should not discourage us from asserting, in the cold light of dawn, that ghosts simply don't make biological sense.

New Scientist, ***140 (1905),*** 25 December 1993, p. 67 ”

Activity 29 Do you believe in ghosts?

Use your notes from Activity 28 to present arguments for or against the belief in ghosts. If circumstances allow it, pair up with someone of the opposite opinion to yourself and carry out the argument as a (polite) discussion. You should back up your point of view with arguments and also deal with your opponent's counter-arguments.

Project hint

Discussing a point of view with someone who disagrees with you can help clarify your thinking. Look for ways in which you and other students can help one another in this way when working on your Research project.

Further work

Write up your précis of the Whalley article as a mini-essay, including in your report the main points of his argument and your own evaluative comments, saying whether you agree with his point of view and whether (and why) you consider his arguments to be valid.

4.3 Identify yourself

Personal identity

A central philosophical puzzle surrounds the question of **personal identity**. What is it that makes an individual the same person at different times? Each person changes in many ways during the course of his or her life, yet we tend to think that one and the same person can exist through the period of change. When I draw my pension, I will be very different in many ways from how I was when my life began, yet, for all that, I assume that the pensioner and the baby are the same person. But what makes this true? How are we to tell what personal identity consists of (Figure 29)?

▲ ***Figure 29*** *Personal identity?*

The question is an important one since many ethical disputes turn on questions of whether a person exists. The obvious ones are those concerning the start of life (at what stage is an embryo a person?), the end of life (is a comatose patient on life support still a person? Is a patient who has serious dementia still the same person?), and cloning (is our identity fixed by our genetic make-up?). This is an area where the *ethical* question of how we should act is affected by the *philosophical* question about the concept of the person. The ethical questions are addressed in the *Ethics* part of this course, where issues surrounding the beginning and ending of life are explored in Section 2. Here, we shall inquire a little more closely into how philosophers have handled issues of personal identity.

Activity 30 *Define yourself*

Complete a copy of Table 1 to show which features you consider to be essential to your personal identity. Compare your views with other students.

Table 1 Define yourself

Feature	*Essential to your identity? (yes/no/don't know)*
mobile phone	
clothes	
body	
brain	
memories	
soul	
feelings	
beliefs	

Parrot in person

The topic of personal identity is one often approached, for better or worse, by means of **thought experiments**. A thought experiment is a description of a real or imaginary situation which should help us understand how our concepts work. The experiment is an opportunity to test out different ways of thinking by asking yourself what you would say in the situation. It is always worth bearing in mind that honest agnosticism is a valid response, especially when the thought experiments get to be pretty far-fetched, as they can sometimes do in philosophy.

A famous example of a thought experiment is Locke's rational parrot. The philosopher John Locke (1632–1704, Figure 30) believed that a person is a thinking thing, with memory and self-consciousness. He drew support for this view from the story of the rational parrot. Locke reported this as though the bird really existed.

> "I had a mind to know, from Prince Maurice's own mouth, the account of a common, but much credited story, that I had heard so often from many others, of an old parrot he had in Brazil, during his government there, that spoke, and asked, and answered common questions, like a reasonable creature …
>
> When it came first into the room where the prince was, with a great many Dutchmen about him, it said presently, What a company of white men are here! They asked it, what it thought that man was, pointing to the prince. It answered, Some General or other. When they brought it close to him, he asked it, D'ou venez-vous? It answered, De Marinnan. The Prince, A qui estes-vous? The Parrot, A un Portugais …
>
> The Prince, it is plain, who vouches this story, and our author, who relates it from him, both of them call this talker a parrot: and I ask any one else who thinks such a story fit to be told, whether, if this parrot, and all of its kind, had always talked, as we have a prince's word for it this one did,– whether, I say, they would not have passed for a race of rational animals; but yet, whether, for all that, they would have been allowed to be men, and not parrots?
>
> *Locke, J.* An Essay Concerning Human Understanding, *Book II, Ch. XXVII, section 8*"

▲ ***Figure 30*** *John Locke.*

We shall adopt the more cautious route of treating the parrot as a creature in a thought experiment. Locke's question is, if the parrot showed clear evidence of being able to think and discuss things, wouldn't you want to call it a person? If you agree with Locke's proposal, you have learned something about your concept of a person – namely that it is not the same as a human being. There can be non-human persons, or so the thought experiment is meant to suggest. If you don't agree, you also learn something – namely that it is not enough in your view to be capable of thought. Perhaps the term 'person' cannot be separated from 'human being' so easily.

Activity 31 *Parrot in person*

In a small group of students, discuss your thoughts about Locke's rational parrot. If you think the parrot counts as a person, explain why. If you don't think this, say what it is that makes you unwilling to call the parrot a person. As part of your discussion you might also like to think about other cases, such as intelligent aliens (as in *Star Trek*).

What makes me me?

Philosophers have thought long and hard about the **criteria** for personal identity. What they are looking for is a way of telling when an individual at one time counts as the same person at another time.

There are various possibilities here. One is that you are the same person that you were last week because you possess the same brain. This would be a form of **physical continuity**. A problem here is that talking about the same brain is problematic, since some brain cells may well have died in the past week, raising the tricky question 'how many brain cells could you lose before you ceased to be you?'

Another possibility is that you are identical with some past person by virtue of **psychological continuity**. You are the same as the past person because you are able to remember experiences had by this past person. This seems sensible since our self-awareness is shaped by our memories, but what about cases in which a person loses his or her memory? If you suffered from serious amnesia, would you cease to be you?

A third view is that the essential part of a person is his or her **soul**, where this is understood in dualist terms as something non-physical. Philosophers have generally felt that dualism does not help us to understand what personal identity consists of, since the concept of the soul is such a mysterious one. It seems comparatively easier to identify people than to identify souls, so explaining personal identity in terms of soul identity seems rather back to front.

Project hint

If you are exploring a topic within the general area of the beginning and ending of life, questions about the meaning of personal identity are particularly relevant.

Activity 32 *What makes me me?*

Consider each of the different views given above about what a person is. What reasons and what objections can be given to each? Record these by making a list of bullet points for each view.

Further work

One of the main motivations philosophers have in thinking about the concept of personal identity is that it plays a central role in ethical debates about the beginning and ending of life. If you have already discussed this topic in the Ethics part of the course, look back to the work you did on the abortion and euthanasia debates in Lessons 2.2 and 2.3. How do the different theories of personal identity relate to the viewpoints you discussed there?

4.4 Animal minds

Animal feelings

Do animals have minds? This is a question that spans science, ethics and philosophy. In Section 3 of the *Ethics* part of this course, the question of animal welfare is addressed. In the debates over how animals should be treated, a central issue is whether they have a mind and, in particular, whether they are capable of feeling pain.

It might seem that this is a factual question which could be answered simply by doing some experiments. Things are not so simple, though, since there are philosophical questions to consider as well. Does it make sense to talk about animals thinking and feeling? If it does, is there evidence that they do these things?

The philosopher René Descartes (1596–1650) denied that animals had a mind. His view was that they were rather like robots (Figure 31). Descartes was a dualist who thought that the mind/soul (he did not distinguish between these) was something separate from the body. Since he thought animals had no soul, it followed that they lacked a mind. They may behave in ways that seem to manifest intelligence, but they are merely like automata (robots), which lack conscious self-awareness.

Yet, as another French philosopher, Michel de Montaigne (1533–92) argued, the similarities between humans and animals strongly suggest that they do have a mind. This theme of similarity was developed in the nineteenth century when Darwin's theory of evolution gave support to a picture of the biological world in which all living things are related.

When discussing the question, it is helpful to make some distinctions. The question of whether animals have feelings is different from the question of whether they think. Almost all our thoughts are expressed in language. Language is particularly important in conscious self-awareness. When you were a baby, unable to speak, you might have been able to feel happiness, but you would not have been able to think to yourself 'here I am, feeling happy' – that thought would have to wait until you had learned quite a bit of language.

Creatures may have all sorts of sensations but only a creature with language could think about what it is experiencing. This is one reason for questioning what it means for animals to have a mind. For reasons like this, philosophers have felt more confident attributing sensations to animals rather than conscious, rational thought processes.

Project hint

If you are exploring a topic within the general area of animal welfare, questions about whether animals have a mind are particularly relevant.

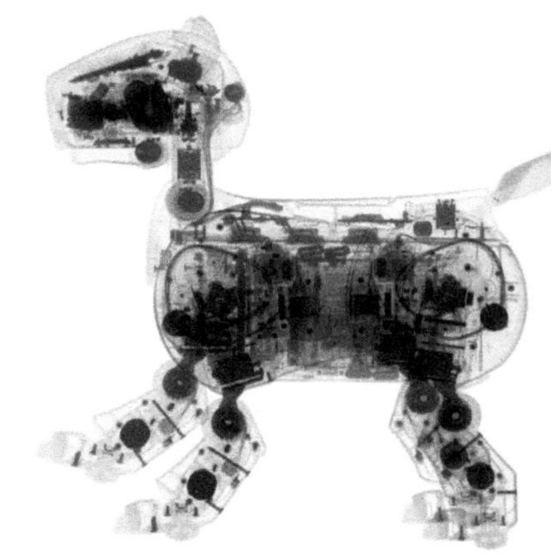

▲ **Figure 31** *Are animals like robots?*

Activity 33 *Animal feelings*

Consider the question of whether animals have feelings, and in particular, whether they experience the sensation of pain. With a small group of other students, discuss the criteria by which we tell whether something can be said to feel and decide whether you think (some or all) animals meet these criteria.

Do fish feel pain?

The utilitarian philosopher Jeremy Bentham (1748–1832) argued, when defending animal rights, 'The question is not, Can they reason? nor, Can they talk? but, Can they suffer?' From a utilitarian point of view, causing pain is a bad thing to do, regardless of whether it is humans who suffer or animals. Bentham's point was that, even if animals (who lack language) could not think to themselves that they were suffering, the fact that they were in pain was what counted from an ethical point of view.

An interesting debate in this regard concerns fish. The question is a live one since angling is the biggest hobby amongst UK men and a very large number of fish are caught as part of this pastime. The ethical question of whether this is a legitimate pursuit turns largely on the philosophical question of whether fish experience pain.

How would you tell if a creature is in pain? The main source of evidence is their behaviour. We recognise certain forms of behaviour (wincing, screaming, grimacing) as indicating pain. But what does this behaviour prove? Some philosophers would argue that the behaviour proves that the creature is suffering. Others argue that since you can't experience another's sensations, you can never be absolutely sure what a creature is feeling, although the evidence may point towards suffering. Perhaps the behaviour is a mere reflex and there is no conscious sensation of pain being felt. For example, creatures such as slugs have a withdrawal reflex which is activated in potentially harmful situations, but it is unlikely that their brains are capable of processing pain stimuli.

The argument at this point usually takes the form of an analogy: we know that we experience pain and we can find out what parts of our nervous system are responsible for mediating these feelings. If we find similar structures in other creatures, this provides a good reason for saying that they too experience pain. Fish are a difficult case since their behavioural reactions are quite different from those of humans and there is also controversy about the way their nervous system works.

Activity 34 *Do fish feel pain?*

Read the article that follows, then discuss these questions.

1 Do you agree with Professor Bateson that it is impossible to know whether another person is feeling pain? Is it easier or harder to be sure in the case of animals?

2 What reasons are given in the article for saying that fish can feel pain? What counter-arguments are offered?

3 What is your own point of view on the question of whether fish can feel pain? What reasons would you give for it and how would you respond to objections?

4 Write a short essay making a case for your point of view on the question of whether fish can feel pain.

“*Fish ‘capable of experiencing pain’*

Fish are capable of experiencing pain. This is the conclusion of researchers who observed rainbow trout behaviour after the animals were given injections that would be painful to people. Other scientists reject their interpretation, but the study could still be used by anti-angling campaigners.

The argument over whether fishing is a ‘blood sport’ in the same vein as fox hunting and hare coursing has hinged on whether fish feel pain in a similar way to mammals. If they do not, as most researchers currently believe, then the animal welfare argument against angling largely falls apart.

Lynne Sneddon at the Roslin Institute, near Edinburgh, Scotland, and her colleagues, took measurements from individual neurons in anaesthetised fish while they poked the fish’s heads and applied acid and heat.

They identified up to 22 neurons that fire in response to the stimuli. What is more, the firing pattern looked much the same as neurons in humans that transmit the pain message. So fish have the neural hardware to transmit the message but does it register as pain in the fish brain?

It is of course impossible to really know whether another person is feeling pain, let alone another species, notes Patrick Bateson, an animal behaviour expert at Cambridge University, UK. But the next best thing, he says, is to look for behavioural responses that resemble those exhibited by a human in pain.

Bee venom

The team compared the behaviour of fish that had either bee venom or acetic acid injected into their lips with animals that had received harmless saline.

The fish given the nasty chemicals showed clear signs of physiological stress, the researchers found. They took 90 minutes longer to resume feeding and their rate of gill breathing was characteristic of a fish swimming at top speed.

More surprisingly, they displayed very unusual behaviours such as rocking from side to side. Sneddon believes this may be similar to repetitive behaviours sometimes seen in zoo animals. The fish treated with acid also rubbed their lips on the sides and bottom of the tank.

‘These behaviours are not just reflex responses,’ argues Sneddon. If a human touches a hot iron then, before any pain is registered, a local neural reflex circuit pulls the hand away to prevent damage. But the throbbing discomfort felt after the event is pain. She believes that the strange trout behaviours are evidence of something similar.

Cry out

But James Rose, an expert in fish neurobiology at the University of Wyoming in Laramie disagrees: ‘It has nothing to do with pain – the fish brain just hasn’t got the hardware to experience pain.’

Resource link

Read the *New Scientist* articles on this topic in the online archive.

He points out, for example, that even people in a persistent vegetative state are able to make complex responses to painful stimuli. They can cry out or screw up their faces without ever being conscious of their surroundings.

Whether it can be classed as pain or not, Sneddon's work has identified that fish experience prolonged discomfort following an injection that would be painful to humans.

For Bateson that is a significant step forward in the argument: 'There seems, already, to be a good argument to say that fish should be treated carefully.'

Randerson, J. New Scientist *news service (April 2003);* Proceedings of the Royal Society B *(DOI 10.1098/rspb.2003.2349)* ”

4.5 Artificial intelligence

Robot mind

Since the advent of computers, people have been fascinated with the question of whether it is possible to build a machine that could think. In 1996, a chess-playing computer called Deep Blue (Figure 32) beat world champion Gary Kasparov. Can Deep Blue think?

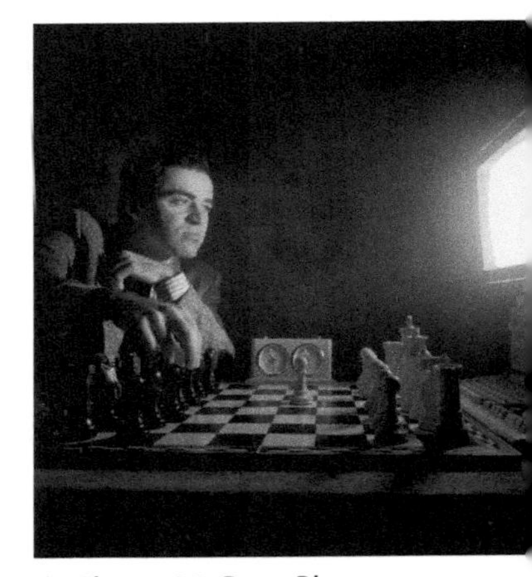

▲ ***Figure 32*** *Deep Blue.*

Project hint

The field of artificial intelligence could provide an interesting topic for a Research project.

The programme of seeking to build intelligent machines is termed **strong artificial intelligence** (or strong AI for short). It is not by any means the only thing which AI researchers do, and in some ways it has not been the most successful part of their work. Another central activity has been building systems – such as **neural networks** – which simulate activities such as perception or face recognition. The aim here is to use such systems to help us better understand what is going on in the brain when we perform these activities.

Consider the following thought experiment. Neuroscientists devise a tiny silicon chip which is capable of exactly replicating the function of one of your neurones. They replace the neurone with the chip. Then they do the same with a second neurone, then a third, and so on, until all the neurones in your head have been replaced with silicon chips.

Activity 35 *Robot mind*

Would you be able to think if one neurone was replaced with a silicon chip that did the same job? How about if two were replaced? Or three? If all the neurones in your head had been replaced with silicon chips, would you still be able to think? Does this suggest that thinking machines could exist? Discuss your views on these questions with other students and try to find objections to the arguments implied here.

The Turing test

▲ **Figure 34** *An early computer.*

▲ **Figure 33** *Alan Turing.*

Alan Turing (1912–54, Figure 33) was a brilliant mathematician who played a central role in the development of the first computers (Figure 34). During the Second World War, he was drafted to Bletchley Park, a secret British Intelligence base where analysts worked on decoding intercepts of German military messages. Much of the driving force in the development of computing technology came from the demand for machines to do large numbers of calculations swiftly as part of the immensely complex decrypting process.

In 1950 Turing wrote a pioneering paper entitled 'Computing machinery and intelligence' in which he argued that the way to tell whether a machine was capable of intelligent thought would be as follows. Place a person in front of a computer terminal and let them type in questions. If a machine can produce answers which are so convincing that the questioner is unable to tell whether they have been talking to another person or a machine, the machine has passed the test; it counts as intelligent. This famous idea has become known as the **Turing test**.

Activity 36 *The Turing test*

Discuss the Turing test using these questions as a guide.

- Is it necessary for thinking things to pass the test?
- Would you pass the test (what about when you were very young)?
- Might an intelligent computer nevertheless fail the test (perhaps it can't see the point in proving itself or is simply shy)?
- Assuming that the test is passed, does it follow that we are dealing with a genuinely intelligent machine?

The Chinese room

The American philosopher John Searle (b.1932) has argued that the fact that a machine passes the Turing Test is not in itself a reason for attributing to it a mind. Specifically, he believes that an ability to process information does not demonstrate the existence of conscious understanding. Searle's Chinese room thought experiment is designed to make this point.

Assume that you speak Chinese and are able to construct any question you like in the language by putting symbols into a big basket then passing them

◀ ***Figure 35*** *The Chinese room.*

through a slot in a wall. Back comes a basket of characters containing the answer to your question. So whatever is behind the wall passes the Turing test. However, inside the room there is a man who speaks no Chinese. He is answering the questions with the help of a huge book which lists all possible combinations of Chinese characters (all possible questions) and tells him which characters to put in the basket in answer to each question. Yet the man himself understands no Chinese – he is simply doing very complex symbolic processing (Figure 35).

The point of the thought experiment, according to Searle, is that it shows that even if computers did pass the Turing test, we would not be entitled to say that they understood what they were doing. They could simply be seen as immensely complex symbolic processors which act according to rules but lack conscious awareness of what they are doing. So, even if a machine passes the Turing test, we may still be reluctant to say it has a mind.

Resource link

Read an overview of the philosophical debate about the Chinese room argument.

Activity 37 *The Chinese room*

Discuss your reaction to the Chinese room thought experiment. Do you agree with Searle that it shows that there is more to understanding than processing information according to rules? What more could there be? What are the implications of the thought experiment for the programme of strong AI? Write a paragraph that a defender of strong AI might use to respond to Searle.

5 Think again

5.1 Professor Spector's genetic determinism

What have you learned?

This part of the course has been all about developing the thinking and analytical skills needed to think philosophically about scientific questions. These skills can be summarised as follows.

- Surveying the main viewpoints on the topic – since philosophical questions are hard, it is worthwhile beginning by finding out how other people have tried to answer them.
- Explaining clearly and precisely your own viewpoint – this involves trying to define precisely the key terms in the question you are considering (using a dictionary, examples and contrasts). It also means 'locating' where you stand in the debate. There will be positions with which you agree and others that you are opposed to.
- Giving reasons – ideally, a point of view should be backed up by supporting arguments. The very nature of philosophy is that truth is to be found by reasoned debate.
- Identifying objections to your viewpoint – even though you hold a particular viewpoint, much can be gained by trying to see why other people disagree.
- Replying to these objections – being able to support an argument both with reasons and with answers to objections is a tremendously valuable skill, not only when discussing philosophical issues related to science but in any area of work or life where debatable questions arise.

Using these skills is a key aspect of your Research project, so these final two lessons are designed to review the work from this part of the course and help you look ahead to your project.

Project hint

The steps outlined here provide a structure for the Discussion section of your Research project.

Fateful genes

Where do our actions originate from? We like to think of ourselves as making choices by exercising something we call 'free will'. Yet it can come as a surprise to learn how much of what we choose is affected by factors that are beyond our control. The focus for the age-old debate between nature and nurture in recent years has been the idea of **genetic determinism**. This is the view that your behaviour is the product of your genetic make-up (Figure 36).

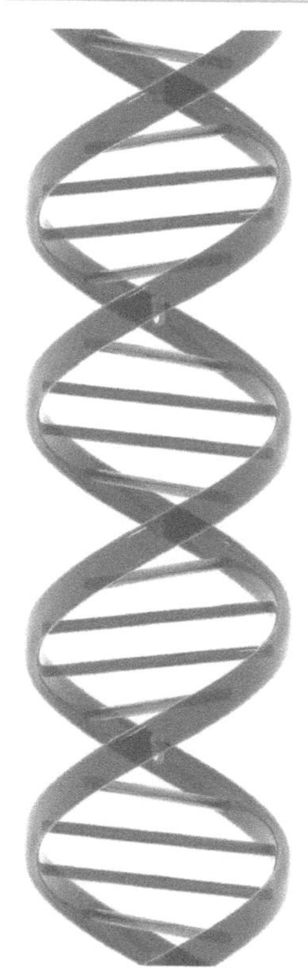

▲ ***Figure 36*** *Genes carried on DNA may determine aspects of your behaviour.*

Resource link

Wikipedia provides more on this debate.

The following extract, from an article by *Times* Science Correspondent Anjana Ahuja, describes research on twins which raises intriguing questions about free will.

Activity 38 *Fateful genes*

As you read the article below, make about half a page of notes to sum up the key points. Try to identify the point of view that Professor Spector holds, his reasons for holding it, any objections he considers and his response to objections. Also consider what is meant by key terms such as 'heritability' and 'genetic influence'.

Project hint

If you are exploring a topic within the general area of genetics, questions about determinism could be relevant.

Project hint

You will probably use articles like this when working on your Research project. Use this activity as an opportunity to practise your note-taking skills.

“ *Science: Our fateful genes*

Professor Tim Spector, 45, made his name by studying twins[Figure 37]. Twelve years ago he set up the Twin Research Unit at St Thomas', which, with about 5000 sibling pairs on its books, has become one of the most famous and detailed twin registers in the world. Twins volunteer eagerly, Spector says, partly because it gives them privileged access to excellent clinical care but also because they are fascinated by their 'twinness'.

By comparing large groups of identical twins and non-identical (fraternal) twins, scientists can tease out the influences of nature and nurture on health and personality. If a condition or trait is more common among identical twins, who share 100 per cent of their genes, than fraternal twins, who share just 50 per cent, then that condition is

▲ ***Figure 37*** *Twins.*

deemed to have a measurable 'heritability'. The higher the heritability, the more dominant are genes.

Common medical conditions such as heart disease and diabetes are highly heritable. But twin studies around the world suggest that aspects of personality, and even religious and moral beliefs, are also moulded heavily by the genes bequeathed to us by our parents.

During the research for his book, subtitled *How Your Genetic Inheritance Shapes Your Life*, Spector dusted off a little-known but controversial 1970s study on twins. More than 800 pairs were asked how much they agreed with such statements as 'coloureds are innately inferior'. Disturbingly, Spector says, some 50–60 per cent of the variation between people was down to genes, a figure later confirmed in an Australian twin study. Spector writes of a 'clear genetic influence on attitudes to racism'.

'I was surprised by the findings on race,' he admits. 'I had assumed that, although I could understand that there might be a basis for tribal beliefs, education should have got rid of them or negated them.' It is ironic, he says, because geneticists are coming to believe that there is no such thing as race. This is because there is more genetic variation within a single race than between races. Skin colour is determined by only a handful of genes, with the distinctively pale European hue regarded as a mutation from the more common palette of blacks and browns.

Doesn't a genetic basis for racism suggest that it is fighting against human nature to adopt a policy of equality? Just because a trait is heritable, Spector retorts, doesn't mean that we should practise eugenics. Knowledge is the key: 'If (white supremacists) see themselves as mutations, they won't see themselves at the centre of the universe. We can slowly change beliefs.'

Whether a person likes exercising is also partly genetic. 'If people don't exercise they are seen as weak-willed and we blame them,' says Spector, who says his work has made him more understanding of his wayward patients. 'But some people don't have a genetic make-up that gives them a buzz out of exercise. Some enjoy it more than others. I don't think modern doctors realise this. They treat everyone the same and think that everyone gets the same rewards.'

Being burdened with the genes for laziness, however, doesn't justify slacking. It means trying that little bit harder to make the best of the hand you've been dealt. Spector says: 'It does seem like an excuse but the current medical model of bashing people and making people feel bad about themselves has the opposite effect. This doesn't change the advice you give to people to lose weight but it means that, for certain patients, for every kilo they lose they should feel ten times as proud.'

Ahuja, A. The Times, *4 December 2003* ”

Activity 39 *All in the genes?*

Discuss your thoughts about Professor Spector's research and findings and write a few sentences in response to the following questions.

1 Does the research prove that there is a genetic influence on people's beliefs about race?

2 Should this research make us less ready to criticise some people for not exercising more?

3 If there were a genetic basis for racist beliefs, would this provide an excuse for racism?

5.2 From your own point of view

What do you think?

In this final lesson, you are asked to look back over your earlier work and carry out a mini-research project.

Activity 40 *What do you think?*

Follow up one of the topics that has interested you most during this part of the course. Consult at least two other sources for material on the topic. Prepare a short summary to present to other students in your class.

Structure your summary using the steps set out at the start of Lesson 5.1. You may find it helpful to prepare a summary of the main viewpoints and your own view first, then discuss with a friend who agrees to act as 'devil's advocate', putting forward objections to your point of view, to which you can then work out replies.

PART 4

CARRYING OUT A RESEARCH PROJECT

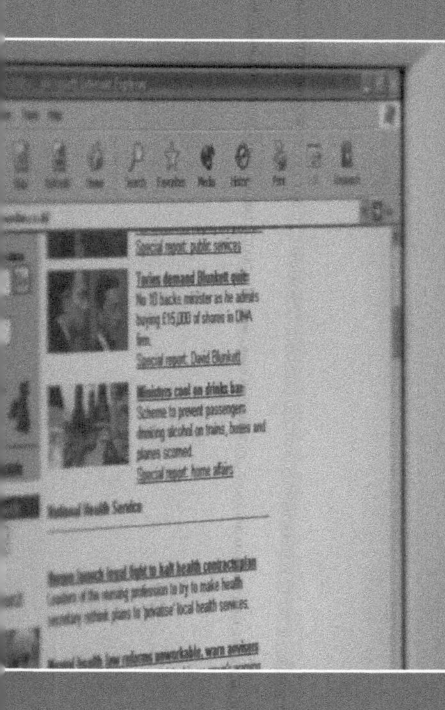

1 Introduction to carrying out a Research project

1.1 The *Perspectives on Science* Research project

What is the Research project?

A major part of your work for *Perspectives on Science* is the Research project. During the second half of the course, you will spend approximately half the lesson and homework time researching a topic of your choice. You will need to write a report of your research, which should be about 6000 words (maximum 7000) and give a 10-minute oral presentation on your project to an audience including your teacher/lecturer. Your teacher/lecturer will mark the report and presentation and your overall grade for the whole course will be determined by these marks.

For your Research project you will need to do the following.

- Decide on a research topic. It is very helpful to write your project title in the form of a question. Your project then involves researching how the question might be answered.
- Produce a summary of the science 'story' behind your question. You will need to consult a range of information sources and use them to give an account of the science as it is currently understood and how this understanding has developed.
- Discuss philosophical and ethical aspects of your question. You will need to state a point of view, and present and discuss philosophical and ethical arguments that relate to this viewpoint.

The research proposal

About half-way through your course, you will be asked to decide the topic for your project. You will need to discuss and agree your proposal with your teacher/lecturer.

The Course specification lists the broad research topic areas (Figure 1) within which you may do your project. They are:

- the origins of the universe
- the human mind
- the beginning and ending of life
- genetics
- animal welfare
- scientific revolutions
- the mechanistic universe.

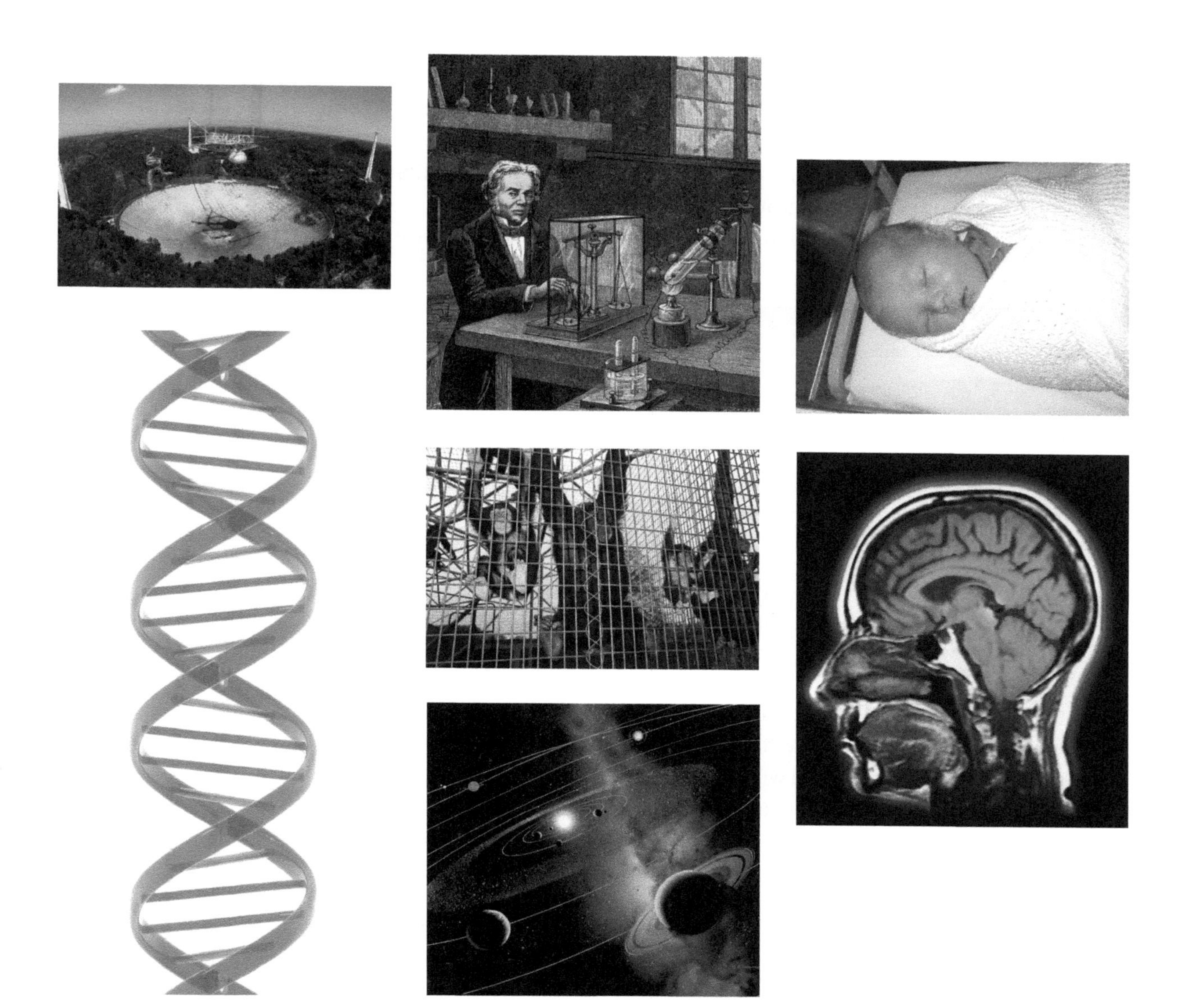

▲ ***Figure 1*** *The Research project must lie within one of seven broad topic areas.*

You need to think of a research question within one of these areas. Your project is most likely to be successful and enjoyable if you can answer yes to the following:

- Do you find the topic interesting?
- Does the topic relate to areas of science where you feel reasonably confident of your understanding?
- Does your project title raise a question that people have strong (and different) opinions about? Are there ethical and philosophical aspects to this question?
- Do you have some idea as to where you can start finding out more information about the topic?

Your research proposal should contain brief notes on:

- your choice of research question (which should fall within one of the specified topics)
- a rationale for the project – why you propose to research this question
- an outline of the science background to your question
- an identification of the philosophical and ethical aspects of your question.

Activity 1 *Writing a research proposal*

Write a proposal for your Research project. State the question you are proposing to research, write a few sentences explaining why you want to research this particular question, give a brief outline of the relevant science and indicate the ethical and philosophical aspects that you propose to discuss.

Discuss your proposal with your teacher or lecturer and modify it as necessary before submitting it.

1.2 Planning the Research project

Research and writing

You will have several weeks to carry out your Research project. A substantial amount of work will be involved and it is important to make the best use of your time. During this period you will probably have some lessons in which you are asked to take part in particular activities or tasks which contribute to your project, and others in which the time is made available for your own individual work. To make the best use of your time, you will need to keep in mind the two end-products of your project: the written report and the oral presentation. The written report is the main way in which you will report on your research (Figure 2). The report should be about 5000–6000 words long (maximum 7000 words).

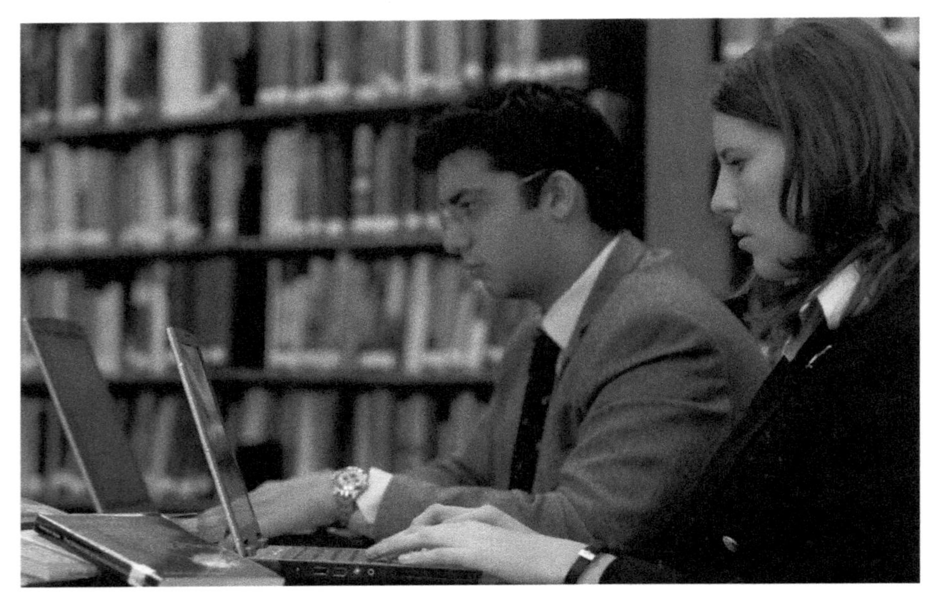

▲ ***Figure 2*** *Writing up.*

It's a good idea to write up your project as you go along. You might want to make some changes as your work progresses, but that's better than leaving all the writing until the last minute.

Your project report should be organised into the following headed sections. However, the order in which they appear in the report is *not* the order in which you should work on them and write them up.

Abstract (200–250 words)

To include:

- the project s aims
- the main arguments that you explored
- the conclusions that you reached.

Write this section last!

Introduction (750–1000 words)

- To include a statement of your research question.

  This should be an expanded and more detailed statement of your project's title.

- To outline a rationale for your choice of research topic.

  Why did you choose to explore this question?

  What, briefly, are the relevant areas of science?

  What philosophical and ethical issues are related to this question?

- To give definitions and explanations of key terms used in your project.

  Some of the terms you use will probably have been introduced in your earlier work on this course. Look back at your notes and the course materials to see how they are defined and explained. Try to provide similar definitions for any other terms that you use. Use reference books to help.

Write a first draft of this section when you write your research proposal. Then come back and change or add to it as you go along.

Literature review (1850–2500 words)

- To include an account of the science 'story' behind your research question.

  What is the relevant science?

  How has the accepted understanding of that science changed over time?

  Where and when did key developments take place?

  Who are, or were, the key people involved?

  What are, or were, the main influences on these people and their work?

- To provide a critical account of the sources you have consulted.

  Are they primary or secondary sources?

  How reliable are they likely to be?

All your sources should be identified and there should be full references to them in a **bibliography**. (The account of sources can be integrated with the science 'story'. It does not need to be a separate subsection.)

This section is the best place to start the main work on your project. As you put together the information for this section, your ideas for the Discussion should be taking shape. You should also construct your Bibliography while you work on this section.

Discussion (2650–3500 words)

- To begin with a statement of your own point of view on your research question.
- There should follow a detailed philosophical and ethical argument making a case for the point of view you have adopted, including your response to any counter-arguments that could be raised.

  What arguments can you use to support your own viewpoint?

  What are the counter-arguments and how can you address them?

  What are the assumptions underlying any of the arguments you discuss?

  Are the arguments logically valid?

  What philosophical and ethical positions have other people adopted?

  How can the various arguments and viewpoints be described using terms such as realist, utilitarian, and so on?

Start thinking about this section and making notes for it as you produce the Literature review. Start to write this section when you have more or less completed the Literature review. If you draw on any additional sources, be sure to include references to them and add them to the Bibliography.

Conclusion (570–750 words)

- To give a statement of your conclusion and the case you have presented for it.
- To include an evaluation of your project.

  What skills have you developed during your work?

  What have you learned about the research process?

  With hindsight, what might you have done differently?

  How might the project be extended by further work?

Write this section when you have finished work on your Literature review and Discussion. Then summarise it in a few sentences to help you write the Abstract.

Bibliography (no word limit)

- This is a list of all your information sources presented in a clear and logical fashion and following recognised conventions, to include full details of author, title, publication and date for each source.

Construct this section at the same time as you are writing the Literature review and the Discussion. Then, at the end, go through it and check that it is complete and correct.

Oral presentation

When you have completed your written report, you will be asked to make a 10-minute oral presentation to an audience including your teacher/lecturer. The oral presentation will contribute to the overall mark you receive for your project. The written report contributes 80 per cent of the marks and the oral presentation 20 per cent, so don't let the presentation dominate your research efforts; on the other hand, don't neglect it as 20 per cent is a substantial fraction of the total marks.

During the research period you will have several opportunities to develop your oral presentation skills. Try to take full advantage of these opportunities, particularly if you are nervous about speaking to an audience. Oral presentation is something that improves with practice, and increased skill leads to increased confidence.

Activity 2 *Planning*

In consultation with your teacher or lecturer, draw up a timetable for your Research project using Table 1 on page 192. Keep a copy in a safe and prominent place.

Table 1 Research project plan.

Research question:	
Deadline date for written report:	Date of oral presentation:
Section	*Time allowed (e.g. hours/lessons/weeks)*
Research proposal and planning	
Introduction	
Literature review	
Discussion	
Conclusion	
Abstract	
Bibliography and final revisions	
Preparing for oral presentation	
Week/date	*Section(s)*

2 Written report

2.1 Introduction

The Introduction

The Introduction is the first main section of your project report. Its purpose is to set the scene for your readers and draw them in to the report. Drafting the Introduction at an early stage can also help to focus your own mind on your research question. Then, as you gather information and refine your ideas, you can come back and revise your draft.

In writing your research proposal, you will have already done some work towards your project. Turning your research proposal into the first draft of your Introduction is a good way to get started on your project.

Your Introduction should have three main subsections, as follows.

Research question

As you begin work on your project, write a few sentences saying what you intend to research. During your research period, you might find that your work develops in ways that you did not anticipate. For your final report, you will need to rewrite your Introduction to describe the work you actually did. Any major changes of direction should be noted in the Conclusion to your report, where you reflect on the way your work developed during the research period.

Rationale and background

This is probably the longest subsection of your Introduction. To start, you should explain why you chose your research question. (Perhaps a personal experience has drawn your attention to a particular issue. Maybe your project relates to an intended future career or area of further study. Or maybe you read something, or saw a TV programme, that started you thinking about a particular question.)

You should also outline the science background to your project and note any relevant ethical and philosophical issues (you might do this as you are explaining why you chose this particular question). Here is an opportunity to demonstrate your knowledge of some of the terminology that you have learned earlier in the course and refer to relevant ethical and philosophical frameworks.

Course reference

You met ethical frameworks in Activities 5, 6, 7 and 8 of the Ethics part of the course. Key philosophical positions relating to science were introduced in Lessons 1.4–1.7, 3.2 and 4.1 of the Philosophy part of this course.

Definitions of key terms

Here you should note and define any key terms that you use in your report. Some of these might be unfamiliar technical terms that you come across during your research, but others will be 'everyday' terms (such as 'rights' or 'life') whose meaning needs to be made clear in the context of your project. Use dictionaries to help you, and try also to clarify the meanings by giving examples and 'criteria for use'.

Course reference

Section 2.3 in the Philosophy part of this course is about the careful use of language and techniques for defining terms.

Activity 3 *Drafting the Introduction*

Look back at your research question then write about 700 words as a draft Introduction to your project, using the guidelines above. Keep this draft in a safe place. As you prepare the final report on your project, return to your draft and modify it accordingly.

2.2 Literature review

The Literature review

It is best to start the main work on your project by gathering some information and working on the Literature review section of your report. The work you do here will also contribute to the Discussion section.

The Literature review is a summary of the science behind your project and an account of other work that has already been published which relates to your research question. It is essentially an account of who did what and what they have written (or said) about the topic. As far as possible, put the information in your own words rather than copying straight from the source.

A good literature review should tell a coherent 'story'. You can only really do this, however, after you have consulted several sources and found out what they contain. To start with, it is a good idea to keep a separate page of notes (either paper or electronic) for each source you consult. Then, when you have consulted several sources (Figure 3), you can start to sort your notes into a logical order and put them together to make your Literature review.

Use Table 2 opposite to help you plan your work for this part of your project.

▲ **Figure 3** *Visiting the Salford University library.*

Getting started

Here are some things to think about before you start.

- Where will you begin to look for information?
- Are there some useful books in your school/college library?
- Do you know of any relevant websites?
- Are there people or organisations that might be able to give you information? How do you plan to contact or visit them?
- Might you be able to find relevant items in newspapers or magazines (e.g. *New Scientist*) or from TV programmes?

Table 2 Planning the Literature review.

Research question	
What will you research? Consider the science story, context, key individuals and dates, influences on the principal characters. Also consider source evaluation (reliability, primary or secondary, fact, speculation or opinion).	
What sources will you use? Consider libraries, museums, websites, people worth talking to.	
What will you do? Collecting materials, note-taking, building the bibliography, assembling the Literature review, editing, adding evaluation of sources, further research.	
Deadline (date)	
Week (date)	*Actions*

For each information source that you use, keep a careful record of the following:

- full details of the source
- for books and articles: the author(s), title, publisher and date
- for websites: the full URL, the name(s) of the person or organisation that produced the site (if available) and the date when you consulted the site
- for any relevant quotes within the source: full details of their origin.

You will need this information for your Bibliography. In case you should want to revisit the same source later, collate the following information:

- A summary of the relevant information that it contains.

  Look for the '5 Ws' – who, what, where, why, when (and how).

- A summary of any relevant philosophical and/or ethical arguments used or quoted by the authors.

  What assumptions are being made?

  Is the argument valid?

  Are there any flaws?

  What is the philosophical position adopted?

  What ethical framework is being used?

- A brief review of the nature of the source.

  Is it a primary or secondary source?

  Does it contain reliable fact, subjective opinion or speculation?

  Could the author(s) have a vested interest, and might they be biased?

Course reference

You met the '5 W's in Activities 2 and 3 of the History part of this course and used them in later activities to analyse and summarise information (e.g. History Activities 5 and 13).

Course reference

Lessons 1.2 and 3.3 in the History part of the course describe various types of source material.
In the History part of the course you met several techniques for summarising and presenting information. See, for example, History Activities 5, 12, 18, 19, 20 and 32.
Activities 5, 11, 26, 30 and 32 in the History part of the course included a critical discussion of sources.

Course reference

Some key philosophical positions relating to science were introduced in Lessons 1.4–1.7, 3.2 and 4.1 of the Philosophy part of this course.

Course reference

You met ethical frameworks Activities 5, 6, 7 and 8 of the Ethics part of the course and used them in many later activities (e.g. Ethics Activities 12, 14, 15, 19, 34 and 36).

Activity 4 *Starting the Literature review*

Choose *three* information sources that you have consulted for your project and write an account of how they contribute to your research question.

Later, as you consult more sources and your project develops, you can modify and add to this account and hence produce your Literature review.

2.3 Good communication

Written communication

When consulting source materials for your project, you probably found some that were clear and easy to read, and others that were more difficult. Of course, the 'difficulty' of a piece of text depends partly on its content, but the way it is written and presented can also make a huge difference to whether it is easy to read and understand.

Your experience of reading other people's work should help you with your own writing. You should aim to make your project report as clear and readable as possible. You want your readers to know what you have found out, to follow your arguments and to understand your point of view.

Course reference

The style in which a report is written can affect the way readers respond to it. See, for example, Ethics Activity 23.

Activity 5 *Written communication*

Figure 4 overleaf lists various features that might make a project report easier, or more difficult, to read. Work in a small group to sort the features in Figure 4 into three categories: those that, in your experience, make a long piece of text easier to read and understand; those that make it more difficult or off-putting; and those that make no difference. Then write a checklist of points to look out for in your own report.

Activity 6 *Well written?*

As you write your report, bear in mind your checklist from Activity 5 and try to write as clearly as possible. When you have written a section, put it aside for a day then re-read it. Something that you thought was very clear when you first wrote it might not read quite so well when you come to it with fresh eyes.

If possible, exchange drafts with another student. Try to give one another polite but honest feedback on readability, then act upon it.

Course reference

In the History part of the course you met several techniques for summarising and presenting information (e.g. History Activities 5, 12, 18, 19, 20 and 32). Consider how you might use these in your Research project report.

In Philosophy Lesson 2.3 you used various techniques to define and clarify key terms.

2.4 All my own work

Whose work is it anyway?

Using someone else's work and pretending it is your own is called **plagiarism**. It is a form of cheating. For example, a scientist who 'borrowed' someone else's results and published them under his or her own name would be committing plagiarism.

Activity 7 *Whose work is it anyway?*

In a small group, discuss situations in which plagiarism might occur.

short, clear sentences

text organised under main headings and subheadings

lots of rambling repetition (is the writer not worried about boring or confusing you?)

a logical development with a clear beginning, middle and end

numbered pages

very small print and narrow margins

lots of unexplained unfamiliar words to keep you guessing

long sentences with little or no punctuation (the writer is really making you work hard)

short, clear paragraphs

colourful illustrations

a quirky style with lots of slang words to show how cool the writer is (cool or annoying?)

no clear structure (the writer keeps losing track of where he or she is going – and so do you)

summaries of important points (the writer is sure about what he/she wants to tell you)

contradictions and inconsistencies (how do you know what the writer really means?)

'signposting' to alert you to what's coming next (e.g 'There are three key ideas here: first…')

clear explanations of unfamiliar words and ideas

a pompous style with lots of long words and long sentences to show how clever the writer is (or thinks he/she is)

▲ ***Figure 4*** *Factors affecting the readability of a report.*

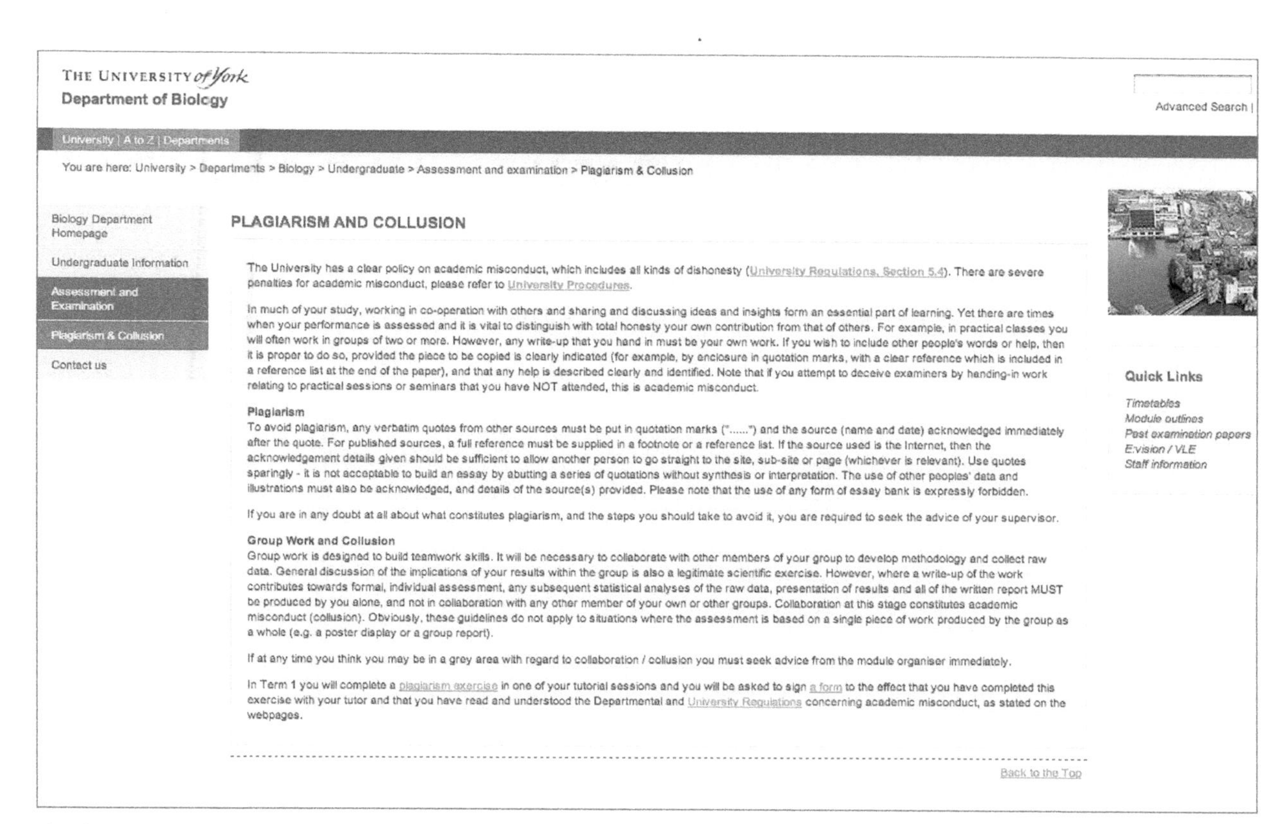

THE UNIVERSITY *of York*
Department of Biology

Advanced Search |

University | A to Z | Departments

You are here: University > Departments > Biology > Undergraduate > Assessment and examination > Plagiarism & Collusion

Biology Department Homepage
Undergraduate Information
Assessment and Examination
Plagiarism & Collusion
Contact us

PLAGIARISM AND COLLUSION

The University has a clear policy on academic misconduct, which includes all kinds of dishonesty (University Regulations, Section 5.4). There are severe penalties for academic misconduct, please refer to University Procedures.

In much of your study, working in co-operation with others and sharing and discussing ideas and insights form an essential part of learning. Yet there are times when your performance is assessed and it is vital to distinguish with total honesty your own contribution from that of others. For example, in practical classes you will often work in groups of two or more. However, any write-up that you hand in must be your own work. If you wish to include other people's words or help, then it is proper to do so, provided the piece to be copied is clearly indicated (for example, by enclosure in quotation marks, with a clear reference which is included in a reference list at the end of the paper), and that any help is described clearly and identified. Note that if you attempt to deceive examiners by handing-in work relating to practical sessions or seminars that you have NOT attended, this is academic misconduct.

Plagiarism
To avoid plagiarism, any verbatim quotes from other sources must be put in quotation marks ("......") and the source (name and date) acknowledged immediately after the quote. For published sources, a full reference must be supplied in a footnote or a reference list. If the source used is the Internet, then the acknowledgement details given should be sufficient to allow another person to go straight to the site, sub-site or page (whichever is relevant). Use quotes sparingly - it is not acceptable to build an essay by abutting a series of quotations without synthesis or interpretation. The use of other peoples' data and illustrations must also be acknowledged, and details of the source(s) provided. Please note that the use of any form of essay bank is expressly forbidden.

If you are in any doubt at all about what constitutes plagiarism, and the steps you should take to avoid it, you are required to seek the advice of your supervisor.

Group Work and Collusion
Group work is designed to build teamwork skills. It will be necessary to collaborate with other members of your group to develop methodology and collect raw data. General discussion of the implications of your results within the group is also a legitimate scientific exercise. However, where a write-up of the work contributes towards formal, individual assessment, any subsequent statistical analyses of the raw data, presentation of results and all of the written report MUST be produced by you alone, and not in collaboration with any other member of your own or other groups. Collaboration at this stage constitutes academic misconduct (collusion). Obviously, these guidelines do not apply to situations where the assessment is based on a single piece of work produced by the group as a whole (e.g. a poster display or a group report).

If at any time you think you may be in a grey area with regard to collaboration / collusion you must seek advice from the module organiser immediately.

In Term 1 you will complete a plagiarism exercise in one of your tutorial sessions and you will be asked to sign a form to the effect that you have completed this exercise with your tutor and that you have read and understood the Departmental and University Regulations concerning academic misconduct, as stated on the webpages.

Back to the Top

Quick Links
Timetables
Module outlines
Past examination papers
E:vision / VLE
Staff information

▲ ***Figure 5*** *Many organisations have strict policies and codes of practice against plagiarism.*

Any writer, scientist or historian who is found to have plagiarised someone else's work is likely to have their career and reputation permanently damaged or destroyed. Author Dan Brown was accused of plagiarising someone else's work to write his bestselling novel *The Da Vinci Code*, and in spring of 2006 he fought – and won – a long and expensive court case to clear his name and reputation. In July 2004 the BBC was fined several thousand pounds for including, in a history programme about Harlech Castle, several phrases that were extremely similar to those used in a Channel 4 programme on the same building. Hamish Mykura, head of history at Channel 4, described the incident as 'unprecedented' and said 'I am absolutely astonished. Imitation may be the sincerest form of flattery, but I'm not sure what this is.' He went on to say 'When a programme claims to have an author's voice, it should be that author's voice and no one else's.' (*Guardian*, June 2004)

Activity 8 *What's wrong with plagiarism?*

Plagiarism is regarded as a serious wrongdoing. Discuss reasons for this and consider how you might use various ethical frameworks to make the case against (or in favour of) plagiarism.

Course reference

You met ethical frameworks in Section 1 of the Ethics part of the course; see Ethics Activities 5, 6, 7 and 8. The ethical behaviour of scientists is discussed in Ethics Section 5.

Avoiding plagiarism

By now, it will probably be obvious where this is leading: your own Research project. Plagiarism is a potential issue with any written coursework, so it is important that you understand what is, and is not, acceptable. As well as reading this Student book, you should also read the relevant parts of the Course specification.

The Internet is a huge resource and contains not only 'raw material' for research but websites from which it is possible to obtain entire essays and projects. *It is most important that you resist the temptation to paste such material into your own project*. In addition to the ethical aspect, such material is likely to be detected by your teacher/lecturer and the coursework moderator, with serious consequences – your project could be disqualified. And when you come to give your oral presentation, you will find it difficult to talk convincingly and answer questions about work you have copied from elsewhere while pretending to have done it yourself.

Deliberate plagiarism as described above is easy to avoid: just don't do it. But in practice, plagiarism is more likely to be accidental. In your project, you are expected to use a range of resources to gather information and to help you discuss your research question. 'Research' does not mean 'developing absolutely everything from scratch'. Indeed, the very nature of the project means that you will need to draw on a large body of existing literature and synthesise your own project from the work of others together with your own ideas.

There is absolutely nothing wrong with quoting exactly what somebody else has said or written. But the key term here is 'quoting'. Any material quoted from elsewhere should be clearly indicated either by quotation marks or by consistently using a different font, and full details of the source should be given either in the main text (e.g. using footnotes) or in the Bibliography. (For example, material quoted in this Student book is always distinguished from the rest of the text and always followed immediately by details of the source.) Only if quoted material is 'hidden' and passed off as your own original work does quoting become plagiarism.

2.5 Bibliography and footnotes

This lesson shows you two techniques that are widely used by authors of academic books and articles. You should aim to use both while writing your Research project.

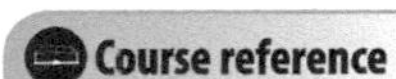

Course reference

Activities 17 and 32 in the History part of the course drew attention to the importance of keeping careful records of source material.

Bibliography

A bibliography is a list of all the sources referred to in a project, essay or research paper. It is usually placed at the end under the heading 'bibliography' or 'references'. Its purpose is to make clear to readers exactly how other people's work has been used, and to enable readers to consult the same sources themselves if they so wish.

When you draw on or refer to work from another source (Figure 6), this must be made clear in the main text (otherwise you are probably committing plagiarism) and you must give clear details to enable readers to find the same source.

Bibliography

K. Ansell-Pearson & D. Large, *The Nietzsche Reader*. Blackwell, Oxford (2005).

D. Cadbury, *The Dinosaur Hunters*. Fourth Estate, London (2001).

W. Ellwood & J. McMurty, *The No-nonsense Guide to Globalisation*. New Internationalist Publications (2001).

E. Evans, *The Birth of Modern Britain 1780–1914*. Longman, London (1997).

L. Freedman, *Atlas of Global Strategy*. Macmillan, London (1985).

A. Hunt & R. Millar, *AS Science for Public Understanding*. Heinemann, Oxford (2000).

E. Nisbet, *Getting heated over glaciation*. Nature **422**, 812–813 (2003).

R. Rees, *Poverty and Public Health 1815–1948*. Heinemann, Oxford (2001).

M. B. Steger, *Globalization: A Very Short Introduction*. Oxford University Press, Oxford (2003)

D. Watts, *Whigs, Liberals and Radicals 1815–1914*. Hodder & Stoughton, London (1995).

J. Watson & F. Crick, *Molecular structure of nucleic acids*. Nature, **171**, 737–738 (1953).

▲ ***Figure 6*** *All sources must be referenced in a bibliography.*

There are two main conventions for organising references: alphabetical and numerical. An advantage of the alphabetical system is that readers immediately get some information about the source you have used without having to turn to another page, and an advantage of the numerical system is that it is a bit more compact, particularly when referring to websites. For your own project, choose whichever you prefer and stick to it consistently.

Alphabetical

In the main text, where you quote or refer to a printed source, give the surname(s) of the author(s) in brackets followed by the year of publication, e.g. (Close, 1990) or (Pears and Shields, 2004). If there are three or more authors, it is usual just to list the first one then write 'et al.' (meaning 'and others'), e.g. (Cobley et al., 2006). If you are referring to a website, the brackets should contain the author, if known, and the URL of the home page, e.g. (Atyiah, www.bmj.com).

In your Bibliography, each reference should be given as shown below.

For books:

Surname, initials (year) *Name of book in italic*, publisher, place of publication, chapter number, page number(s)

Details of publication are usually printed on the reverse of the title page at the front of the book.

For journals (or magazines):

Surname, initials (year) Title of article, *Name of journal in italic*, **Volume number (issue number if applicable) in bold**, page number(s)

Details of volume and issue number are usually given on the contents page and/or in the header or footer running along each page.

For websites:

Author or editor (year) *Title* [online]. Publisher, place of publication. Available from: URL [date of access]

Ideally your reference should contain all these details, but in practice many websites do not include such full information so include as much as you can find. Sometimes the 'author' is an organisation rather than a named person.

In the bibliography, sources should be listed in alphabetical order of surname of first author, regardless of the order in which they relate to your main text. For example:

Atiyah, M. (1999) *Science for Evil: the Scientist's Dilemma* [online]. British Medical Journal, London. Available from: www.bmj.bmjjournals.com/cgi/content/full/319/7207/448 [accessed 4 January 2005]

Close, F. (1990) *Too Hot to Handle*, W. H. Allen, London, Ch 11, pp. 192–3

Holmes, B. (2004) Squeeze gently to clone monkeys, *New Scientist*, **184 (2477)**, p. 8

Pears, R and Shields, G. (2004) *Cite them Right: Referencing Made Easy,* Northumbria University Press.

Royal Society (2004) *The Use of Non-human Animals in Research: A Guide for Scientists* [online]. Royal Society, London. Available from: www.royalsoc.ac.uk/displaypagedoc.asp?id=10298 [accessed 4 January 2005]

Numerical

In the main text, refer to sources by numbers in either square brackets [1] or superscripts[1] – use either one system or the other, not a mixture. The first source you refer to is [1], the second [2], and so on. If you need to refer to the same source later, use the same number as before.

The references are then listed in numerical order in your bibliography. The conventions for listing names of authors and publications are similar to the alphabetical system, only the initials come before the surnames and the publication years are put in a different place. For example:

1 B. Holmes, Squeeze gently to clone monkeys, *New Scientist*, 2004, **184 (2477)**, p. 8

2 M. Atiyah., *Science for Evil: the Scientist's Dilemma* [online], 1999. British Medical Journal, London. Available from: www.bmj.bmjjournals.com/cgi/content/full/319/7207/448 [accessed 4 January 2005]

3 R. Pears and G. Shields, *Cite them Right: Referencing Made Easy*, 2004, Northumbria University Press

4 F. Close, *Too Hot to Handle*, 1990, W. H. Allen, London, Ch 11, pp. 192–3

5 Royal Society *The Use of Non-human Animals in Research: A Guide for Scientists* [online], 2004. Royal Society, London. Available from: www.royalsoc.ac.uk/displaypagedoc.asp?id=10298 [accessed 4 January 2005]

Activity 9 *References*

Look at some examples of publications and notice how they refer to other sources.

Use one of the conventions described above to produce references for a selection of printed and web-based materials. Ideally, use sources that you are consulting for your project.

Footnotes

The point of a footnote, in an academic document, is to provide supplementary information without interrupting the main flow of the text. Specifically, footnotes may be used to provide such information as the following:

- details of a reference – either textual or web-based. This is particularly helpful if the reference is lengthy, as it will be if it is a full URL
- comments on a source which has been used in the text
- comments on the main argument.

Suppose, for example, that you were making an argument about the rights of animals. You may well have chosen a particular definition for the term 'rights', and in a footnote you might explain that this was your own choice and that other people have different definitions. The footnote could also contain a reference so that the reader can follow up these other definitions, if he or she so chooses.

When writing your literature review, footnotes are a sensible place for the evaluation of your sources. If you incorporate all this information (whether your source is primary or secondary, whether it contains facts, speculation or opinion, and whether it is objective or biased) in the flow of the text, it will distract the reader from the main point. On the other hand, leaving it to the end makes it seem disconnected from your science story. Here is an ideal opportunity to demonstrate that you can make good use of footnotes.

Footnotes are usually indicated by superscript letters or numbers that refer the reader to additional information at the foot of the page. Most word-processing packages allow you to insert footnotes very easily[a] . If you are using the numerical convention for your bibliography, make sure you don't have two confusing numbering systems – use letters for your footnotes and/or use numbers in square brackets for your references.

Activity 10 *Footnotes*

Select one page of your Literature review, or mini-literature review if you have not yet begun writing the main thing. Insert some footnotes to do some of the tasks listed above.

2.6 Using web resources

Strengths and weaknesses of web resources

In the course of your Research project, you will almost certainly want to make use of the vast resources available via the Internet (Figure 7). Just as you would with any source, it is important to think critically about what you read on the Internet. You cannot assume that what you are reading is objective, unbiased fact.

Activity 11 *Strengths and weaknesses of web resources*

List all the possible strengths and weaknesses of web-based resources that you can think of. Compare your list with those of other students.

▲ ***Figure 7*** *Using the Internet.*

---

[a] If you are using Word on a PC, you will find footnotes by selecting 'Insert' on the main toolbar, then selecting 'Reference' followed by 'Footnote'.

Evaluating web resources

When you are browsing the web to help your research, you should be asking yourself questions both in order to understand what you read and also to evaluate reliability.

The '5 W's

In the *History* part of this course you encountered the '5 W' questions: what, who, when, where and why. These can be applied to the material you find on the web. When doing web research, key questions to ask include:

- What is this site telling me?
- Who put this material on the web?
- When was this information placed here (is it still up to date)?
- Where is the information placed (what site does it belong to)?
- Why has this information been placed on the web (is it there merely to inform or is it meant to convince me of a particular point of view)?

> **Course reference**
>
> Activities 5, 11, 26, 30 and 32 in the History part of the course included a critical discussion of sources.

Primary or secondary?

In the *History* part of this course you learned about the importance of distinguishing between primary and secondary sources. This is especially significant when reading material published on the Internet since much of it is not factual but represents a personal point of view, or speculation. The key questions here are:

- Is this material a primary or secondary source?
- Is the material fact, subjective opinion or speculation?

Reliability

Establishing the reliability of web material is not easy, but questions that can be asked include the following:

- How much authority does the author have (e.g. is he/she a recognised expert, a student or an interested amateur)?
- Is the site where the work is published a reputable source? (E.g. does it have a reputation for impartiality? Has the research been peer reviewed?)
- Is the process by which the information was obtained rigorous? (E.g. is it based on controlled testing? Was the sample used sufficiently large and unbiased?)

> **Activity 12** *Evaluating web resources*
>
> Choose a website with information relevant to your Research project and carry out an evaluation using the questions listed above.

2.7 What do you think?

What's the point of a point of view?

If you look back to the research proposal you wrote before beginning your Research project, you will remember that you chose a particular research question. Ideally, you chose this question because you found it interesting and worth studying. It is likely that you have a point of view – you think one particular answer to the question is true. Perhaps you are cautious and would prefer just to say that one answer is better than another. However you express it, your Research project will be much stronger if you can identify clearly what you really think about your research question. You need to have a clearly defined point of view.

When discussing ethical and philosophical questions, some people can only see things from their own point of view. They cannot understand the opposite side of the debate at all. At the other extreme, some people shrug their shoulders and decide that we can never know what to believe since there are always good arguments on both sides of the debate.

The best approach lies between these extremes. In the Discussion section of your Research project, you should definitely consider arguments on both sides of the debate. Doing this is part of recognising that people who think deeply about the issues still come to different conclusions. However, it is also important that you form a view of your own and try to defend it. It might seem as though you are being fairer by just stating both sides of the argument. In reality, though, you will learn more and understand the issues better if you try to argue for your own viewpoint. It is when you do this that you will discover where the real strengths and weaknesses in your ideas lie.

Course reference

Much of the Philosophy part of this course is devoted to developing thinking skills and setting out arguments relating to a point of view. See Philosophy Sections 2 and 5 in particular.

There are many activities in the Ethics part that relate to the discussion of a point of view, including Activities 12, 14, 15, 18, 22, 28, 31 and 39. See also History Activities 12, 25, 30 and 31.

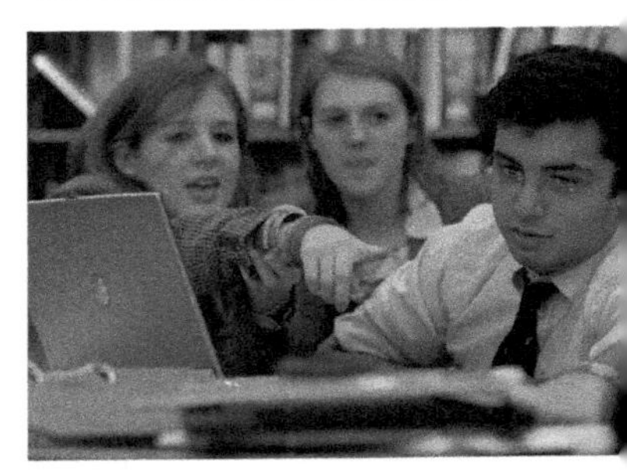

▲ ***Figure 8*** *Discussing points of view.*

Course reference

To clarify your thinking, it can be helpful to list arguments both for and against a point of view. See for example Ethics Activities 15, 18 and 27, and Philosophy Activities 17, 21, 25, 29 and 34.

Activity 13 *Identifying a point of view*

Re-read your research proposal, then briefly explain to others in your class what your research question is and how you would answer the question.

Clarifying your point of view

Philosophy is a subject which is all about thinking clearly. People hold all sorts of opinions on philosophical or ethical questions but their ideas are often quite vague. A central skill that you will be expected to demonstrate in the Discussion section of your Research project is that of expressing your point of view clearly. This is a skill which you began to develop when you looked at how to define key words.

Course reference

Lesson 2.3 in the Philosophy part of this course is about the careful use of language and techniques for defining terms.

Example 1

Suppose you are writing a Research project about embryonic stem cell research. You will need to define each of the following words:

- Embryonic: what is an embryo? Is it the same as a fetus? Is an embryo a human being? Is an embryo an individual? Is an embryo a person?
- Stem cell: what are stem cells? How are they different from other cells? Can there be different types of stem cell?
- Research: what types of activity do scientists do with embryonic stem cells? Is research different from medical treatment? Could some research also involve treatment?

As well as thinking about the definitions of key words, you can clarify your point of view by considering the viewpoint of those with whom you disagree. This is one reason why it is important to have a viewpoint of your own – you can then sharpen your ideas by contrasting them with opposing viewpoints.

Example 2

Suppose your point of view is that embryonic stem cell research is a good idea. This is a point of view which you could defend in your Research project. But before you started arguing for it, you would need to clarify exactly what it is that you believe.

- Do you think every type of embryonic stem cell research is a good idea?
- Do you think that some types are acceptable while others are not?
- What do the opponents of such research believe?
- Do you disagree with them completely or are there some cases where you agree?

Asking questions such as these is a way of helping to clarify your point of view.

It is also helpful to think about what general ethical and/or philosophical frameworks you accept. In lessons 1.4 and 1.6 of the *Philosophy* part of this course, you came across frameworks such as realism, relativism and falsificationism. When studying the *Ethics* part of this course, you looked at common ethical frameworks including utilitarianism, divine command, rights and virtues. When you are thinking about your point of view, you should consider which of these frameworks you accept. You can then classify your position – you will know where you stand in the debate.

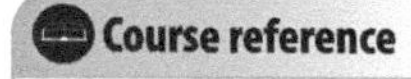
Course reference

For a summary of commonly used ethical frameworks, see Ethics Section 1. For philosophical frameworks relating to science, see Philosophy Lessons 1.4–1.7, 3.2 and 4.1.

Example 3

Suppose you decide to defend the point of view that embryonic stem cell research, up to a certain time limit and for certain purposes, is acceptable. Why do you think this? Is it because of utilitarian reasons (this research will bring more benefit than any harm it involves)? Or is it because you have thought about the rights involved and think that embryos up to a certain time limit do not have rights? Perhaps you prefer to adopt the divine command theory – in which case your point of view will be a religious one.

When you have thought about such questions as these, you will be able to describe and explain your viewpoint more clearly (e.g. 'I adopt a utilitarian viewpoint', 'My viewpoint is religious', 'My viewpoint is based on rights').

Activity 14 *What do they think?*

Using a copy of the questionnaire in Table 3, work with another member of your class and interview one another about your Research project and your points of view. When you are the interviewer, write your partner's answers in the spaces provided in the questionnaire. Then make some suggestions about what he or she could do to make his/her point of view clearer still. Bear in mind that this is a constructive exercise – you are not aiming to criticise someone else's ideas just for the sake of being critical.

Course reference

It can be helpful to use a table to list evidence and arguments that support, or undermine, a point of view. See, for example, History Activity 26, and Ethics Activities 15, 18 and 27.

Table 3 Thinking clearly about points of view.

Name of interviewer:	*Name of interviewee:*
1. What is the interviewee's research question?	
2. What is the interviewee's point of view about his/her research question?	
3. What are the key words the interviewee has used in describing his/her point of view?	
4. How does the interviewee define each of these key words?	
5. What viewpoints does the interviewee disagree with?	
6. What philosophical and/or ethical frameworks does the interviewee use when defending his/her point of view?	
7. In what ways could the interviewee make his/her point of view clearer or more precise?	

▲ ***Figure 9*** *Interviewing a peer.*

Activity 15 *What do you think?*

Write a summary of the answers you have given to the interview questions and a short response to the comments made by your interviewer about how your point of view could be made clearer.

2.8 Discussing discussions

The Discussion

The Discussion section of your Research project is the section where you describe your own point of view and why you believe it. This means defining what it is you believe as clearly as possible, then going on to find arguments in favour of your viewpoint as well as answers to arguments against it.

What is the difference between the Discussion section and the Literature review? The Literature review looks mainly at the background science for your project, the people who discovered this science and the context in which they worked. It also involves assessing the reliability of the source materials which you are using. In the Discussion section, you will also want to make use of source material but for a different purpose. The source material will mainly be philosophical and ethical arguments about your research question. Your aim will be to analyse these arguments critically and to build up a strong case for your own point of view. This will involve presenting arguments in favour of your point of view, as well as considering and trying to answer objections.

Course reference

The Philosophy part of the course is particularly relevant to the Discussion section of your project. See Philosophy Sections 2 and 5 in particular.

Activities in other parts of the course are also relevant. See, for example, History Activities 30 and 31, and Ethics Activities 15, 18 and 27.

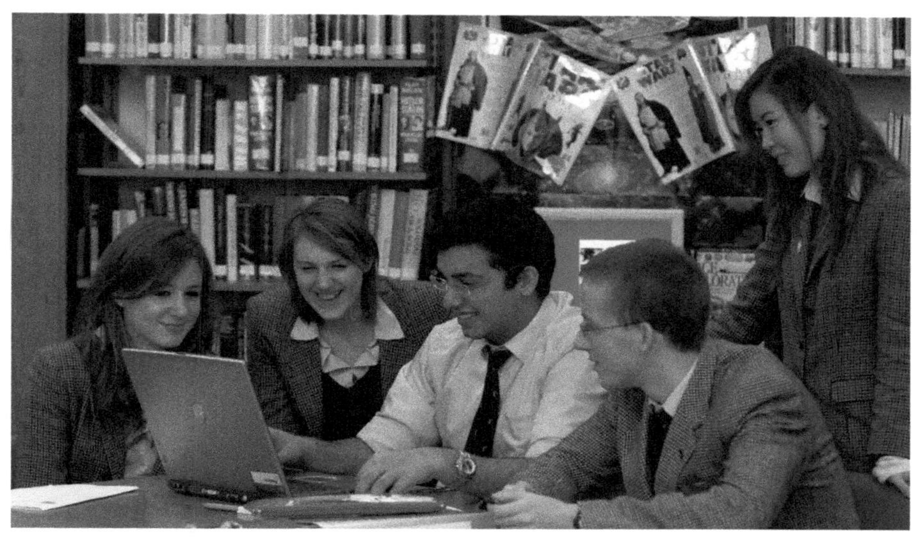

▲ ***Figure 10*** *Discussing discussions.*

Activity 16 Analysing the news

Working in a small group or with a partner, look through a recent edition of a newspaper.

Find an article in which the author is arguing for his/her particular point of view. Make notes using the headings from Table 4 to help you analyse the author's arguments. (Your headings should refer to the author's point of view, arguments and so on, rather than your own.)

Write a letter to the newspaper replying to the author of the argument you have read. Before doing this it may be helpful to look at how letters to the paper are written. They tend to be brief (no more than 400 words). They contain criticism of the author's arguments and usually also a defence of the letter writer's point of view. You should aim to write in the style appropriate to the newspaper you have read.

Use Table 4 to help you plan your work for this part of your project.

Table 4 Discussion planner.

Research question	
Central philosophical and ethical theories which people use to answer your question	
Statement of your point of view	
Supporting lines of argument for your point of view	
Objections to your point of view	
Response to objections	
General comments about the limitations of your case	

2.9 Conclusion

Reaching a conclusion

The purpose of the Conclusion of your Research project is to look back and to look forwards. Looking back means summarising what you have argued for – what your point of view is and how you have tried to argue your case. It also means looking back to see how your ideas have changed. It may be that your point of view has altered, either because you have changed your mind or because you have learned to define your position more clearly. Look back at your original research question, and to the first draft of your Introduction (Lesson 2.1) and reflect on the ways your project developed. Even if you have not changed your point of view, you will almost certainly have learned more about the arguments for and against your position. The Conclusion provides you with an opportunity to step back and put all of this experience into context. You will have learned a great deal, not just about your particular research topic but about the nature of research and philosophical debate. You now know a good deal more about how arguments work and how to cope in a rational manner with the differences of opinion about deep ethical and philosophical questions.

▲ ***Figure 11*** Talking can help clarify your Conclusion.

Activity 17 *The story of your project*

Working with another student, take it in turns to interview one another in order to help tell the story of your Research project. Don't worry about making notes. The aim of the exercise is to give one another a chance to think about how the research process has gone – how your ideas have changed and what you have learned about research itself. It is not easy to do this kind of thinking (the technical name is 'metacognition' – thinking about thinking). You will need to be a patient and helpful interviewer.

The key questions to address (along with others if you find them helpful) are:

- Can you summarise your point of view and the case you have made for it?
- How have your ideas developed during the course of the project?
- What have you learned about the research process?
- If you could continue your project, what further work would you do?

Activity 18 *Telling your story*

Your experience in Activity 17 will have helped you to reflect on the work you have done for your Research project. A good conclusion is one in which this story is also well presented. Working with a different partner, tell the story of your Research project. You should cover all the points that have come up in the course of your interview:

- a summary of your point of view
- how your ideas have developed in the course of the project
- what you have learned about the research process
- what further work you could do.

Activity 19 *Writing your story*

Write the story of your Research project, making sure that you answer all the four key questions asked in Activity 17. What you write will form the basis of the Conclusion of your Research project.

2.10 Abstract

Abstract questions

In carrying out your Literature review, you may have come across articles that begin with a short **abstract** summarising their key points. Academic journal articles generally include an abstract, and you will need to provide one for your Research project.

Course reference

Several earlier activities in this course involve summarising information. See, for example, History Activities 5, 10 and 17, Ethics Activity 22, and Philosophy Activities 14, 24 and 28.

Activity 20 *Abstract questions*

In a small group, spend a few minutes discussing the following questions.

- What do you think is the purpose of an abstract? Who is it written for?
- What are some key features of a good abstract?

For your Research project, you are asked to write an abstract of 200–250 words summarising your work. Although it is placed at the start of your report, you should write it last! After you have written the report, you should write an abstract that summarises the main points of your work, then read carefully through your work and make sure that the abstract really does reflect what the report says.

Activity 21 *Writing an abstract*

Read carefully through an article or a book chapter and write an abstract in no more than 250 words summing up its main points.

Compare your abstract with one written by someone else for the same article or chapter. Discuss any similarities and differences between what you have written and try to come to an agreement about what should, or should not, be included in the abstract. Then revise your own abstract as you feel necessary.

2.11 The final report

The final report

When you have written all the sections of your project report, before you finally hand it in you will want to edit it to make sure that it reads well, that your point of view is clear and that the main lines of your argument can be clearly followed. There are two aspects to this – content (what you have written) and communication (the way you have written it) – and your report will be assessed on both these aspects. Activities 5 and 6 (Lesson 2.3) referred to communication, and you might like to revisit them as you prepare your final draft. Here we are concerned with the content of your report and the way it is organised.

Activity 22 *Editing*

Use the checklists below to make sure your project report contains everything that it needs to, and that things are in the correct sections.

Abstract

- Have you stated the point of view you defend in your project?
- Have you outlined the aims, arguments and conclusions of your project?
- Is your abstract in a logical order?
- Have you related your project to the main theories relevant to your topic?

Introduction

- Do you have a well-defined research question?
- Have you stated your rationale for your choice of question?
- Have you described the scientific, ethical and philosophical aspects of your question?
- Have you given an analysis of the key terms used in your project?
- Is your introduction well structured?
- Does your introduction lead into your project?
- Have you explained how your project fits into discussion of your topic?

Literature review

- Have you chosen material which provides an original context for your project?
- Have you given a detailed outline of the science story?
- Do you include key dates and people involved in the science story?
- Do you discuss the influences on the principal characters?
- Have you evaluated the reliability of your sources?
- Have you considered which sources are primary and which are secondary?
- Have you distinguished between fact, speculation and opinion?

Discussion

- Is your point of view defined using terms drawn from central philosophical and ethical theories?
- Have you given supporting arguments for your point of view?
- Have you considered and responded to objections to your point of view?
- Have you considered any limitations of your arguments?
- Is the overall argument well balanced (have you considered opposite viewpoints to your own)?
- Do the different parts of the discussion link together to form an integrated case?
- Is your discussion logically argued and have you been careful to use language precisely throughout?

Conclusion

- Does your conclusion provide a clear summary of your point of view?
- Have you reflected on how your ideas have developed during the course of the project?
- Have you explained what you have learned about the research process?
- Have you included ideas about possible extensions to your Research project?

References and bibliography

- Have you included references to all your sources?
- Have you used a consistent system of references throughout the report?
- Do you use footnotes to provide additional information?
- Is your bibliography properly constructed (listing author, title, publisher, publication date, edition number, page numbers)?

General

- Is your report within the word limit?
- Have you checked the spelling?

3 Oral presentation

3.1 Preparing to speak

Planning an oral presentation

You will be asked to give a 10-minute presentation on your Research project. Afterwards you will be expected to answer questions on your work.

Some of the discussions and debates in the first half of the course will have helped you to develop the necessary skills of oral presentation. The activities in this lesson are designed to help you plan and deliver your oral presentation, and during the research period you should have some opportunities to practise for the presentation by giving short oral reports on you work in progress.

Giving an oral presentation can be daunting. Sometimes it can be easier if the audience is made up of people you know well (you are talking to friends so can relax); on the other hand, sometimes it is easier to talk to complete strangers (you can put on an act that is quite different from your usual shy self). Either way, you need to prepare carefully. In summary, the main tips are:

- plan the content of your talk in some detail
- prepare some visual aids to help both the audience and yourself
- practise the talk out loud.

▲ ***Figure 12*** *Oral presentation.*

Course reference

Several earlier activities in this course involve oral presentation. See, for example, History Activities 21, 22, 26, 31, 32 and 39.

Activity 23 *The rumour clinic*

Work in a group of at least five people. One person will be told some information out of earshot of the rest. The first person must secretly tell the second person what he/she has heard, who in turn tells the third person and so on. At the end, compare the final and intermediate versions of the message with the original.

The rumour clinic

Activity 23 illustrates an important point about communicating information orally: however carefully you concentrate, it is very difficult to pick up information just by listening, particularly if you only hear it once. This has three important implications for the way you plan your presentation:

- keep it simple
- repeat key points
- use visual aids.

First, don't try to say too much. Concentrate on saying why you chose your topic, stating your point of view and summarising the main arguments and conclusion of your work. In a 10-minute talk, you will only have time to discuss, at most, two major points in any detail.

If something is really important, don't just say it once. Officers in the army are sometimes advised to 'tell them what you're going to tell them, tell them, then tell them what you've told them' – in other words, introduction, main body, conclusion.

Visual aids let your audience see, as well as hear, the key points that you want them to take in. You may decide to use PowerPoint, an overhead projector, a blackboard or whiteboard, flip-chart, posters, slides, video, or any combination of these to accompany your presentation. But whatever you choose, keep it simple. As a rough rule of thumb, use no more than one PowerPoint slide or overhead transparency for each minute of your talk – so that's 10 maximum – and keep the content clear and simple. People need to be able to take in the content at a glance, so write bullet points rather than continuous text, use a large font (at least 24 pt) and include just a few big, clear pictures (Figure 13).

As well as helping your audience, visual aids will help you stick to your planned structure without reading from notes. If you put each of your main points on a PowerPoint slide (or equivalent) then you will be reminded to talk in more detail about each in turn. Visual aids also support you by leading the audience to focus on the content of your talk rather than looking at you – this can be a great advantage if you are feeling a bit nervous.

Primates in medical research

UK research programmes

Surgical techniques developed using primates

Drugs tested on primates

Protocols for animal research

Ethical arguments

Animal rights

Conclusion

Was it right for scientists to join the Manhattan atomic bomb project in World War II?

In this talk I will describe the Manhattan project using information from primary and secondary sources and explain the physics of nuclear bombs.

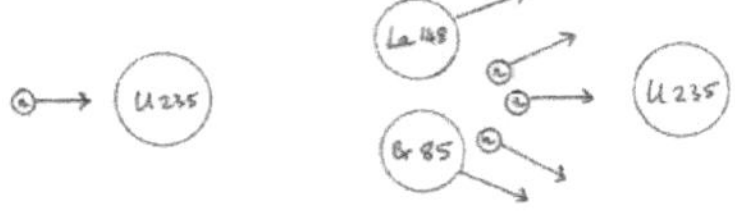

My point of view is that the use of weapons of mass destruction is never justified. Scientists should behave ethically and not get involved in WMD research.

I will show how a utilitarian argument might be used to justify using nuclear weapons but my arguments about rights and virtue ethics reach a different conclusion.

▲ ***Figure 13*** *Good or bad examples of visual aids?*

Activity 24 *Telling a story*

You will be given about five overhead transparencies in random order. Decide how these can be arranged so as to tell a 'story'. Then use the transparencies to help you tell the story to other people.

3.2 Speaking well

One of the best ways to learn how to speak to an audience is to observe other people doing it. You can probably think of situations when you have been in the audience of a good, or a bad, speaker – either live (for example, at school or college, in a public lecture, at a religious service) or while watching a TV or video. Use these experiences to help you prepare for and practise your own oral presentation.

Activity 25 *Speaking well, speaking badly*

In a small group, discuss your own experiences of being in the audience of good and bad speakers. List things that help keep you interested in what the speaker is saying, and things that make you switch off your attention.

Table 5 lists some things that you might have mentioned in Activity 25. You might be able to add some more.

Table 5 Speaking well, speaking badly.

How to make your audience switch off	*How to hold your audience's attention*
Start your talk without looking at the audience.	Begin by smiling at the audience.
Read from notes.	Talk to and look at the audience.
Speak in a flat boring voice all the time.	Vary your tone of voice.
Speak very slowly all the time, or very quickly.	Vary the pace. Avoid gabbling.
Use a lot of unexplained technical jargon.	Define any technical terms.
Talk down to your audience.	Use suitable language for you audience.
Hunch your shoulders and keep your arms crossed.	Smile. Try to look relaxed.
Say 'um' and 'er' a lot.	Try not to 'um' and 'er'.
Stare at a fixed point in the room.	Skim the whole audience. Try to find some friendly faces to focus on in different parts of the room.
Break off from the talk and spend a few minutes setting up your visual aids.	Make sure all your visual aids are ready before you start, and that any equipment is working and you know how to use it.
Fiddle with papers, hair, clothing, etc.	Hold a set of prompt cards.
Ramble on without a break.	Break up your talk into clear sections. Give the audience signals such as 'first of all … my next point is … and finally …'

If you don't have much experience of speaking to an audience, the right-hand column of Table 5 might make you think 'easier said than done'. But the main thing is to prepare carefully then smile at the audience, take some slow deep breaths and try to look relaxed. As with many things, speaking to an audience is something that improves with practice, so don't worry if at first you do find yourself umming and erring and speaking too fast. But do look for plenty of opportunities to practise before you give your main presentation.

The professionals

As you become more confident in speaking to an audience, you can begin to develop more techniques for grabbing people's attention and persuading them of your point of view. Actors, politicians and broadcasters (Figure 14) all have expertise in this, so watch them at work and see how they do it.

▲ **Figure 14** *News presenters are professional communicators.*

Activity 26 *The professionals*

Watch a clip from a movie in which one of the characters makes an emotional speech (e.g. a scene from a courtroom drama). Analyse the speech by considering the following questions:

- Are there any facts presented in this speech?
- What opinions are given?
- Is there a clear, logical structure here?
- What is the speaker's argument and the conclusion?
- Pick out what is effective for the viewer/listener.
- Is it persuasive? If it is, try to identify what makes it so.

As you might have seen in Activity 26, a speech can sometimes be persuasive because of the way it is delivered as much as the content. When you make a presentation about your project, you will be assessed on both content and delivery. So the message is: plan and prepare the content carefully, then try to communicate it as effectively as possible.

3.3 Speak out

Assessment criteria

A good way to become familiar with the assessment criteria for your oral presentation, and to prepare for your own presentation, is first to apply the criteria to other speakers (Figure 15).

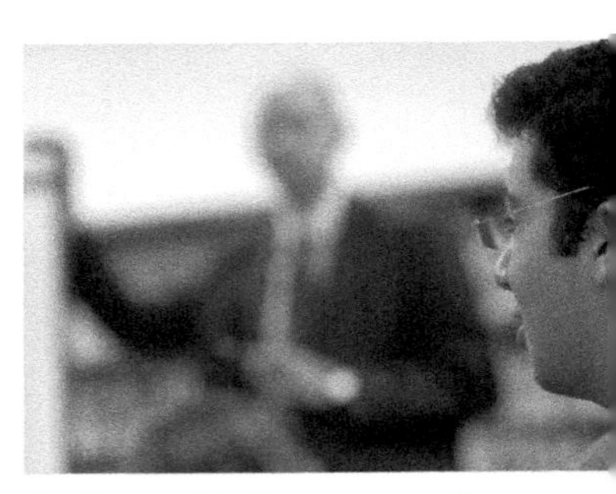

▲ **Figure 15** *Assessment of oral presentation.*

The following aspects of your presentation will be assessed:

- content – purpose, target audience, clarity of argument, conclusion
- organisation – preparation, structure, timing
- pace – delivery, response to feedback
- voice – tone, volume, diction, explanations
- visual aids – variety, relevance, clarity
- contact with audience – posture, eye contact, engaging
- handling questions – confidence, subject knowledge, in control.

The *Perspectives on Science* Course specification sets out these criteria in more detail.

Activity 27 *Assessing oral presentation*

Watch some examples of people (e.g. a TV presenter, lecturer or actor) giving a presentation and see how well, in your opinion, they perform against the assessment criteria listed above. Discuss your opinions with other students and with your teacher/lecturer.

3.4 Research seminar

Work in progress

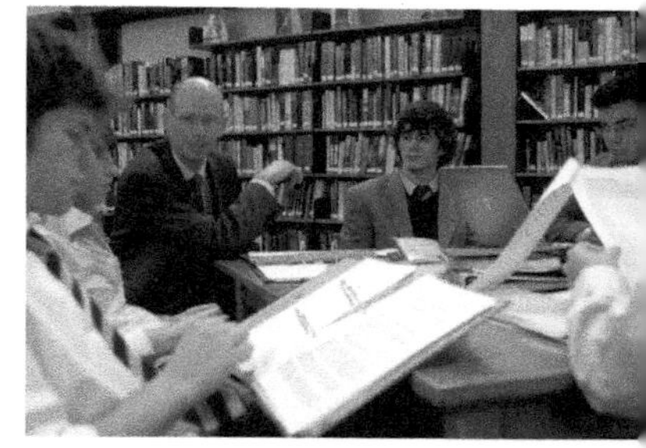

▲ ***Figure 16*** *Work in progress.*

During your work on your Research project, you will probably be asked to take part in one or more research seminars (Figure 16). The purpose of these seminars is to help you clarify your thinking about your topic, to receive advice from your teacher/lecturer and other students, and to contribute your advice to other people's work. Academic researchers, be they scientists, historians, philosophers or from some other subject area, often take part in such seminars for precisely the same purposes.

Activity 28 *Work in progress*

Plan, prepare and deliver a short oral presentation on one aspect of your Research project. Raise any questions relating to your project that you would find it helpful to discuss. Respond to questions from the rest of the class, and listen to other people's comments and suggestions.

In a research seminar, you will be asked to give a short presentation on some aspect of your work in progress. This might be a report on some literature sources that you have been consulting, a discussion of some arguments relevant to your topic or a discussion of a point of view. Whichever is the case, you need to prepare to speak for a few minutes to the rest of your class and respond to questions. This is also an opportunity for you to ask questions and gather other people's views on aspects of your chosen topic. If you are wondering how best to move your work forward, other people's suggestions and comments can be very valuable. If people disagree with your particular point of view, hearing their arguments can help you to sharpen your own thinking and develop counter-arguments.

Use research seminars as an opportunity to practise and develop your oral presentation skills. Plan what you will say and prepare some suitable visual aids. This will be valuable when you come to give your main presentation – you will probably be able to adapt or reuse what you have prepared earlier.

Questions and discussion

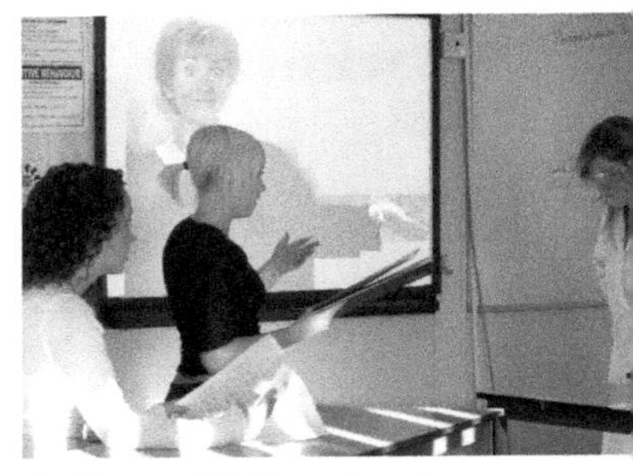

▲ *Figure 17* Question time.

Responding to questions will be an important part of your final presentation, so any experience gained beforehand will be helpful. 'Question time' (Figure 17) can be more daunting than the rest of your presentation because you cannot prepare for it in the same way, but the following points are worth bearing in mind.

- You will almost certainly know more about your research topic than anyone else in the room, including your teacher or lecturer.
- The more interesting your talk, the more questions people will ask. So take every question as a compliment, even if the questioner is disagreeing with you.
- Pause for thought before launching into an answer – particularly if you are not sure what to say.
- If you don't know the answer to a question, be honest and say so.
- If someone asks about an aspect of your topic that has not previously occurred to you, be grateful. It might be something worth researching as your project develops.
- Keep your answers short so as to give several people a chance to ask questions.
- Try not to let one person dominate. Try to take questions from a range of people.
- If someone persists in demanding a more detailed response to their question, offer to discuss it with him or her privately afterwards.
- Be polite if someone tries to put you down; don't enter into a disagreement. Try to use phrases such as 'that's an interesting point of view' or 'well, that's a different way of looking at things' or 'that's something I'll have to think about'.

Do unto others ...

Listening to other people's presentations and asking them questions is an important aspect of taking part in a seminar. When someone else is giving a presentation, try to imagine yourself in his/her situation and behave as you would wish your own audience to behave. In short:

- remember, the speaker may be nervous even if he or she doesn't look it
- listen to the presentation with respect
- try to think of a constructive question to ask – and listen attentively to the answer.

Activity 29 *Reflection*

After the seminar, reflect on how it went for you. Start by trying to think of the good points, then think of aspects that you can work to improve next time. Your teacher/lecturer will probably be able to give you some helpful feedback.

3.5 Presentation

Be prepared

After you have finished the written report of your project, you can focus your attention fully on your oral presentation.

You will be told the date and time in advance. Make sure you are well prepared in good time. In particular:

- plan the content and timing of your presentation carefully
- prepare your visual aids
- practise giving your presentation to an audience.

For the first two of these, refer to previous lessons for guidance and draw on the experience that you have built up during your work for this course. When you are fairly sure you have prepared a more-or-less final version of your presentation, hold a dress rehearsal. Ideally, the dress rehearsal will take place in the same room as your final presentation, in front of a small audience of students from your class (Figure 18).

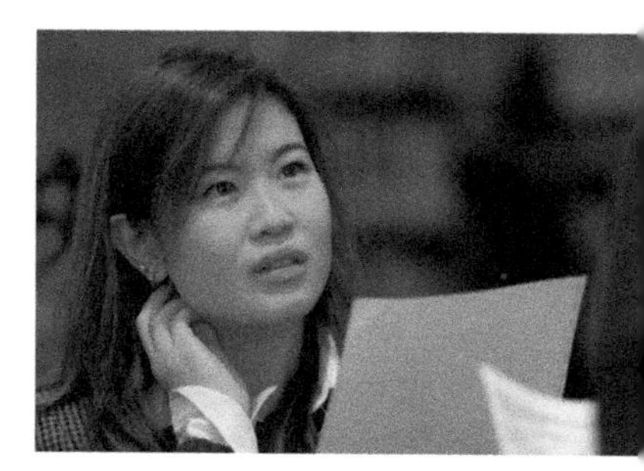

▲ ***Figure 18*** *Dress rehearsal.*

Planning

When planning your presentation, it is useful to keep in mind the same '5 W's (and one H) that you have met in the context of historical research:

- What – make your theme statement.
- Why – state your purpose clearly.
- When – know the time you are presenting and also the timings of when you will be saying things.
- How – make a plan of your structure.
- Where – check every aspect of your venue, particularly for suitability for your audience.
- Who – note down any important information about your listeners.

Your presentation should take approximately 10 minutes. In such a short time, you cannot attempt to describe everything that you did for your project. Concentrate on talking about the conclusions that you reached, summarise your literature review and discussion very briefly and choose one or perhaps two arguments to discuss in detail.

Plan what you are going to say in three parts.

Introduction (1 min)

This should take about 10 per cent of the allotted time (in this case, 1 minute). Try to find some way of grabbing people's attention immediately – perhaps display a picture or read a quotation, state an opinion or pose a question. Your introduction should be long enough to set the scene for the presentation but short enough to mark its own end clearly.

Main body (7.5 min)

The main 'meat' of your talk should take about 75 per cent of the time. You will need to be very selective – you cannot possibly communicate your entire Research project in this short time.

Conclusion (1.5 min)

Take about 15 per cent of your time to reinforce the 'take home' messages from your talk. Make sure you audience knows you are drawing to an end purposefully and not just stopping. Say 'and finally ...', sum up your main points, thank your audience for their time and ask if they have any questions.

Start to plan your presentation while you are working on the Discussion section of your written report. Then, when you have more or less finished the written report, spend some time on more detailed preparation for the presentation.

Activity 30 *Dress rehearsal*

Practise giving your presentation to an audience. Try to do it 'for real' – in other words, don't keep stopping to ask whether it's going OK. Afterwards, ask for feedback then act on the comments that you receive. In particular:

- Adjust the timing if your presentation is too long or too short.
- Make sure your visual aids are clear and legible from all parts of the room.
- Check that you are speaking clearly and engaging your listeners' attention.
- Check that the structure of your talk was made clear to your audience.
- Check that your audience grasped the main points that you were trying to make.

Glossary

absolutism Absolutism assumes the existence of an objective reason for a statement. Thus, someone might argue that it is absolutely wrong to torture people because such behaviour is forbidden in scripture, is inherently disrespectful to people, contravenes their rights or always leads to unhappiness.

abstract A short summary of a report, article or book. Its purpose is to highlight the main points made in the text.

agnosticism The point of view of someone who is unsure whether or not there is a god

argument In philosophy, a piece of reasoning designed to provide rational support for a conclusion; a statement of one or more premises leading logically to a conclusion. (When an argument is presented, the conclusion is not necessarily the final statement.)

atheism The belief that there is no god.

autonomy The ability to make decisions for oneself. A person acts autonomously when such decisions can be put into practice.

bibliography A list of references to all the sources used in a project, essay or research paper. It is usually placed at the end in a separate headed section. The bibliography must contain enough detail to enable other readers to find the sources in a library or on the Internet.

conclusion What an argument seeks to establish.

consequentialism The view that the consequences (results) of a course of action alone are sufficient to let a person decide the rightness or otherwise of the course of action.

counter-arguments Arguments that are designed to undermine or contradict a particular point of view.

criterion (plural **criteria**) A way of telling whether something is the case. For example, 'having feathers' is one criterion for deciding whether something is a bird; 'knowing the meaning of road signs' is one criterion for deciding whether someone should be awarded a full driving licence.

criterion of falsifiability This is the suggestion, made by Karl Popper, that we can tell whether a theory is scientific or not by whether it makes predictions that can, in principle, be proved false. Popper thought that while it is impossible ever to prove a theory true, scientific theories could, in principle, be disproved because they make testable predictions. This distinguishes them from activities such as astrology that make such vague predictions that they are never disproved, and from theories such as Marxism that are constantly changed to avoid the charge that they have been falsified. (See *falsificationism*).

deduction A type of reasoning in which the logical consequences of a proposition are derived. For example, if all dogs are noisy (proposition), you can reason that any given dog must be noisy (consequence).

distributive justice The view that scarce resources should be allocated among people in a way that is fair.

divine command For people with a religious faith, right conduct is often seen as fulfilling what is required by divine command. These commands are generally revealed in holy scriptures and the teachings of a specialised group of people, such as priests or imams.

dualism The view that a human being is made up of two parts: a non-physical soul/mind and a physical body.

duties Things each of us ought to do. For example, if you have a child, you have a duty to look after him or her.

ethical frameworks Conceptual structures that allow a person to decide the rightness or wrongness of actions. Standard ethical frameworks include utilitarianism, rights and duties, and virtue ethics.

ethics Reasoned views about why certain things are morally wrong and other things are morally right.

evidence A means of proving an unknown or disputed fact, or supporting a point of view. Well established facts and primary sources of information provide much more compelling evidence than secondary sources, subjective opinion or speculation.

fact A statement about which there is no uncertainty or dispute. For example, it is a fact that Tony Blair became UK Prime Minister in 1997, and that light travels in a vacuum at 300 million metres per second.

In moral philosophy, facts are the relatively unproblematic happenings to which moral value may or may not be attached. For example, it is a fact that the use of contraception reduces the likelihood of a woman becoming pregnant, but this doesn't tell us whether the use of contraception is good, bad or morally of no significance.

facts and values Since David Hume it has been widely accepted that there is no logical connection between facts (what are) and values (what ought to be the case). For example, the frequency of occurrence of earthquakes and dishonesty tells us nothing about how morally good or bad these are.

falsificationism The view that what makes an activity or a theory scientific is that it gives rise to predictions that could, in principle, be proved false when tested by observation or experiment.

first cause The name given to whatever generated the universe, if indeed anything did.

genetic determinism The view that a person's characteristics are completely determined by his or her genetic make-up.

homeopathy The view that 'like cures like' and that medical substances become more powerful when they are diluted. For example, a nut called nux vomica is known to cause vomiting when eaten. According to homeopathy, nausea and vomiting can be cured by very dilute doses of nux vomica – and, the more severe the nausea, the greater the dilution required for a cure.

hypothesis An 'educated guess' at an explanation, usually based on observation or experiment. A scientific hypothesis often gives rise to propositions that can be tested by further experiment or observation.

induction A type of reasoning in which the conclusion is made probable by the premises but not strictly proven. Reasoning by induction involves generalising from experience, or going beyond the data to find an explanation.

intelligent design theory The view that the complexity and orderliness of the natural world are best explained by the existence of an intelligent designer.

interaction problem The problem, faced by dualists, of how a non-physical thing like the mind/soul can interact with a physical body.

invalid An invalid argument is one in which the conclusion does not follow from the premises. If an argument is invalid, it is possible for the premises to be true, but the conclusion false.

materialism The view that the human being is made up of physical stuff alone: there is no non-physical mind or soul.

model A simplified representation of some aspect of the physical world. In everyday language, the term usually means a physical small- or large-scale representation. In science, a model is usually a description involving words, symbols, equations or numbers.

monism The same as *materialism*.

morals Beliefs about which things are right and which are wrong. For example, a person might believe that hunting animals for their fur is always wrong but that eating meat is acceptable provided that the animals from which the meat comes do not suffer.

naturalism The view that explanations should be given in purely natural terms, without relying on anything supernatural. (See *materialism*, *reductionism*.)

neural networks Computing systems that use similar structures to those found in the brain (parallel connections between nodes).

non-reductionist The view that, although a person is made of purely physical stuff, not all his or her properties can be explained in purely physical terms – in particular, that consciousness is fundamentally different from physical brain processes.

objections The same as *counter-arguments*.

objective Unaffected by a person's emotions, sensations or beliefs. Facts are objective (whereas opinions are subjective).

opinion Someone's personal judgement about what seems to be true. For example, it is a matter of opinion whether Margaret Thatcher was a good prime minister, or whether chocolate is delicious.

paradigm A set of theories and methods that a group of scientists share and which guides them in their scientific work.

peer review In Science and other academic disciplines, the process by which people's work is checked by others with knowledge of the field before publication.

personal identity The relationship that is supposed to hold between a person at one stage in his/her life and the same person at a later stage. (See *physical continuity*, *psychological continuity*.)

philosophy The discipline in which fundamental ideas are discussed, with the aim of understanding these ideas more clearly and thinking critically about the reasons people give for their fundamental beliefs.

physical continuity The view that what makes a person at one time identical with a person at some other time is that enough of the person's body or brain has persisted in existence. (See *personal identity*, *psychological continuity*.)

plagiarism Using someone else's work and pretending it is your own. Plagiarism occurs whenever someone's work is used without being acknowledged. A scientist copying someone else's results, a student buying an essay from a website and a writer quoting from a book without giving the source are all committing plagiarism.

points of view Beliefs about philosophical (or ethical) matters.

premises The starting points for an argument. (When an argument is presented, the premises are not necessarily placed at the beginning.)

primary source A record produced during an event, or by someone who was present when it happened. A scientist's lab notebook and a video recording are both examples of primary sources. Historians generally prefer to use primary sources as they give a more direct record of an event than secondary sources. But primary sources might still be subject to bias, for example, when someone involved in an event is not aware of all the facts or wishes to promote a particular interpretation.

problem of induction The problem of justifying conclusions that go beyond the data gained by experience.

proposition In philosophy, arguments are used to provide support for particular propositions. For example, the 'first cause' argument is designed to establish the proposition that God exists.

pseudo-science Activities or theories that are meant to look as though they are genuinely scientific but which are not.

psychological continuity The view that what makes a person at one time identical with a person at some other time is that the later person can remember enough of what the earlier person experienced. (See *personal identity*, *physical continuity*.)

realism The view of those who (unlike relativists) believe that there is an objective reality which our theories try to describe.

reasons Statements that provide support for a point of view.

reductionist The view of someone who believes that only physical things exist, and that everything can be explained by fundamental scientific laws.

relativism The view of those who (unlike realists) believe that truth is relative: it depends upon your point of view. Moral relativism is the view that maintains that nothing is absolutely right or wrong (i.e. right or wrong at all times, in all places and in all circumstances). The context can mean that any action normally considered wrong (e.g. telling lies, being sexually unfaithful, even torture or murder) may be justifiable.

rights Things that should nearly always be allowed. Most people believe that humans have such rights as the right to life, the right to freedom of speech, the right to a fair trial and so on. Under certain circumstances a person may lose a right – for example, you don't have the right to freedom of speech if that means shouting 'fire' in a crowded public place when there is no fire. If someone has a right to something, it usually means that one or more people have duties to that person.

scientific realism The view of someone who believes that science is progressing towards an objectively true description of reality.

scientific revolution A transformation from one scientific paradigm to another.

secondary source A record produced after an event by someone who was not present. An encyclopedia entry and a TV documentary are examples of secondary sources. Secondary sources rely on other sources of information, some of which might be primary sources.

soul The non-physical essential part of a human being, according to the dualist point of view.

speculation Guessing what might happen or what might have happened, or the reasons why an event or action took place.

strong artificial intelligence The view that, by implementing appropriate programmes, intelligent computers can be created.

subjective Affected by a person's emotions, sensations or beliefs. Opinions are subjective (whereas facts are objective).

theism The belief in the existence of a god.

theistic evolution The belief that Creation and evolution are compatible with one another since God creates the world using a process of evolution.

theory In everyday language, the term is often used to mean 'hypothesis'. In science, a theory is an idea, or set of laws, that can be used to explain some observations and make predictions about the outcome of future observations. (See *hypothesis*, *falsificationism*.)

thought experiment An imaginary scenario used to test how our concepts work in cases completely unlike those in which we normally use them.

Turing test A test to see whether a machine is capable of intelligent thought, in which a person types questions into the machine. If the person cannot tell whether he/she has been talking to a person or a machine, the machine has passed the test.

utilitarianism The ethical framework which holds that the right course of action is that which maximises the amount of happiness or pleasure in the world. If you are a utilitarian it means that while you might, for example, normally respect other people's property, there could be occasions when you would believe that the right thing to do would be to steal.

valid A valid argument is one in which the conclusion follows from the premises. In a valid argument it is not possible for the premises to be true and the conclusion false.

values In moral philosophy, values are the ethical meanings attached to certain facts. In science, internal ethical values are those that are intrinsic to the scientific way of arriving at knowledge. They include such things as the accurate recording of data and honest reporting of findings. External ethical values include such things as undertaking work intended to benefit humanity or enhance animal welfare.

virtue ethics Ethical framework that stresses the development of good character traits, i.e. virtues. Precisely what the virtues are is open to disagreement, and may vary from place to place and at different times in history. However, certain virtues, such as kindness and courage, are valued by most cultures.

Index